Elements of
GENERAL TOPOLOGY

HOLDEN-DAY SERIES IN MATHEMATICS

Earl A. Coddington and Andrew M. Gleason
Editors

Elements of

GENERAL TOPOLOGY

Shih-chen

Sze-Tsen Hu

Department of Mathematics
University of California, Los Angeles

HOLDEN-DAY, INC
San Francisco, London, Amsterdam
1964

Library of Congress Catalog Card Number: 64–16576

Printed in the United States of America

PREFACE

Topology is now included in the undergraduate curricula of most universities. The present book is designed as a text for a one-semester course in general topology for upper division undergraduates as well as first-year graduate students. Its aim is to provide a systematic exposition of the essentials of this subject in a desirably leisurely fashion, to students who have reached at least the level of mathematical maturity following two or three years of sound undergraduate mathematics study. Apart from the arithmetic of real numbers and the continuity of rational fractions, no specific mathematical knowledge is required except at a few isolated spots.

The first three chapters of this book cover the more or less standard elements of general topology. Instead of covering as much ground as possible, we elect to put almost all emphasis on the absolutely basic concepts, fundamental properties, and important constructions, presenting them carefully and painstakingly. In giving proofs, we include details which might ordinarily be omitted, preferring intelligibility over brevity. The examples are chosen so as to be used later and to produce minimal distraction from the main lines of development. These readers who are interested in pathological examples can find plenty of these in the existing books on the subject.

The last three chapters present some more specific topological topics, which either have not yet appeared in book form (Chapter IV) or have appeared but only in advanced treatises (Chapters V and VI). We believe that the notions treated here—namely cellular polytopes, function spaces, and fundamental groups—should be of interest to all mathematicians, and not reserved for specialists in topology. These are treated in the same style as the topics in the first three chapters. Definitions of the elementary algebraic notions used but not defined in the final chapter can be found in Chevalley's *Fundamental Concepts of Algebra*.

As a rule, brief mention of facts extraneous to our argument, without proof, is avoided. This is part of our deliberate intent to leave it to the instructor's option whether to mention a specific fact related to the material treated in the book. In addition, we do not want to educate the student to accept anything without an intelligible proof.

The bibliography at the end of the book comprises two parts, "Books" and "Papers." The former contains almost all books on general topology, while the latter has been reduced to the minimum essential to the text and the exercises. References to this bibliography are cited in the text or in the exercises by letters and numbers enclosed in brackets. Cross references are given in the form (III; 8.1), where III stands for Chapter III and 8.1 for the numbering of the statement in the chapter.

A list of special symbols and abbreviations used in this book is given immediately after the Table of Contents. Certain deviations from standard set-theoretic notations have been adopted in the text; namely, $\square$ is used to denote the empty set and $A \setminus B$ the set-theoretic difference usually denoted by $A - B$. We have used the symbol $||$ to indicate the end of a proof and the abbreviation iff for the phrase "if and only if."

The author acknowledges with great pleasure his gratitude to Professors Robert F. Brown and Barrett O'Neill who used the manuscript in their classes and made several useful suggestions. He is especially grateful to Mr. James Baugh who assisted through all its stages, showing great patience at all times. It is a pleasure to acknowledge the invaluable assistance the author received in the form of partial financial support from the Air Force of Scientific Research during the years since 1957 while the present book was gradually developed as various lecture notes. Finally, it is a pleasure to thank the publisher and the printer for their courtesy and cooperation.

Sze-Tsen Hu

University of California
Los Angeles, Calif.

TABLE OF CONTENTS

SPECIAL SYMBOLS AND ABBREVIATIONS

$\Rightarrow$	implies, sufficiency	
$\Leftarrow$	is implied by, necessity	
‖	end of proof, q.e.d.	
iff	if and only if	
$\in$	is an element of	2
$\notin$	is not an element of	2
$\subset$	is a subset of	2, 8
$\supset$	contains	2
$=$	equals	3
$\bigcup$	union	4
$\cup$	union	3
$\bigcap$	intersection	4
$\cap$	intersection	3
$\prod$	Cartesian product	12, 13
$\times$	Cartesian product	12, 13
Σ	sum	40
$\{\ \}$	set	2
$\{\ \mid\ \}$	set such that	2, 12
$\square$	empty set	2
X^M	Cartesian power	14
f^{-1}	inverse of f	7
$f \circ g$	f composed with g	8
$f \mid A$	f restricted to A	9
$f \times g$	Cartesian product	12, 13
$f : A \rightarrow B$	function, f, from A to B	8
$f : A \subset B$	inclusion f of A into B	8
$e(f, \mu)$	evaluation function	15
$d(x, y)$	distance function	97
exp	exponential map	194
$\chi_A, \chi_{A.B}$	characteristic function, map	10, 94

deg (σ)	degree σ	196
dim P	dimension P	142
$\sim$	is equivalent to	89, 175
$\simeq$	is homotopic to	48, 52
$\cong$	is isotopic to	48, 52
∞	ideal element	103
$+\infty, -\infty$	ideal elements	107
Ext (E)	exterior of E	21
Int (E)	interior of E	21
$\partial\,(E)$	boundary of E	21
Cl (E)	closure of E	23
$\overline{E}$	closure of E	23
$N_\delta(p), N_r(p)$	δ, r-neighborhood of p	19, 99
St(F)	closed star of F	120
st(F)	open star of F	120
X^*	one-point compactification	103
β	Stone-Čech compactification	105
Con (E)	cone over E	45
Cyl f	mapping cylinder of f	45
S(X)	suspension of X	90
$\Omega(X), \Omega(X, x_i)$	space of paths in X, space of paths in X at x_0	151
$\Lambda(X), \Lambda(X, x_0)$	space of loops in X, space of loops in X at x_0	171, 172
Map (X, Y)	space of maps from X to Y	150
$C(X)$	cellular carrier of X	136
$S = S(K)$		116
$\|K\|$	topological realization of, support of	116
F_σ	F-sigma	93
G_δ	G-delta	93
I^n, I^N	n-Cube, Hilbert Cube	37
P^n	Projective n-space	44
R	Real line	17
R^n	Euclidean n-space	37
S^n	n-sphere	54
Δ^n	n-simplex	41
Ω^1	ordinals $\leqslant$ the first uncountable ordinal	110
$[f]$	homotopy class of f	
$\pi(X)$	fundamental groupoid	176, 184
$\pi_1(X, x_0)$	fundamental group	186
$\pi_n(X)$	n-th homotopy group	204
$\pi_n(X, x_0)$	n-th homotopy group	204

Chapter I: SETS AND FUNCTIONS

In this introductory chapter of the book, we will give an elementary account of sets and functions, with the primary purpose of introducing the notation to be used in the sequel. To save the reader unnecessary effort, this topic will be developed at as naïve a level as possible and with minimal coverage. Among the materials omitted from an earlier manuscript are the basic logical notions, relations, the cardinality of sets, etc. These are so fundamental that we can safely assume that the student has already learned them in some earlier course. Further, we will not indulge in the various forms of the Axiom of Choice and their equivalence. With the single exception in the proof of (III, 2.10), this axiom is used in the book only in its naïve form of allowing an unlimited number of choices.

1. SETS

We will adopt a naïve viewpoint in developing an elementary theory of sets. A *set* is to be thought of intuitively as a collection of objects which are either enumerated or are determined by the possession of some common property. This is not a definition, because the word "collection" is only a synonym for the word "set." In the text, we will occasionally use synonyms, namely, "aggregate," "family," etc. The following examples of sets will be helpful in understanding the intuitive meaning of this undefined term.

(a) The set AMS of all members of the American Mathematical Society.

(b) The set MAA of all members of the Mathematical Association of America.

(c) The set N of all natural numbers, i.e. positive integers.

(d) The set Z of all integers, positive, zero, or negative.

(e) The set R of all real numbers.

The symbols for the special sets given in the last three examples will be used throughout the book.

The objects in a set X will be called the *members*, the *elements*, or the *points* of X. These may be concrete things or abstract notions. We shall use the symbol $\in$ to stand for the phrase "is a member of." Thus, the notation

$$x \in X$$

reads that "x is a member of X" or equivalently "x belongs to X." The negation of $x \in X$ will be denoted by

$$x \notin X.$$

To determine a set is to determine its members. In other words, a set X is determined iff one can tell whether or not any given object x belongs to X. Frequently, the members of a set X are determined by the possession of some common property. For example, if $p(x)$ denotes a given statement relating to the object x, then we write

$$X = \{x \mid p(x)\}$$

to state that X is the set of all objects x for which the statement $p(x)$ holds.

A set X is said to be *empty* iff it has no members. The empty set will be denoted by the symbol $\square$. Thus, $X = \square$ reads that X is empty.

A set X is said to be a *singleton* iff it has one and only one member. If the lone member of a singleton X is x, then we denote

$$X = \{x\}.$$

On logical grounds, it is necessary to distinguish between an object x and the set $\{x\}$. However, as a matter of notational convenience, we will frequently use the same symbol x for an object x and the singleton $\{x\}$ which consists of this object x.

More generally, if $x_1, x_2, \ldots, x_n$ are n given objects, then

$$X = \{x_1, x_2, \ldots, x_n\}$$

stands for the set X which consists of these objects $x_1, x_2, \ldots, x_n$ as members.

Now, let A and B denote two given sets. If every member of A belongs to B, then we say that A *is contained in* B, or equivalently, B *contains* A; in symbols,

$$A \subset B, \qquad B \supset A,$$

where the symbol $\subset$ is called the *inclusion*. In this case, A is said to be a *subset* of B. Among the sets in the examples (c)–(e) given above, we have

$$N \subset Z \subset R.$$

If $A \subset B$ and $B \subset A$, then we say that A and B are equal; in symbols,

$$A = B.$$

In other words, two sets are equal iff they have the same members. If $A \subset B$ and $A \neq B$, then A is said to be a *proper subset* of B.

The subsets of a given set X are frequently defined by imposing further conditions upon the members of X. For example, if $p(x)$ denotes a given statement relating to the member x of X, then

$$\{x \in X \mid p(x)\}$$

stands for the subset of X which consists of all members x of X for which $p(x)$ holds. In this way, we can define the *unit interval I* of real numbers by the formula:

$$I = \{t \in R \mid 0 \leqslant t \leqslant 1\}.$$

There are many ways leading to the formation of new sets from old ones. The following three operations are fundamental. The *union* $A \cup B$ is defined to be the set which consists of those objects x which belong to at least one of the sets A and B. The *intersection* $A \cap B$ is defined to be the set which consists of those objects x which belong to both A and B. The *difference* $A \setminus B$ is defined to be the set which consists of those objects x which belong to A but not to B. These definitions may be stated in the form of the following equations:

$$A \cup B = \{x \mid x \in A \text{ or } x \in B\},$$
$$A \cap B = \{x \mid x \in A \text{ and } x \in B\},$$
$$A \setminus B = \{x \mid x \in A \text{ and } x \notin B\}.$$

THEOREM 1.1. *For arbitrary sets A, B, C and X, the following laws are valid:*

(1.1.1)   *The commutative laws:*

$$A \cup B = B \cup A,$$
$$A \cap B = B \cap A.$$

(1.1.2)   *The associative laws:*

$$A \cup (B \cup C) = (A \cup B) \cup C,$$
$$A \cap (B \cap C) = (A \cap B) \cap C.$$

(1.1.3)   *The distributive laws:*

$$A \cap (B \cup C) = (A \cap B) \cup (A \cap C),$$
$$A \cup (B \cap C) = (A \cup B) \cap (A \cup C).$$

(1.1.4)   *De Morgan formulae:*

$$X \setminus (A \cup B) = (X \setminus A) \cap (X \setminus B),$$
$$X \setminus (A \cap B) = (X \setminus A) \cup (X \setminus B).$$

The proofs of these are straightforward and hence will be left to the student as exercises. As an illustrative example, we will prove the last equality of the De Morgan formulae as follows.

The proof of an equality of sets usually breaks up into two parts.

(*i*) *Proof of the inclusion*

$$X \setminus (A \cap B) \subset (X \setminus A) \cup (X \setminus B).$$

Let x be any member of $X \setminus (A \cap B)$. Then, by the definition of the difference, we have $x \in X$ and $x \notin A \cap B$. The latter implies that $x \notin A$ or $x \notin B$. Since $x \in X$, $x \notin A$ implies $x \in X \setminus A$ and $x \notin B$ implies $x \in X \setminus B$. Hence we have $x \in X \setminus A$ or $x \in X \setminus B$; in other words, x must be a member of the set $(X \setminus A) \cup (X \setminus B)$. ‖

(*ii*) *Proof of the inclusion*

$$(X \setminus A) \cup (X \setminus B) \subset X \setminus (A \cap B).$$

Let x be any member of $(X \setminus A) \cup (X \setminus B)$. Then $x \in X \setminus A$ or $x \in X \setminus B$. If $x \in X \setminus A$, then $x \in X$ and $x \notin A$. Since $x \notin A$ implies $x \notin A \cap B$, it follows that x is in $X \setminus (A \cap B)$. Similarly, one can prove that $x \in X \setminus B$ also implies that x is in $X \setminus (A \cap B)$. ‖

Two sets A and B are said to be *disjoint* iff $A \cap B = \square$; otherwise, they are said to be *overlapping*.

The concept of union and intersection can be generalized to any number of sets as follows. If Φ is a family of sets, then

$$\bigcup_{X \in \Phi} X = \{x \mid x \in X \text{ for some } X \in \Phi\},$$

$$\bigcap_{X \in \Phi} X = \{x \mid x \in X \text{ for each } X \in \Phi\}.$$

One can verify that the laws in Theorem 1.1 also hold for any number of sets.

If A is a subset of a set X, then the difference $X \setminus A$ will be called the *complement* of A with respect to X. In symbols,

$$\mathscr{C}_X A = X \setminus A.$$

If A is also a subset of some other set Y, then $\mathscr{C}_X A$ and $\mathscr{C}_Y A$ are different sets. If we consider, in a certain situation, only subsets of a fixed set X, then we write $\mathscr{C}A$ instead of $\mathscr{C}_X A$.

EXERCISES

1A. Prove all of Theorem 1.1 (including the De Morgan Formulae).

1B. Verify the following relations for arbitrary sets A and B:
  (a) $\square \subset A$.
  (b) $A \subset A$.
  (c) $A \cup \square = A$.
  (d) $A \cap \square = \square$.
  (e) $A \cap A = A = A \cup A$.
  (f) $A \cap B \subset A \subset A \cup B$.

1C. Establish the following propositions for arbitrary sets A, B, C:
  (a) If $A \subset B$ and $B \subset C$, then $A \subset C$.
  (b) If $A \subset C$ and $B \subset C$, then $A \cup B \subset C$.
  (c) If $A \supset C$ and $B \supset C$, then $A \cap B \supset C$.

1D. Show that the following three statements are equivalent for arbitrary sets A and B:
  (a) $A \subset B$.
  (b) $A \cup B = B$.
  (c) $A \cap B = A$.

1E. Prove the following properties of subsets of a fixed set X:
  (a) $\mathscr{C}X = \square$.
  (b) $\mathscr{C}\square = X$.
  (c) $A \cup \mathscr{C}A = X$.
  (d) $A \cap \mathscr{C}A = \square$.
  (e) $\mathscr{C}\mathscr{C}A = A$.
  (f) $\mathscr{C}(A \cup B) = \mathscr{C}A \cap \mathscr{C}B$.
  (g) $\mathscr{C}(A \cap B) = \mathscr{C}A \cup \mathscr{C}B$.
  (h) $\mathscr{C}(A \setminus B) = B \cup \mathscr{C}A$.
  (i) If $A \cup B = X$ and $A \cap B = \square$, then $B = \mathscr{C}A$.
  (j) If $A \subset B$, then $\mathscr{C}B \subset \mathscr{C}A$.

1F. Verify the following equalities for arbitrary sets A, B, C:
  (a) $A \setminus (A \setminus B) = A \cap B$.
  (b) $A \cap (B \setminus C) = (A \cap B) \setminus (A \cap C)$.
  (c) $(A \setminus B) \cup (A \setminus C) = A \setminus (B \cap C)$.

(d) $(A \setminus C) \cup (B \setminus C) = (A \cup B) \setminus C$.
(e) $(A \setminus B) \cup (B \setminus A) = (A \cup B) \setminus (A \cap B)$.
(f) $A \cup (B \setminus A) = A \cup B$.
(g) $A \cap (B \setminus A) = \square$.

2. FUNCTIONS

Let X and Y be given sets. By a *function* $f: X \rightarrow Y$ from X into Y, we mean a rule which assigns to each member x of X a unique member $f(x)$ of Y.

EXAMPLE 1. Consider the set N of all natural numbers and the set Z_p of all non-negative integers less than a given positive integer p. For any $x \in N$, let us divide x by p and obtain a remainder $f(x)$. This number $f(x)$ is in Z_p. The assignment $x \rightarrow f(x)$ defines a function $f: N \rightarrow Z_p$.

EXAMPLE 2. Consider the equation $y = x^2$. For each real number $x \in R$, $y = x^2$ is also a real number. Hence, the assignment $x \rightarrow x^2$ defines a function $f: R \rightarrow R$ from R into itself. This function is frequently denoted by x^2; therefore, $x^2 : R \rightarrow R$.

Let $f: X \rightarrow Y$ be a given function. The set X is called the *domain* of the function f and the set Y is called the *range* of f. For each point x of the domain X, the point $f(x)$ of the range Y which is assigned to x by the function f is called the *image* of x under f. Sometimes, $f(x)$ is called the *value* of the function f at the point x.

For any subset A of X, the subset of Y which consists of the points $f(x)$ for all $x \in A$ is called the *image* of A under the function f and will be denoted by $f(A)$; in symbols,

$$f(A) = \{f(x) \in Y \mid x \in A\}.$$

In particular, the image $f(X)$ of the whole domain X of f is simply called the *image* of f and denoted by Im (f).

PROPOSITION 2.1. *For any two subsets A and B of the domain X of a function $f: X \rightarrow Y$, we have*

(2.1.1) $\qquad\qquad f(A \cup B) = f(A) \cup f(B)$,
(2.1.2) $\qquad\qquad f(A \cap B) \subset f(A) \cap f(B)$.

The proofs of (2.1.1) and (2.1.2) are left to the student as exercises;

he can also easily generalize these to any number of subsets of the domain X.

That the two sides of the inclusion (2.1.2) are not always equal can be seen by the following example. Let

$$X = \{a, b\}, \quad A = \{a\}, \quad B = \{b\}, \quad Y = \{y\},$$

and let $f : X \to Y$ denote the unique function. Then we have

$$f(A \cap B) = f(\square) = \square, \quad f(A) \cap f(B) = Y.$$

If $f(X) = Y$, then we say that $f : X \to Y$ is a function from X *onto* Y; frequently, we shall also say that the function $f : X \to Y$ is *surjective*. Therefore, $f : X \to Y$ is surjective iff, for every point y in Y, there exists at least one point x in X such that $f(x) = y$. The function in Example 1 is surjective while that in Example 2 is not surjective.

If $f(X)$ consists of a single point y of Y, then we say that $f : X \to Y$ is a *constant function* from X into Y. If X is nonempty, then, for each $y \in Y$, there is a unique constant function $f_y : X \to Y$ such that $f_y(X) = y$.

For any subset B of Y, the subset of X which consists of the points $x \in X$ such that $f(x) \in B$ is called the *inverse image* of B under the function $f : X \to Y$ and will be denoted by $f^{-1}(B)$; in symbols,

$$f^{-1}(B) = \{x \in X \mid f(x) \in B\}.$$

In particular, if B is a singleton, say $B = \{y\}$, then $f^{-1}(B)$ is called the *inverse image* of the point y under f denoted by $f^{-1}(y)$. Thus, a point $y \in Y$ belongs to the image $f(X)$ of a function f iff $f^{-1}(y)$ is nonempty.

PROPOSITION 2.2. *For any two subsets A and B of the range Y of a function $f : X \to Y$, we have*

(2.2.1) $\qquad\qquad f^{-1}(A \cup B) = f^{-1}(A) \cup f^{-1}(B),$
(2.2.2) $\qquad\qquad f^{-1}(A \cap B) = f^{-1}(A) \cap f^{-1}(B),$
(2.2.3) $\qquad\qquad f^{-1}(A \setminus B) = f^{-1}(A) \setminus f^{-1}(B).$

The proofs of (2.2.1)–(2.2.3) are left to the student as exercises; he can also easily generalize the first two equalities to any number of subsets of the range Y.

By a comparison of the propositions (2.1) and (2.2), one will find that the inverse images behave much better than the images. This explains why the notion of inverse images will be used more than that of images.

If A and B are disjoint subsets of Y, then it follows from (2.2.2) that the inverse images $f^{-1}(A)$ and $f^{-1}(B)$ are also disjoint. In particular, the inverse images of distinct points of Y are disjoint.

A function $f: X \to Y$ is said to be *one-to-one* or *injective* iff, for every point $y \in Y$, the inverse image $f^{-1}(y)$ is either empty or a singleton. Thus, f is injective iff the images of distinct points of X are distinct. As an example of injective functions, let us consider the case $X \subset Y$. Then, the function $i: X \to Y$ defined by $i(x) = x \in Y$ for every $x \in X$ is called the *inclusion function* of X into Y. To indicate that $i: X \to Y$ stands for the inclusion function, we write

$$i: X \subset Y.$$

It is obvious that every inclusion function is injective.

A function $f: X \to Y$ which is both surjective and injective will be called a *bijective function*. If $f: X \to Y$ is bijective, then, for every $y \in Y$, the inverse image $f^{-1}(y)$ is always a singleton, i.e. a point in X; the assignment $y \to f^{-1}(y)$ defines a function $g: Y \to X$, which is called the *inverse function* of f and may be denoted by

$$f^{-1}: Y \to X.$$

One can easily see that f^{-1} is also bijective. As an example of bijective functions, we mention the inclusion function $i: X \subset X$ of X into itself. This special inclusion function i will be called the *identity function* on X. For this special case, we have $i^{-1} = i$.

Two functions f and g are said to be *composable* iff the range of f is equal to the domain of g, i.e.

$$X \xrightarrow{f} Y \xrightarrow{g} Z.$$

In this case, we define a function $\phi: X \to Z$ by assigning to each point x of X the point

$$\phi(x) = g[f(x)]$$

of the set Z. This function ϕ is called the *composition* of f and g denoted by

$$\phi = g \circ f: X \to Z.$$

PROPOSITION 2.3. *If $\phi = g \circ f$ denotes the composition of the functions $f: X \to Y$ and $g: Y \to Z$, then we have:*

(2.3.1) $\qquad\qquad \phi(A) = g[f(A)] \quad$ *for each $A \subset X$;*

(2.3.2) $\qquad\qquad \phi^{-1}(C) = f^{-1}[g^{-1}(C)] \quad$ *for each $C \subset Z$.*

The proofs of (2.3.1) and (2.3.2) are left to the student as exercises.

It follows from (2.3) that the composition of surjective functions is surjective and that the composition of injective functions is injective. As partial converse of this, we have the following proposition which will be useful in the sequel.

PROPOSITION 2.4. *If $\phi = g \circ f$ denotes the composition of the functions $f : X \to Y$ and $g : Y \to Z$, then the following statements are true:*

(2.4.1)   *If ϕ is surjective, then so is g.*
(2.4.2)   *If ϕ is injective, then so is f.*

Proof. Assume that ϕ is surjective. Then $\phi(X) = Z$ by definition. According to (2.3.1), we have

$$Z = \phi(X) = g[f(X)] \subset g(Y) \subset Z.$$

It follows that $g(Y) = Z$ and hence g is surjective. This proves (2.4.1).

Next, assume that ϕ is injective. Let a and b be any two points in X such that $f(a) = f(b)$. Then we have

$$\phi(a) = g[f(a)] = g[f(b)] = \phi(b).$$

Since ϕ is injective, it follows that $a = b$. This proves (2.4.2).   ‖

Let $f : X \to Y$ be a given function and A be a subset of X. Define a function $g : A \to Y$ by taking $g(x) = f(x)$ for every $x \in A$. This function g will be called the *restriction* of the given function f to the subset A; in symbols

$$g = f \mid A.$$

If $g = f \mid A$, then the function $f : X \to Y$ is said to be an *extension* of the function $g : A \to Y$ over the set X. In this case, we obtain a triangle

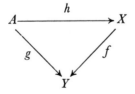

of functions, where $h : A \subset X$ stands for the inclusion function. The relation $g = f \mid A$ is equivalent to the commutativity of the triangle, i.e., $g = f \circ h$.

While there is only one restriction of a given function $f : X \to Y$ to a given subset A of X, the extensions of a given function $g : A \to Y$ over a set

X which contains A are usually numerous. For example, let y be an arbitrary point in Y; the function $e_y : X \to Y$ defined by

$$e_y(x) = \begin{cases} g(x), & (\text{if } x \in A), \\ y, & (\text{if } x \in X \setminus A), \end{cases}$$

is an extension of the given function $g : A \to Y$ over the set X.

The definition of the function $e_y : X \to Y$ given above is a special case of the construction of *combined functions* which will be frequently used in the sequel. Let F be a given family of subsets of a set X. Assume that F *covers* X, that is to say, X is equal to the union of the sets in F. Assume that, for each $A \in F$, there has been given a function $f_A : A \to Y$. Thus, we obtain a family

$$\Phi = \{f_A \mid A \in F\}$$

of functions *indexed* by the members of the family F. The family Φ of functions is said to be *combinable* iff, for any two sets $A, B \in F$, the functions $f_A : A \to Y$ and $f_B : B \to Y$ *agree* on the intersection $A \cap B$, i.e.

$$f_A \mid A \cap B = f_B \mid A \cap B.$$

If the family Φ of functions is combinable, then Φ defines uniquely a function $f : X \to Y$ given by taking $f(x) = f_A(x)$ if $x \in A \in F$. This function f will be called the *combined function* of the family Φ of functions.

To conclude the present section, we will give a few more examples of functions of special kinds.

EXAMPLE 3. A function $f : N \to X$ from the set N of natural numbers into a given set X is called a *sequence* (of points) in X. For each $n \in N$, the image $x_n = f(n)$ is called the *nth term* of the sequence f. Customarily, the sequence f can be written in the form

$$f = \{x_1, x_2, x_3, \ldots, x_n, \ldots\}.$$

In particular, if X is the set R of real numbers, then f is called a sequence of real numbers; if X is the set Z of integers, then f is called a sequence of integers.

EXAMPLE 4. Let X be a given set. For an arbitrary subset A of X, define a function $\chi_A : X \to R$ by taking

$$\chi_A(x) = \begin{cases} 1, & (\text{if } x \in A), \\ 0, & (\text{if } x \in X \setminus A). \end{cases}$$

This function χ_A is called the *characteristic function* of the subset A in X.

EXAMPLE 5. Let 2^X denote the set of all subsets of a given set X. Consider an arbitrary function $f: M \to 2^X$ from a set M into 2^X. For each element $\alpha \in M$, the image $E_\alpha = f(\alpha)$ is a subset of X. Customarily, the function f can be written in the form

$$f = \{E_\alpha \subset X \mid \alpha \in M\}$$

and is called an *indexed family* of sets with M as the *set of indices*. In particular, if M is the set N of natural numbers, then f is called a *sequence of sets*.

EXERCISES

2A. Prove the propositions (2.1), (2.2), and (2.3).

2B. Establish the following relations for any function $f: X \to Y$ with $A \subset X$ and $B \subset Y$:

   (a) $f^{-1}(f(A)) \supset A$.
   (b) $f(f^{-1}(B)) \subset B$.
   (c) $f(X \setminus A) \supset f(X) \setminus f(A)$.
   (d) $f^{-1}(Y \setminus B) = X \setminus f^{-1}(B)$.
   (e) $f(A \cap f^{-1}B) = f(A) \cap B$.

2C. Prove that a function $f: X \to Y$ is bijective iff there exist two functions $g, h : Y \to X$ such that the compositions $g \circ f$ and $f \circ h$ are the identity functions on X and Y respectively. In this case $g = f^{-1} = h$.

2D. Prove that the composition is associative, i.e., for arbitrary functions $f: X \to Y$, $g: Y \to Z$, and $h: Z \to W$, we have

$$h \circ (g \circ f) = (h \circ g) \circ f.$$

   Hence, we may denote this composed function by $h \circ g \circ f$.

2E. Verify the following equalities for the characteristic functions of subsets of X at an arbitrary point x of X:

   (a) $\chi_{A \cap B}(x) = \chi_A(x)\chi_B(x)$.
   (b) $\chi_{A \cup B}(x) = \chi_A(x) + \chi_B(x) - \chi_A(x)\chi_B(x)$.
   (c) $\chi_{A \setminus B}(x) = \chi_A(x)[1 - \chi_B(x)]$.

2F. If $f: X \to Y$ is a function and $\{E_\alpha \mid \alpha \in M\}$ is an indexed family of subsets of Y, then the following two equalities hold:

   (a) $f^{-1}(\bigcup_{\alpha \in M} E_\alpha) = \bigcup_{\alpha \in M} f^{-1}(E_\alpha)$.
   (b) $f^{-1}(\bigcap_{\alpha \in M} E_\alpha) = \bigcap_{\alpha \in M} f^{-1}(E_\alpha)$.

3. CARTESIAN PRODUCTS

Let us consider an arbitrarily given indexed family of sets

$$\mathscr{F} = \{X_\mu \mid \mu \in M\}$$

and denote by X the union of the sets X_μ for all $\mu \in M$.

By the *Cartesian product* of the family $\mathscr{F}$ of sets, we mean the set Φ of all functions

$$f : M \to X$$

such that $f(\mu) \in X_\mu$ for every $\mu \in M$. The Cartesian product of the family $\mathscr{F}$ is denoted by

$$\Phi = \Pi_{\mu \in M} X_\mu.$$

In particular, if M consists of the first n natural numbers, then a point f in Φ is essentially an ordered n-tuple $(x_1, \ldots, x_n)$ with $x_i = f(i)$ for each $i = 1, \ldots, n$. In this case, the Cartesian product of the family $\mathscr{F}$ is denoted by

$$\Phi = X_1 \times \cdots \times X_n.$$

If $X_\mu = \square$ for some $\mu \in M$, then one can easily see that the Cartesian product Φ is empty; otherwise, we have $\Phi \neq \square$. Hereafter, we will always assume that $X_\mu \neq \square$ for every $\mu \in M$.

For each $\mu \in M$, consider the function

$$p_\mu : \Phi \to X_\mu$$

defined by $p_\mu(f) = f(\mu)$ for every $f \in \Phi$. By the axiom of choice, p_μ is surjective for every $\mu \in M$. We will call p_μ the *projection* of the Cartesian product onto its μ-th *coordinate set*.

If each member X_μ of the family $\mathscr{F}$ is equal to a given set X, then the Cartesian product Φ of the family $\mathscr{F}$ will be called the *Mth Cartesian power* of the set X denoted by

$$\Phi = X^M.$$

Hence, X^M is the set of all functions from M into X. In particular, if M consists of the first n natural numbers $1, \ldots, n$, Φ is called the *nth Cartesian power* of the set X; in symbols,

$$\Phi = X^n.$$

Thus, X^n is the set of all n-tuples $(x_1, \ldots, x_n)$ with $x_i \in X$ for every $i = 1, \ldots, n$.

Assume $M \neq \square$ and consider the function

$$d : X \to X^M$$

defined by taking $d(x) \in X^M$ to be the constant function

$$[d(x)](M) = x$$

for every point $x \in X$. Obviously, the function d is injective. It is called the *diagonal injection* of the set X into the Cartesian power X^M.

Next, let us consider an arbitrarily given indexed family

$$\mathscr{H} = \{h_\mu : X_\mu \to Y_\mu \mid \mu \in M\}$$

of functions. Denote

$$X = \bigcup_{\mu \in M} X_\mu, \quad Y = \bigcup_{\mu \in M} Y_\mu,$$
$$\Phi = \Pi_{\mu \in M} X_\mu, \quad \Psi = \Pi_{\mu \in M} Y_\mu.$$

Define a function

$$H : \Phi \to \Psi$$

as follows. For an arbitrary point $f \in \Phi$, $H(f) \in \Psi$ is defined to be the function $H(f) : M \to Y$ given by

$$[H(f)](\mu) = h_\mu[f(\mu)]$$

for every $\mu \in M$. To justify this definition, we observe that, for each $\mu \in M$, $f(\mu)$ is a point of X_μ and hence $h_\mu[f(\mu)]$ is a well-defined point of Y_μ. This function $H : \Phi \to \Psi$ will be called the *Cartesian product* of the family $\mathscr{H}$ of functions and will be denoted by

$$H = \Pi_{\mu \in M} h_\mu.$$

In particular, if M consists of the first n natural numbers, then the Cartesian product of the family $\mathscr{H}$ is denoted by

$$H = h_1 \times \cdots \times h_n.$$

If $X_\mu = X$ for every $\mu \in M$, then $\Phi = X^M$ and the diagonal injection d is defined. The composed function

$$h = H \circ d : X \to \Psi$$

of the d and H in the following diagram

$$X \xrightarrow{\ d\ } X^M \xrightarrow{\ H\ } \Psi$$

will be called the *restricted Cartesian product* of the family

$$\mathscr{H} = \{h_\mu : X \to Y_\mu \mid \mu \in M\}.$$

When there is no risk of ambiguity, this function h will also be called the Cartesian product of the family $\mathscr{H}$ and also be denoted by

$$h = \Pi_{\mu \in M} h_{\mu}.$$

EXERCISES

3A. Show that if $A \subset X$ and $B \subset Y$, then
(a) $A \times B \subset X \times Y$,
(b) $(X \times Y) \setminus (A \times B) = [(X \setminus A) \times Y] \cup [X \times (Y \setminus B)]$.
show that

3B. Show that if $A \subset X$, $B \subset Y$, $C \subset X$, and $D \subset Y$, then
(a) $(A \times B) \cap (C \times D) = (A \cap C) \times (B \cap D)$,
(b) $(A \times B) \cup (C \times D) \subset (A \cup C) \times (B \cup D)$.
Give an example showing that the two members of (b) fail to be equal.

3C. Consider the function $\theta : X^2 \to X^2$ defined by $\theta(a,b) = (b,a)$ for every point (a,b) of the Cartesian square X^2.   Verify
$$\theta \circ d = d,$$
where $d : X \to X^2$ denotes the diagonal injection.   Generalize this fact to an arbitrary Cartesian power X^M.

3D. Consider the Cartesian product Φ of an arbitrarily given family $\mathscr{F} = \{X_{\mu} \mid \mu \in M\}$ of sets and its projections
$$p_{\mu} : \Phi \to X_{\mu}, \quad (\mu \in M).$$
Prove that the restricted Cartesian product of the family $\{p_{\mu} \mid \mu \in M\}$ is the identity function on Φ.

3E. Consider the diagonal injection $d : X \to X^M$ and the projections $p_{\mu} : X^M \to X$, $(\mu \in M)$, of a Cartesian power X^M.   Prove that the composed function
$$p_{\mu} \circ d : X \to X$$
is the identity function on X for every $\mu \in M$.

3F. Assume that the set X consists of the integers 0 and 1.   Define a function
$$\beta : 2^M \to X^M$$
from the set 2^M of all subsets of the set M into the Cartesian power X^M as follows: for each subset S of M, take $\beta(S)$ to be the characteristic function of the set S, i.e.
$$\beta(S) = \chi_S : M \to X.$$

Prove that the function β is bijective. This explains the meaning of the classical notation 2^M for the set of all subsets of a given set M.

3G. Define a function

$$e : X^M \times M \to X$$

by taking $e(f, \mu) = f(\mu)$ for each $\mu \in M$ and each $f \in X^M$. This function is called the *evaluation* of the Cartesian power X^M. For any given $\mu \in M$, verify

$$p_\mu(f) = e(\mu, f)$$

for every $f \in X^M$. Hence, e can be considered as the projections collected all together.

Chapter II: SPACES AND MAPS

Our main objective in this chapter is the introduction of spaces and maps. We will adopt as a definite principle that the topology of a space means the totality of its open sets and nothing else. While there are various ways to determine the topology of a space, we shall not regard these as the topology itself. Most of the chapter will be devoted to the methods of constructing new spaces from old ones by forming subspaces, topological sums, topological products, or quotient spaces, and also of constructing new maps from old ones by means of composition or combination.

1. TOPOLOGICAL SPACES

Let X be a given *set* of objects called the *points* of X.

A *topology* in X is a nonempty collection

$$\tau \subset 2^X$$

of subsets of X called *open sets* satisfying the following four axioms:

(OS1)   *The empty set $\square$ is open.*
(OS2)   *The set X itself is open.*
(OS3)   *The union of any family of open sets is open.*
(OS4)   *The intersection of any two (and hence of any finite number of) open sets is open.*

A set X is said to be *topologized* if a topology τ has been given in X. A topologized set X will be called a *topological space* or simply a *space* and the topology τ in X is called the *topology of the space X*. The open sets U in τ will be called the *open sets of the space X*.

EXAMPLES OF SPACES:

(1) *Discrete spaces.* Let X be any set. The collection of *all* subsets of X obviously satisfies the axioms for open sets and hence is a topology in X called the *discrete topology* in X. If X is topologized by its discrete topology, it is called a *discrete space*.

16

(2) *Indiscrete spaces.* Let X be any set. The collection $\{\square, X\}$ satisfies the axioms for open sets and hence is a topology in X called the *indiscrete* (or *trivial*) topology in X. If X is topologized by its indiscrete topology, it is called an *indiscrete space.*

(3) *The real line.* Let R denote the set of all real numbers. Define a collection τ of subsets of R as follows: A subset U of R is in τ iff, for an arbitrarily given point $u \in U$, there exists a positive real number δ_u such that a real number x is in U if $| x - u | < \delta_u$. It can be verified that this collection τ forms a topology in R which will be referred to as the *usual topology* in R. If R is topologized by its usual topology, it is called the (topological) *real line.*

Since topologies in a set X are special collections of subsets of X, we can compare topologies in the same set X by means of the inclusion relation. Let σ and τ be any two topologies in X. If $\sigma \subset \tau$, then we shall say that σ is *smaller* than τ and τ is *larger* than σ. It is also said that σ is *coarser* than τ and τ is *finer* than σ. Unfortunately, the more familiar terms "stronger" and "weaker" are used in contradictory senses in algebraic topology and functional analysis: If $\sigma \subset \tau$, in algebraic topology σ is said to be stronger than τ, while in functional analysis σ is said to be weaker than τ. On the other hand, τ is said to be weaker than σ in algebraic topology and τ is said to be stronger than σ in functional analysis.

A *basis* of a topology τ in X is a subcollection β of τ such that every open set U in τ is a union of some open sets in β. In other words, for every $U \in \tau$ and each point $x \in U$, there is a $V \in \beta$ such that

$$x \in V \subset U.$$

The open sets of a given basis β will be called the *basic open sets* of the space X.

A *sub-basis* of a topology τ in X is a subcollection σ of τ such that the finite intersections ($=$ the intersections of the finite families) of open sets in σ form a basis of τ. In other words, for every $U \in \tau$ and each $x \in U$, there are a finite number of open sets in σ, say $W_1, \ldots, W_n$, such that

$$x \in W_1 \cap \cdots \cap W_n \subset U.$$

The open sets in a given sub-basis σ will be called the *sub-basic open sets of* the space X.

It is obvious from the definitions that the topology τ of a space X is completely determined by any given basis or sub-basis of τ.

EXAMPLE OF BASIS AND SUB-BASIS. Let us consider the real line R as a space defined in Example 3 above.   For any two distinct real numbers a and b, $a < b$, the set

$$(a, b) = \{x \in R \mid a < x < b\}$$

is called an *open interval* of R.   It follows from the definition of open sets in R that the collection β of all open intervals of R forms a basis of the real line R.   On the other hand, for each real number a, the sets

$$L_a = \{x \in R \mid x < a\}, \qquad R_a = \{x \in R \mid x > a\}$$

are called the *open half lines* determined by the real number a.   Since

$$(a, b) = R_a \cap L_b,$$

it follows that the collection σ of all open half lines forms a sub-basis of R.

A space X is said to satisfy the *second axiom of countability* iff its topology has a countable basis.   As we shall see further on, such spaces have many pleasant properties.   From the definition of sub-basis, one can easily see that a space X satisfies the second axiom of countability iff its topology has a countable sub-basis.

Let X be a given space and p be a given point in X.   A set $N \subset X$ is said to be a *neighborhood* of the point p in the space X iff there exists an open set U of X such that

$$p \in U \subset N.$$

Hence a neighborhood of a point p in a space X is a set in X containing not only the point p itself but also some open set of X which contains p.

PROPOSITION 1.1.   *A set U of a space X is open iff U contains a neighborhood of each of its points.*

Proof: Necessity.   Assume that U is an open set of a space X.   Then, by the definition of neighborhood of points in X, U is a neighborhood of each point of U.   This implies the necessity.

Sufficiency.   Assume that U is a set in X such that U contains a neighborhood of each of its points.   Let p be an arbitrary point of U.   Then, by assumption, there exists a neighborhood N_p of the point p in X which is contained in U.   By the definition of neighborhoods, there exists an open set U_p of the space such that

$$p \in U_p \subset N_p.$$

By (OS3), the union

$$U = \bigcup_{p \in U} p \subset \bigcup_{p \in U} U_p \subset U.$$

Hence, we obtain:

$$\bigcup_{p \in U} U_p = U.$$

Since U_p is open for each p, this implies the sufficiency. ||

For an arbitrarily given point p in a space X, the family of all neighborhoods of p in X will be called the *neighborhood system* of the point p in the space X.

Properties of neighborhood systems are given by the following proposition.

PROPOSITION 1.2. *If $\mathscr{N}$ denotes the neighborhood system of a point p in a space X, then finite intersections of members of $\mathscr{N}$ belong to $\mathscr{N}$ and each set in X which contains a member of $\mathscr{N}$ belongs to $\mathscr{N}$.*

Proof. Let $N_1, \ldots, N_r$ be given neighborhoods of p in X. Then, by definition, there exist open sets $U_1, \ldots, U_r$ in X such that

$$p \in U_i \subset N_i, \qquad (i = 1, 2, \ldots, r).$$

Let $N = N_1 \cap \cdots \cap N_r$ and $U = U_1 \cap \cdots \cap U_r$. Then we have $p \in U \subset N$. By (OS4), U is an open set. Hence, N is a neighborhood of p in X.

Next, let L be any neighborhood of p in X and M be a set in X which contains L. By the definition of a neighborhood, there exists an open set V of X with $p \in V \subset L$. Since $L \subset M$, it follows that $p \in V \subset M$. Hence, M is a neighborhood of p in X. ||

By a *local basis*, or a *neighborhood basis*, of a space X at a point $p \in X$, we mean a collection β of neighborhoods of p in X such that every neighborhood of p in X contains a member of β. The members of a given local basis β of X at a point $p \in X$ will be called the *basic neighborhoods* of p in X.

EXAMPLE OF LOCAL BASIS. Consider the real line R and any $p \in R$. For each positive real number $\delta > 0$, the set

$$N_\delta(p) = \{x \in R \mid |x - p| < \delta\}$$

is called the *δ-neighborhood* of p in R. Let $\delta_1, \delta_2, \ldots, \delta_i, \ldots$ be any sequence of positive real numbers converging to 0; then the collection $\{N_{\delta_i}(p) \mid i = 1, 2, \ldots\}$ is a local basis of R at p.

A space X is said to satisfy the *first axiom of countability* iff it has a countable local basis at each of its points. For examples, the real line R and all discrete spaces satisfy the first axiom of countability.

Since the family of all open sets in a given basis of a space X containing a given point $p \in X$ is obviously a local basis of X at the point p, we get the following proposition.

PROPOSITION 1.3. *If a space X satisfies the second axiom of countability, then it satisfies also the first axiom of countability.*

The converse of (1.3) is false; for example, every noncountable discrete space fails to satisfy the second axiom of countability.

EXERCISES

1A. Find all topologies on a set of three elements.

1B. Prove that, for any family $\mathscr{F}$ of topologies in a set X, there is a unique largest topology Inf $\mathscr{F}$ in X which is smaller than each member of $\mathscr{F}$, and a unique smallest topology Sup $\mathscr{F}$ in X which is larger than each member of $\mathscr{F}$. Furthermore, prove that
$$\text{Inf } \mathscr{F} = \bigcap \{\tau \mid \tau \in \mathscr{F}\}.$$

1C. Define a collection σ of subsets of R as follows: a set W of R is in σ iff either $W = \square$ or $R \setminus W$ consists of at most a finite number of real numbers. Verify that σ is a topology in R which is properly smaller than the usual topology in R.

1D. Let β denote the collection of all half-open intervals $[a, b)$, which consist of all real numbers x with $a \leqslant x < b$, where a and b are real numbers. Let $\mathscr{F}$ denote the family of topologies in X each containing β and let
$$\eta = \text{Inf } \mathscr{F}.$$
Then η is called the *half-open interval topology* of R. Prove that η is different from both the usual topology τ and the topology σ in (1C).

1E. Prove that the half lines L_a, R_a for all rational real numbers a constitute a sub-basis of the real line R and hence the real line R satisfies the second axiom of countability.

1F. Prove that if the topology τ of a space X has a countable basis, then each basis of τ contains a countable subcollection which is also a basis of τ.

1G. Let σ be any given family of subsets of a set X such that the union of all members of σ is the whole set X. Prove that σ is a sub-basis of the smallest topology τ in X which contains σ.

1H. Let $\mathcal{N}$ denote a function which assigns to each point x of a set X a nonempty family $\mathcal{N}_x$ of subsets of X which satisfies the following three conditions:

   (i) If $N \in \mathcal{N}_x$, then $x \in N$.

   (ii) If M and N are members of $\mathcal{N}_x$, then $M \cap N$ belongs to $\mathcal{N}_x$.

   (iii) If $M \in \mathcal{N}_x$ and $M \subset N \subset X$, then $N \in \mathcal{N}_x$.

Prove that the collection τ of subsets of X defined by

$$\tau = \{U \subset X \mid x \in U \Rightarrow U \in \mathcal{N}_x\}$$

satisfies (OS1–4) and hence is a topology in X. Furthermore, $\mathcal{N}_x$ is precisely the neighborhood system of x in the space X iff it satisfies the following conditions:

   (iv) If $N \in \mathcal{N}_x$, then there is an $M \in \mathcal{N}_x$ such that $M \subset N$ and $M \in \mathcal{N}_y$ for every $y \in M$.

2. SETS IN A SPACE

Let X be an arbitrarily given space. Consider a set E in X and a point p of X. We will first study the relation between p and E with respect to the topology of the given space X.

The point p is said to be an *interior point* of the set E provided that there exists a neighborhood N of p in X contained in E. The point p is said to be an *exterior point* of E if there exists a neighborhood N of p in X which contains no point of E. Finally, the point p is said to be a *boundary point*, or *frontier point*, of E in case every neighborhood N of p in X contains at least one point in E and at least one point not in E.

The set Int (E) of all interior points of E is called the *interior* of E. The set Ext (E) of all exterior points of E is called the *exterior* of E. The set $\partial(E)$ of all boundary points of E is called the *boundary*, or *frontier*, of the set E in the space X. Obviously, we have

$$\text{Int } (E) \subset E,$$
$$\text{Ext } (E) \cap E = \square;$$

and a boundary point of E may be in E and may be not in E.

PROPOSITION 2.1. *The interior* Int (E) *of a set E in a space X is the largest open set of X contained in E.*

Proof. Let U be an arbitrary open set of X contained in E. We are going to show that $U \subset $ Int (E). For this purpose, let p be any point in U. By definition, U is a neighborhood of p in X. Since $U \subset E$, it follows that p is an interior point of E. This implies $U \subset $ Int (E).

Next, for each interior point p of E, choose a neighborhood N_p of p in X such that $p \in N_p \subset E$. By definition of neighborhoods, there exists an open set U_p of X such that $p \in U_p \subset N_p$. Let U denote the union of the open sets U_p for all interior points p of E. This implies that Int $(E) \subset U$. Since U is an open set of X according to (OS3), it follows from the first part of the proof that $U \subset$ Int (E). Hence, Int $(E) = U$ is an open set of X.

Combining both parts of the proof, we conclude that Int (E) is open and contains every open set of X which is contained in E. $\|$

As an immediate consequence of (2.1), we have the following corollary which gives the geometrical significance of the terminology of open sets.

COROLLARY 2.2.   *A set E in a space X is open iff E contains none of its boundary points, in symbols, $E \cap \partial(E) = \square$.*

On the other extreme, we introduce the closed sets to the reader as follows.

A set E in a space X is said to be *closed* iff E contains all of its boundary points, in symbols $\partial(E) \subset E$. Note that a set which contains some but not all of its boundary points is neither open nor closed.

PROPOSITION 2.3.   *A set E in a space X is closed iff its complement $X \setminus E$ is open.*

Proof. It follows immediately from the definition of boundary points that

$$\partial(E) = \partial(X \setminus E).$$

To prove the necessity, let us assume that that E is closed. Then, according to definition, $\partial(E) \subset E$. This implies that $X \setminus E$ contains none of its boundary points. Hence $X \setminus E$ is open according to (2.2).

To prove the sufficiency, let us assume that $X \setminus E$ is open. By (2.2), $\partial(X \setminus E)$ must be contained in E. Hence, $\partial(E) \subset E$ and E is closed by definition. $\|$

The preceding proposition establishes duality between the closed sets and open sets of a space by means of taking complements. Because of this duality, one can easily deduce the properties of closed sets dual to those of open sets. For example, the following proposition can be established in this way.

PROPOSITION 2.4.   *The closed sets of a space X satisfy the following four conditions:*

(CS1)   *The empty set $\square$ is closed.*

(CS2)   *The set X itself is closed.*

(CS3)   *The intersection of any family of closed sets is closed.*

(CS4)   *The union of any two (and hence of any finite number of) closed sets is closed.*

Dual to (2.1), we will define the closure of a set E in a space X as follows.

By the *closure* Cl (E) of a set E in a space X, we mean the smallest closed set of X which contains E. By (CS3), Cl (E) is equal to the intersection of all closed sets of X containing E. Frequently, we will also use the classical notation $\bar{E}$ for the closure of E in X.

PROPOSITION 2.5. *For any given set E in a space X, we have*

$$\mathrm{Cl}\ (E) = E \cup \partial(E) = \mathrm{Int}\ (E) \cup \partial(E).$$

Proof. From the relations $\mathrm{Int}\ (E) \subset E$ and $\mathrm{Ext}\ (E) \subset X \setminus E$, we deduce

$$E \cup \partial(E) = \mathrm{Int}\ (E) \cup \partial(E) = X \setminus \mathrm{Ext}\ (E).$$

Since $\mathrm{Ext}\ (E) = \mathrm{Int}\ (X \setminus E)$ is open, it follows that $E \cup \partial(E)$ is closed and hence

$$\mathrm{Cl}\ (E) \subset E \cup \partial(E).$$

On the other hand, let F be any closed set of X containing E. ~~Then, the set of X containing E.~~ Then, the set $X \setminus F$ is open and is contained in $X \setminus E$. By (2.1), we have

$$X \setminus F \subset \mathrm{Int}\ (X \setminus E) = \mathrm{Ext}\ (E).$$

This implies that $F \supset X \setminus \mathrm{Ext}\ (E)$. In particular, we have

$$\mathrm{Cl}\ (E) \supset E \cup \partial(E).$$

This completes the proof of (2.5). $\ \|$

The duality between Int (E) and Cl (E) is clarified by the following proposition which is an immediate consequence of (2.1) and the definition of Cl (E).

PROPOSITION 2.6. *For any given set E in a space X, we have:*

(i) *E is open iff* Int $(E) = E$;

(ii) *E is closed iff* Cl $(E) = E$.

A characterization of the points in Cl (E) is given by the following proposition.

PROPOSITION 2.7. *A point p is in the closure* Cl *(E) of a set E in a space X iff every neighborhood N of p in X meets the set E.*

Proof: Necessity. Assume that $p \in$ Cl (E). Since Cl $(E) = E \cup \partial(E)$ by (2.5), we must have $p \in E$ or $p \in \partial(E)$. If $p \in E$, then $N \cap E$ contains the point p; if $p \in \partial(E)$, then it follows from the definition of $\partial(E)$ that N contains at least one point of E. Hence $N \cap E \neq \square$ and the necessity is established.

Sufficiency. Assume that every neighborhood of p meets E. We have to prove that $p \in$ Cl $(E) = E \cup \partial(E)$. This is obvious if $p \in E$. Hence, we may assume that $p \notin E$. Then every neighborhood of p contains also a point not in E. By definition, $p \in \partial(E) \subset$ Cl (E). This proves the sufficiency. ||

If p is a point in Cl (E) but not in E, then every neighborhood N of p in X contains at least one point of E other than p. This suggests the following definition.

A point p of a space X is said to be an *accumulation point* (or *cluster point*, or *limit point*) of a set E in X iff every neighborhood N of p in X contains at least one point of E other than p. The set E' of all accumulation points of E in X is called the *derived set* of E in X. Then, we have

$$\text{Cl } (E) = E \cup E'$$

and that a set E in X is closed iff it contains all of its accumulation points.

A set E in a space X is said to be *dense* in X iff Cl $(E) = X$.

PROPOSITION 2.8. *A set E in a space X is dense in X iff the topology of the space X has a basis such that every nonempty basic open set meets E.*

Proof: Necessity. It suffices to show that every nonempty open set U of X meets E. For this purpose choose an arbitrary point $p \in U$. Since E is dense, p is a point of Cl (E). Since U is a neighborhood of p, it follows from (2.7) that U meets E.

Sufficiency. Assume that the topology of the space X has a basis β such that every nonempty basic open set meets E. Let p be an arbitrary point in X and N be any neighborhood of p in X. By the definition of neighborhood and basis, there exists a basic open set V such that $p \in V \subset N$. By assumption, V meets E and hence N also meets E. Hence $p \in$ Cl (E) according to (2.7). Since p is arbitrary, we have Cl $(E) = X$. ||

As an immediate consequence of (2.8), the set Q of all rational numbers is dense in the real line R. In fact, every open interval of real numbers contains a rational number and the collection of open intervals is a basis of the usual topology of R.

A space X is said to be *separable* iff it contains a countable subset which is dense in X. For example, the real line R is separable, because the subset Q of all rational numbers is countable and is dense in R.

PROPOSITION 2.9. *Every space which satisfies the second axiom of countability is separable.*

Proof. Let X be a space satisfying the second axiom of countability. Then, the topology τ of X admits a countable basis β. In each non-empty basic open set $V \in \beta$, let us pick a point $x_V \in V$. Let E denote the set of all points x_V for all $V \in \beta$. Then E must be countable. By (2.8), E is dense in X. Hence X is separable. ||

The converse of (2.9) is false. In fact, a separable space may violate the second axiom of countability. For example, let us consider the set R of real numbers with the topology σ defined in Exercise 1C; that is to say, a set W of R is in σ iff either $W = \square$ or $R \setminus W$ is finite. In this space R topologized by σ, every infinite subset of R is dense in R. In particular, the set N of positive integers is dense in R; hence, R is separable. On the other hand, we will prove that this space R does not satisfy the second axiom of countability. For this purpose, let us assume that β were a countable basis of the topology σ and deduce a contradiction as follows. Let $p \in R$ and consider the intersection of all $V \in \beta$ such that $p \in V$. We assert that this intersection is equal to the singleton set $\{p\}$. In fact, let $q \neq p$. Then $R \setminus \{q\}$ is in σ. There exists a $V \in \beta$ such that $p \in V \subset R \setminus \{q\}$. Hence, q is not in the intersection. This proves our assertion that the intersection is the singleton set $\{p\}$. Now, on one hand, the complement of this countable intersection is the union of a countable number of finite sets and hence countable. On the other hand, this complement contains all real numbers except p and hence is not countable. This contradiction completes the proof.

EXERCISES

2A. Let A and B be any two sets in a space X. Prove the following properties of the operation of forming the interior of a set:

  (a) Int [Int (A)] = Int (A);
  (b) Int $(A \cup B) \supset$ Int $(A) \cup$ Int (B);
  (c) Int $(A \cap B) =$ Int $(A) \cap$ Int (B).

In the case of (b), give an example of two sets A and B in the real line R such that Int $(A \cup B)$ is not equal to Int $(A) \cup$ Int (B).

2B. Let A and B be any two sets in a space X. Prove the following properties of the operation of forming the closure of a set:

 (a) Cl $[\text{Cl } (A)] = \text{Cl } (A)$;
 (b) Cl $[A \cup B] = \text{Cl } (A) \cup \text{Cl } (B)$;
 (c) Cl $[A \cap B] \subset \text{Cl } (A) \cap \text{Cl } (B)$.

In the case of (c), give an example of two sets A and B in the real line R such that Cl $(A \cap B)$ is not equal to Cl $(A) \cap$ Cl (B).

2C. For an arbitrary set E in a space X, establish the following relations between interior and closure:

 (a) Int $(X \setminus E) = X \setminus \text{Cl } (E)$;
 (b) Cl $(X \setminus E) = X \setminus \text{Int } (E)$.

2D. By an *interior operator* on X, we mean a function ϕ which assigns to each subset E of X a subset $\phi(E)$ of X such that the following four conditions are satisfied:

 (IO1) $\phi(X) = X$;
 (IO2) $\phi(E) \subset E$ for each $E \subset X$;
 (IO3) $\phi[\phi(E)] = \phi(E)$ for each $E \subset X$;
 (IO4) $\phi(A \cap B) = \phi(A) \cap \phi(B)$ for each $A \subset X$ and each $B \subset X$.

Let ϕ be a given interior operator on X and let τ denote the collection of all subsets E of X such that $\phi(E) = E$. Verify that τ is a topology in X. Prove that, for each $E \subset X$, $\phi(E)$ is the interior of E in the space X with τ as topology.

2E. By a *closure operator* on X, we mean a function ψ which assigns to each subset E of X a subset $\psi(E)$ of X such that the following four conditions are satisfied:

 (CO1) $\psi(\square) = \square$;
 (CO2) $E \subset \psi(E)$ for each $E \subset X$;
 (CO3) $\psi[\psi(E)] = \psi(E)$ for each $E \subset X$;
 (CO4) $\psi[A \cup B] = \psi(A) \cup \psi(B)$ for each $A \subset X$ and each $B \subset X$.

Let ψ be a given closure operator on X and let τ denote the collection of all subsets E of X such that $\psi(X \setminus E) = X \setminus E$. Verify that τ is a topology in X. Prove that, for each $E \subset X$, $\psi(E)$ is the closure of E in the space X with τ as topology.

2F. Let A and B be sets in a space X. Prove that

$$\partial(A \cup B) \subset \partial(A) \cup \partial(B),$$

and give an example to show that $\partial(A \cup B)$ may be different from $\partial(A) \cup \partial(B)$.

2G. Let E be a dense subset in a space X and U be an open subset of X. Prove that

$$U \subset \text{Cl}\,(E \cap U).$$

3. MAPS

Let us consider a function

$$f : X \to Y$$

of which both the domain X and the range Y are spaces. The function f is said to be *continuous at a point* p of X iff, for every neighborhood N of the point $f(p)$ in Y, there exists a neighborhood M of the point p in X such that $f(M) \subset N$. The function f is said to be *continuous* iff it is continuous at every point of X. Continuous functions will be called *mappings* or *maps*. For example, the constant functions from a space X into a space Y are continuous and will be called the *constant maps*. As another example, the identity function on a space X is continuous and will be called the *identity map* on X.

THEOREM 3.1. *If $f : X \to Y$ is a function from a space X into a space Y with a given basis and a given sub-basis of its topology, then the following statements are equivalent.*

(i) *The function $f : X \to Y$ is a map.*

(ii) *The inverse image $f^{-1}(U)$ of each open set U in Y is open in X.*

(iii) *The inverse image $f^{-1}(V)$ of each basic open set V in Y is open in X.*

(iv) *The inverse image $f^{-1}(W)$ of each sub-basic open set W in Y is open in X.*

(v) *The inverse image $f^{-1}(F)$ of each closed set F in Y is closed in X.*

(vi) $f[\text{Cl}\,(A)] \subset \text{Cl}\,[f(A)]$ *for each $A \subset X$.*

(vii) $f^{-1}[\text{Cl}\,(B)] \supset \text{Cl}\,[f^{-1}(B)]$ *for each $B \subset Y$.*

Proof. (i) $\Rightarrow$ (ii). Let U be an arbitrary open set in Y. We are going to prove that $f^{-1}(U)$ is open in X. For this purpose, let p be any point in $f^{-1}(U)$. Then $f(p)$ is a point in U. Since U is open, it is a neighborhood of $f(p)$ in Y. Since f is continuous at the point p, there exists a neighborhood M of p in X such that $f(M) \subset U$. This implies that $M \subset f^{-1}(U)$. By (1.1), it follows that $f^{-1}(U)$ is an open set in X.

(*ii*) $\Rightarrow$ (*iii*) and (*iii*) $\Rightarrow$ (*iv*) are obvious.

(*iv*) $\Rightarrow$ (*v*). Let F be an arbitrary closed set in Y. We are going to prove that $f^{-1}(F)$ is closed in X. By (2.3), it suffices to show that $X \setminus f^{-1}(F)$ is open in X. For this purpose, let p be an arbitrary point in $X \setminus f^{-1}(F)$. Then $f(p) \in Y \setminus F$. Since F is closed in Y, $Y \setminus F$ is open in Y according to (2.3). By definition, there exists a finite number of sub-basic open sets of Y, say $W_1, \ldots, W_n$, such that

$$f(p) \in W_1 \cap \cdots \cap W_n \subset Y \setminus F.$$

This implies that

$$p \in f^{-1}(W_1) \cap \cdots \cap f^{-1}(W_n) \subset X \setminus f^{-1}(F).$$

By (*iv*), $f^{-1}(W_i)$ is open for each $i = 1, \ldots, n$. By (OS4), $f^{-1}(W_1) \cap \cdots \cap f^{-1}(W_n)$ is open and hence a neighborhood of p in X. Then it follows from (1.1) that $X \setminus f^{-1}(F)$ is open.

(*v*) $\Rightarrow$ (*vi*). Let A be an arbitrary set in X. Then $\mathrm{Cl}\,[f(A)]$ is a closed set in Y. By (*v*), $f^{-1}\{\mathrm{Cl}\,[f(A)]\}$ is a closed set in X. Obviously, $A \subset f^{-1}\{\mathrm{Cl}\,[f(A)]\}$. Since $\mathrm{Cl}\,(A)$ is the smallest closed set in X containing A, we have $\mathrm{Cl}\,(A) \subset f^{-1}\{\mathrm{Cl}\,[f(A)]\}$. This implies

$$f[\mathrm{Cl}\,(A)] \subset \mathrm{Cl}\,[f(A)].$$

(*vi*) $\Rightarrow$ (*vii*). Let B be an arbitrary set in Y and let $A = f^{-1}(B)$. Then, by (*vi*), we have

$$f[\mathrm{Cl}\,(A)] \subset \mathrm{Cl}\,[f(A)] \subset \mathrm{Cl}\,(B).$$

This implies that $\mathrm{Cl}\,(A) \subset f^{-1}[\mathrm{Cl}\,(B)]$. That is,

$$f^{-1}\,[\mathrm{Cl}\,(B)] \supset \mathrm{Cl}\,[f^{-1}(B)].$$

(*vii*) $\Rightarrow$ (*i*). Let p be an arbitrary point of X and N be any neighborhood of $f(p)$ in Y. Then, there exists an open set U of Y such that $f(p) \in U \subset N$. Consider the closed set $B = Y \setminus U$ in Y. According to (*vii*), we have

$$\mathrm{Cl}\,[f^{-1}(B)] \subset f^{-1}[\mathrm{Cl}\,(B)] = f^{-1}(B).$$

Hence $f^{-1}(B)$ is a closed set in X. This implies that the set $M = X \setminus f^{-1}(B)$ is an open neighborhood of p in X and that $f(M) \subset U \subset N$. Therefore, f is continuous at p. Since p is arbitrary, this completes the proof of (3.1).

A map $f: X \to Y$ from a space X into a space Y is said to be *open* iff the image $f(U)$ of every open set U in X is open in Y; similarly,

$f: X \to Y$ is said to be *closed* iff the image $f(F)$ of every closed set F in X is closed in Y.

If a map $f: X \to Y$ is bijective, then its inverse function $f^{-1}: Y \to X$ is well-defined but not always continuous. For example, let X denote the space of all real numbers with the discrete topology and Y denote the real line. Then the identity function $i: X \to Y$ is a bijective map, but its inverse function $i^{-1}: Y \to X$ fails to be continuous. As to the continuity of the inverse function of a bijective map, the following proposition is obvious.

PROPOSITION 3.2. *For any bijective map* $f: X \to Y$, *the following statements are equivalent.*

(a) *The inverse function* $f^{-1}: Y \to X$ *is continuous.*
(b) $f: X \to Y$ *is open.*
(c) $f: X \to Y$ *is closed.*

By a *homeomorphism*, or *topological map*, we mean a bijective map $f: X \to Y$ which satisfies equivalent conditions (a), (b), (c) in (3.2). If a homeomorphism $h: X \to Y$ exists, then the two spaces X and Y are said to be *homeomorphic*, or *topologically equivalent*, and each space is said to be a *homeomorph* of the other. A property which when possessed by a space is also possessed by each of its homeomorphs is called a *topological property*. Formally, topology is the study of topological properties of spaces.

For any two composable functions

$$X \overset{f}{\longrightarrow} Y \overset{g}{\longrightarrow} Z,$$

the relations in (2.3) of Chapter I imply the following proposition.

PROPOSITION 3.3. *If f and g are continuous, so is the composition $g \circ f$. If f and g are homeomorphisms, then f^{-1}, g^{-1} and $g \circ f$ are also homeomorphisms.*

Throughout the remainder of the section, we will consider a function

$$f: X \to Y$$

from a set X into a set Y.

Let τ be an arbitrary topology in X. Define a collection θ of subsets of Y as follows: a subset V of Y is in θ iff the inverse image $f^{-1}(V)$ is in τ. One easily verifies that the collection θ satisfies the axioms for open sets and hence is a topology in Y. In fact, θ is the largest topology in Y which makes f a map. This topology θ is said to be the *induced topology* in Y by the function f and the topology τ in X, and will be denoted by $f_*(\tau)$.

On the other hand, let η be an arbitrary topology in Y. Then it is obvious that the collection

$$\xi = \{f^{-1}(V) \mid V \in \eta\}$$

of subsets of X satisfies the axioms for open sets and hence is a topology in X. In fact, ξ is the smallest topology in X which makes f a map. This topology ξ is said to be the *induced topology* in X by the function f and the topology η in Y and will be denoted by $f^{-1}(\eta)$.

Examples of induced topologies of both kinds will be given in the following sections.

EXERCISES

3A. Consider a function $f: X \to Y$ from a space X into a space Y, a point $p \in X$, and a local basis of Y at the point $f(p)$. Prove that f is continuous at p iff, for every basic neighborhood N of $f(p)$ in Y, there exists a neighborhood M of p in X such that $f(M) \subset N$.

3B. Let E be any subset of a space X; consider the characteristic function

$$\chi_E : X \to R$$

from the space X into the real line R as defined in (I, § 2, Example 4). Prove that χ_E is continuous at a point $p \in X$ iff p is not a boundary point of E.

3C. Let X denote the real line with the usual topology τ and let Y denote the set of all real numbers. Describe the open sets of the topology $f_*(\tau)$ in Y induced by the function

$$f: X \to Y$$

which is defined by taking $f(x) = |x|$, the absolute value of the real number x.

3D. Let E be a subset in a set X, R the real line with the usual topology τ, and $\chi_E : X \to R$ the characteristic function of E in X. Exhibit the open sets in the topology $\chi_E^{-1}(\tau)$ induced in the set X.

3E. Prove that every function from a discrete space into a space or from a space into an indiscrete space is always continuous.

4. SUBSPACES

Let E be a given subset of a space X with a topology τ. Then, the inclusion function

$$i : E \subset X$$

induces a topology $i^{-1}(\tau)$ in E as defined in the previous section. This topology $i^{-1}(\tau)$ in E will be called the *relative topology* in E with respect to τ. When topologized by the relative topology $i^{-1}(\tau)$, E will be called a *subspace* of the space X. It follows immediately from the definition of $i^{-1}(\tau)$ that a set $U \subset E$ is open in E iff there exists an open set V of X such that

$$U = i^{-1}(V) = E \cap V.$$

Similarly, a set $C \subset E$ is closed in E iff there exists a closed set D of X such that $C = E \cap D$.

EXAMPLES OF SUBSPACES. The subset

$$I = \{x \in R \mid 0 \leqslant x \leqslant 1\}$$

of the real line R furnished with the relative topology will be called the *unit interval*. The subspace Z of the real line R consisting of all integers, (positive, negative, or zero) is discrete.

Now, let E be an arbitrary subspace of a space X. It follows immediately from the definition that the inclusion function

$$i : E \subset X$$

is a map which will be called the *inclusion map*.

PROPOSITION 4.1. *A subspace E of a space X is open in X iff the inclusion map $i : E \subset X$ is open. Hence, every open subset of an open subspace is open.*

Proof: Necessity. Assume that E is open in X. We are going to prove that $i : E \subset X$ is an open map. For this purpose, let U be any open set of the subspace E. By definition, there exists an open set V of the space X such that

$$i(U) = U = E \cap V.$$

Since E and V are open in X, so is U. This implies that i is an open map.

Sufficiency. Assume that i is an open map. Since E is open in E and i is an open map, it follows that $E = i(E)$ is open in X. $||$

Similarly, one can prove the following proposition.

PROPOSITION 4.2. *A subspace E of a space X is closed in X iff the inclusion map $i : E \subset X$ is closed. Hence, every closed subset of a closed subspace is closed.*

Next, let us consider two spaces X and Y together with a subspace E of X and the inclusion map $i : E \subset X$.

For an arbitrary map $f: X \to Y$, the composed map

$$g = f \circ i : E \to Y$$

will be called the *restriction* of the map f on the subspace E of X, denoted by

$$g = f \mid E.$$

For every point $p \in E$, we have

$$g(p) = f[i(p)] = f(p);$$

hence g and f are essentially the same map except that the domain of g has been restricted to the subspace E.

By an *extension* of a map $g : E \to Y$ over the space X, we mean a map $f: X \to Y$ such that $f \mid E = g$. The *extension problem* of a given map $g : E \to Y$ over the space X is to determine whether or not g has an extension over X and to find an extension of g over X if such exists. In other words, the extension problem of a given map $g : E \to Y$ over X is to find a map $f: X \to Y$ which makes the triangle

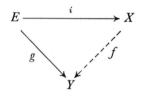

commutative, that is, $f \circ i = g$ where i stands for the inclusion map. As we shall see later, the answer to the extension problem is not always affirmative.

Consider the special case where $Y = E$ and $g : E \to Y$ is the identity map on E. Then an extension of g over the space X will be a map $r : X \to E$ such that $r \mid E$ is the identity map on E. Such a map $r : X \to E$ will be called a *retraction* of X onto E. If a retraction of X onto E exists, the subspace E of X is said to be a *retract* of the space X.

EXAMPLES OF RETRACTS. The space X is a retract of itself. Every singleton subspace of the space X is a retract of X. Finally, the unit interval I is a retract of the real line R with a retraction $r : R \to I$ defined by

$$r(t) = \begin{cases} 0, & (\text{if } t \leqslant 0), \\ t, & (\text{if } 0 \leqslant t \leqslant 1), \\ 1, & (\text{if } t \geqslant 1). \end{cases}$$

This last example shows that frequently a function is constructed by prescribing it on pieces of its domain. In the next few propositions, we will give sufficient conditions for the continuity of functions so constructed.

By a *covering*, or *cover*, of a space X, we mean a collection γ of subspaces of the space X such that the union of all members of γ is the whole space X. If every member of γ is open in X, γ is said to be an *open cover* of X; if every member of γ is closed in X, γ is said to be a *closed cover* of X.

Let γ be a given cover of a space X. For an arbitrary map $g : X \to Y$ from the space X into a space Y, the restrictions

$$g_A = g \mid A : A \to Y, \qquad (A \in \gamma),$$

are well-defined maps and satisfy the relations

$$g_A \mid A \cap B = g_B \mid A \cap B, \qquad (A, B \in \gamma).$$

Our problem is to study the inverse of this process described as follows.

Let us assume that, for each member $A \in \gamma$, there is given a map $f_A : A \to Y$ such that

$$f_A \mid A \cap B = f_B \mid A \cap B$$

for each pair of members A and B of γ. Then we may define a function $f : X \to Y$ by taking

$$f(x) = f_A(x), \qquad (\text{if } x \in A \in \gamma).$$

We are concerned with the problem of whether or not f is continuous.

PROPOSITION 4.3. *If γ is a finite closed cover of X, then the combined function f is continuous.*

Proof. Let F be any closed set in Y. For each member $A \in \gamma$, it follows from the continuity of f_A that $f_A^{-1}(F)$ is a closed set of A according to (v) in (3.1). Since A is closed in X, it follows from (4.2) that $f_A^{-1}(F)$ is also closed in X. Since γ is finite,

$$f^{-1}(F) = \bigcup_{A \in \gamma} f_A^{-1}(F)$$

is a closed set of X according to (CS3) in (2.4). Hence f is continuous. ‖

PROPOSITION 4.4. *If p is an interior point of some member A of γ, then the combined function f is continuous at p.*

Proof. Let N be an arbitrary neighborhood of the point $f(p) = f_A(p)$ in Y. It follows from the continuity of f_A that there exists a neighborhood M of p in A such that $f_A(M) \subset N$. By the definition of a neighborhood, there exists an open set U of A with $p \in U \subset M$. Let

$$V = U \cap \text{Int}\,(A).$$

Since Int (A) is open in X and V is open in Int (A), it follows from (4.1) that V is open in X. Since $p \in V \subset M$, we have

$$f(V) = f_A(V) \subset N.$$

Hence f is continuous at p. ||

   COROLLARY 4.5.   *If γ is an open cover of X, then the combined function f is continuous.*

   Next, we will generalize the notion of the restrictions of a map as follows.   Let

$$f : X \to Y$$

be a given map from a space X into a space Y and consider subspaces

$$A \subset X, \quad B \subset Y$$

such that $f(A) \subset B$.   Define a function

$$g : A \to B$$

by assigning $g(x) = f(x)$ for every x in A.   One can easily verify that g is a map which will be referred to as the *map from A into B defined by f*.

   Let $i : A \subset X$ and $j : B \subset Y$ denote the inclusion maps.   Then the rectangle

$$
\begin{array}{ccc}
A & \xrightarrow{\ \ g\ \ } & B \\
{\scriptstyle i}\downarrow & & \downarrow{\scriptstyle j} \\
X & \xrightarrow[\ \ f\ \ ]{} & Y
\end{array}
$$

is commutative, that is, $f \circ i = j \circ g$.   In case $B = Y$, then j becomes the identity map and $g = f \circ i = f \mid A$ reduces to the restriction of f on A.

   Finally, we will introduce the important notion of an imbedding as follows.

   By an *imbedding* of a space X into a space Y, we mean an injective map $f : X \to Y$ which defines a homeomorphism from X onto $f(X)$. For example, every inclusion map is an imbedding.

EXERCISES

4A.   The open interval (a, b), $a < b$, as a subspace of the real line R, is
      defined by

$$(a, b) = \{t \in R \mid a < t < b\}.$$

Prove that (a, b) and R are homeomorphic by studying the function $h : (a, b) \to R$ defined by

$$h(t) = \begin{cases} \dfrac{t - c}{t - a}, & \text{(if } a < t \leqslant c), \\[2ex] \dfrac{t - c}{b - t}, & \text{(if } c \leqslant t < b), \end{cases}$$

where c denotes the arithmetic mean of a and b.

4B. Let A, B, and C be three subspaces of a space X such that $C \subset A \cap B$. Prove that C is open in the subspace $A \cup B$ if it is open in both A and B, and prove that C is closed in the subspace $A \cup B$ if it is closed in both A and B.

4C. Let A and B be two sets in a space X such that $B \subset A$. Prove:

(a) Int (B) is contained in the interior of B with respect to the subspace A.

(b) Cl $(B) \cap A$ is the closure of B with respect to the subspace A.

(c) $\partial(B) \cap A$ contains the boundary of B with respect to subspace A. Can the words "is contained in" and "contains" in (a) and (c) be replaced by "is identical with"?

4D. Let A and B be two sets in a space X such that $A \cup B = X$. Consider two maps $f, g : X \to Y$ and a given point y_0 in the space Y such that $f(\text{Cl } B) = y_0 = g(\text{Cl } A)$. Define a function $h : X \to Y$ by taking

$$h(x) = \begin{cases} f(x), & \text{(if } x \in A), \\ g(x), & \text{(if } x \in B). \end{cases}$$

Verify that h is well-defined and continuous.

4E. Prove LINDELÖF's THEOREM: *Every open cover of a space satisfying the second axiom of countability has a countable subcover.* A space is said to be a *Lindelöf space* iff each open cover of the space has a countable subcover.

5. SUM AND PRODUCT OF SPACES

Consider a given indexed family

$$\mathscr{F} = \{X_\mu \mid \mu \in M\}$$

of sets. If each of the sets X_μ is a space, $\mathscr{F}$ is called an *indexed family of spaces*. Furthermore, if $\mu \neq \nu$ implies that

$$X_\mu \cap X_\nu = \square,$$

then the family $\mathscr{F}$ is said to be *disjoint*.

To introduce the notion of the sum of spaces, let us consider an arbitrarily given indexed family

$$\mathscr{F} = \{X_\mu \mid \mu \in M\}$$

of spaces and denote by X the union of all sets X_μ, that is,

$$X = \bigcup\nolimits_{\mu \in M} X_\mu .$$

Define a collection τ of subsets of X as follows: A subset U of X is in τ iff $U \cap X_\mu$ is an open set of the space X_μ for every $\mu \in M$. It is obvious that τ satisfies the axioms (OS1)–(OS4) for open sets and hence is a topology in X. When topologized by τ, the space X will be referred to as the *topological sum*, or *sum*, of the family $\mathscr{F}$ of spaces and denoted by

$$X = \sum\nolimits_{\mu \in M} X_\mu .$$

In applications, the given family $\mathscr{F}$ of spaces is usually disjoint.

Since $X_\mu \subset X$ for each $\mu \in M$, the inclusion functions

$$i_\mu : X_\mu \subset X, \qquad (\mu \in M)$$

are well-defined.

PROPOSITION 5.1. *For each $\mu \in M$, the inclusion function*

$$i_\mu : X_\mu \subset X$$

is continuous. If the indexed family $\mathscr{F}$ of spaces is disjoint, then each i_μ is both open and closed.

Proof. To prove the continuity of i_μ, let U be an arbitrary open set of X. Then $U \cap X_\mu$ is an open set of X_μ according to the definition of the topology in X. Since

$$i_\mu^{-1}(U) = U \cap X_\mu ,$$

it follows from (*ii*) of (3.1) that i_μ is continuous.

Next, assume that $\mathscr{F}$ is disjoint. Let U be any open set in X_μ. Since $\mathscr{F}$ is disjoint, we have $U \cap X_\mu = U$ and $U \cap X_\nu = \square$ for each $\nu \neq \mu$. Hence U is also an open set of X. Since $i_\mu(U) = U$, this proves that i_μ is open. On the other hand, let F be any closed set of X_μ and consider the set $V = X \setminus F$. Since $V \cap X_\mu = X_\mu \setminus F$ and $V \cap X_\nu = X_\nu$ for each $\nu \neq \mu$, it follows that V is an open set of X. This implies that $i_\mu(F) = F$ is a closed set of X and hence i_μ is closed. ‖

COROLLARY 5.2. *If the indexed family $\mathscr{F}$ is disjoint, then each i_μ is an imbedding of X_μ as an open and closed subspace of X.*

Next, to introduce the notion of products of spaces, let

$$\mathscr{F} = \{X_\mu \mid \mu \in M\}$$

be an arbitrarily given indexed family of spaces and consider the Cartesian product

$$\Phi = \Pi_{\mu \in M} X_\mu$$

defined in (I, § 3). Then Φ consists of all functions $f : M \to X$ of M into the union X of all sets X_μ in $\mathscr{F}$ such that $f(\mu) \in X_\mu$ for every $\mu \in M$.

We are going to define a topology τ in Φ as follows. For an arbitrary $\mu \in M$, and any open set U_μ of X_μ, the set

$$U_\mu{}^* = \{ f \in \Phi \mid f(\mu) \in U_\mu \}$$

will be called a *sub-basic open set of* Φ defined by $U_\mu \subset X_\mu$. Let σ denote the collection of all sub-basic open sets of Φ. Then we define the topology τ to be smallest topology in Φ containing the collection σ. This topology τ will be called the *product topology* in Φ. When topologized with τ, Φ is said to be the *topological product*, or *product*, of the family $\mathscr{F}$ of spaces, also denoted by

$$\Phi = \Pi_{\mu \in M} X_\mu .$$

Since σ is obviously a cover of Φ and since τ is the smallest topology in Φ containing σ, it follows from Exercise 1G that σ constitutes a sub-basis of τ and that the collection β of all finite intersections of sub-basic open sets of Φ forms a basis of τ.

EXAMPLES OF PRODUCT SPACES. If each member X_μ of the family $\mathscr{F}$ is equal to a given space X, then the topological product Φ of the family $\mathscr{F}$ will be referred to as the *Mth topological power* of the space X denoted by

$$\Phi = X^M.$$

In particular, if M consists of the first n natural numbers, $1, \ldots, n$, Φ is called the *nth topological power* of the space X; in symbols,

$$\Phi = X^n.$$

The nth topological power R^n of the real line R is called the *n-dimensional Euclidean space*. Hence, the points of R^n are the ordered n-tuples $(x_1, \ldots, x_n)$ of real numbers. Similarly, the nth topological power I^n of the unit interval I is called the *unit n-cube*. The Nth topological power I^N of the unit interval I, where N denotes the set of all natural numbers, is called the *Hilbert cube*.

Now, let Φ denote the topological product of an indexed family

$$\mathscr{F} = \{ X_\mu \mid \mu \in M \}$$

of spaces. If $X_\mu = \square$ for some $\mu \in M$, then we have $\Phi = \square$. Hereafter, we assume that $X_\mu \neq \square$ for all $\mu \in M$.

For each $\mu \in M$, consider the projection

$$p_\mu : \Phi \rightarrow X_\mu$$

defined by $p_\mu(f) = f(\mu)$ for every $f \in \Phi$ in (I, § 3). Then, p_μ is surjective for every $\mu \in M$. We will call p_μ the *projection* of the topological product Φ onto its *μ-th coordinate space X_μ.*

PROPOSITION 5.3. *The projection $p_\mu : \Phi \rightarrow X_\mu$ is an open map from Φ onto X_μ for each $\mu \in M$.*

Proof. To prove that p_μ is continuous, let U_μ be any open set in X_μ. Then

$$p_\mu^{-1}(U_\mu) = \{f \in \Phi \mid f(\mu) \in U_\mu\} = U_\mu^*$$

is a sub-basic open set of Φ. Hence p_μ is continuous.

Next, to prove that p_μ is open, let U be an arbitrary open set of Φ. We are going to prove that $p_\mu(U)$ is an open set of X_μ. Let $a \in p_\mu(U)$. Then there exists a point $f \in U$ such that $f(\mu) = a$. Since σ is sub-basis of the product topology, there exist sub-basic open sets $U_{\mu_i}^*$, $(i = 1, \ldots, n)$, such that

$$f \in V = U_{\mu_1}^* \cap \cdots \cap U_{\mu_n}^* \subset U.$$

This implies that

$$a = p_\mu(f) \in p_\mu(V) \subset p_\mu(U).$$

It remains to prove that $p_\mu(V)$ is an open set of X_μ. This follows from the fact that $p_\mu(V) = U_{\mu_i}$ if $\mu = \mu_i$ for some i and that $p_\mu(V) = X_\mu$ if μ is different from μ_i for all $i = 1, \ldots, n$. $\|$

There is a useful characterization of continuity of a function from a space into a topological product.

PROPOSITION 5.4. *A function $f : W \rightarrow \Phi$ from a space W into the topological product Φ is continuous iff, for each $\mu \in M$, the composition $p_\mu \circ f$ is continuous.*

Proof. Since the necessity of the condition is obvious, it remains to prove the sufficiency. Assume that $p_\mu \circ f$ is continuous for each $\mu \in M$ and consider an arbitrary sub-basic open set U_μ^* of Φ. Since $p_\mu \circ f$ is continuous, the set $(p_\mu \circ f)^{-1}(U_\mu)$ is an open set of W. Since

$$(p_\mu \circ f)^{-1}(U_\mu) = f^{-1}[p_\mu^{-1}(U_\mu)] = f^{-1}(U_\mu^*),$$

$f^{-1}(U_\mu^*)$ is an open set of W. Hence, it follows from *(iv)* of (3.1) that f is continuous. $\|$.

For the special case of topological powers X^M, we have the following

PROPOSITION 5.5. *The diagonal injection* (defined in (I, § 3))

$$d : X \to X^M$$

of a space X into the topological power X^M is an imbedding, called the diagonal imbedding.

Proof. To prove the continuity of d, let $U_\mu{}^*$ denote an arbitrary sub-basic open set of X^M defined by an open set U_μ of $X_\mu = X$. Then, the inverse image

$$d^{-1}(U_\mu{}^*) = U_\mu$$

is open in X. By (*iv*) of (3.1), d is a map.

Let $d(X)$ denote the image of d in X^M with relative topology. Then, d defines a map

$$\delta : X \to d(X).$$

We will prove that δ is a homeomorphism.

Since δ is both bijective and continuous, it remains to prove that δ is open. For this purpose, let U be an arbitrary open set of X. Pick an element $\mu \in M$ and let

$$U_\mu = U \subset X = X_\mu.$$

Then $U_\mu{}^*$ is a sub-basic open set of X^M. Since

$$d(U) = U_\mu{}^* \cap d(X),$$

$d(U)$ is an open set of $d(X)$. ||

The image $d(X)$ in X^M of the diagonal imbedding d is called the *diagonal* of the topological power X^M. By means of the diagonal imbedding d, the given space X can be identified with the diagonal $d(X)$ of X^M and considered as a subspace of X^M.

PROPOSITION 5.6. *The diagonal $d(X)$ of a topological power X^M is a retract of X^M.*

Proof. Pick an element $\mu \in M$ and consider the composed map

$$r = \delta \circ p_\mu : X^M \to d(X)$$

of the projection $p_\mu : X^M \to X$ and the homeomorphism $\delta : X \to d(X)$ defined by the diagonal imbedding $d : X \to X^M$. Since r is obviously a retraction of X^M onto $d(X)$, $d(X)$ is a retract of X^M. ||

Finally, let us consider an arbitrarily given indexed family

$$\mathscr{H} = \{h_\mu : X_\mu \to Y_\mu \mid \mu \in M\}$$

of maps.   Then the Cartesian product

$$H = \Pi_{\mu \in M}\, h_\mu : \Phi \to \Psi,$$

as defined in (I, § 3), is a function of the topological product Φ of the spaces X_μ into the topological product Ψ of the spaces Y_μ.   Since H is a function from a space Φ into a space Ψ, we are naturally interested in the continuity of H.

PROPOSITION 5.7.   *The Cartesian product of any indexed family of continuous functions is continuous with respect to the product topologies.*

Proof.   We will prove the continuity of $H : \Phi \to \Psi$.   For this purpose, let $V_\mu{}^*$ denote an arbitrary sub-basic open set of Ψ defined by an open set V_μ in Y_μ with some $\mu \in M$.   Since h_μ is continuous, the inverse image

$$U_\mu = h_\mu{}^{-1}(V_\mu) \subset X_\mu$$

is an open set in X_μ and hence defines a sub-basic open set $U_\mu{}^*$ of Φ. Since obviously

$$U_\mu{}^* = H^{-1}(V_\mu{}^*),$$

it follows from *(iv)* of (3.1) that H is continuous.   **||**

The following corollary is a direct consequence of (5.6) and (5.7).

COROLLARY 5.8.   *The restricted Cartesian product of an arbitrarily given indexed family*

$$\mathscr{H} = \{h_\mu : X \to Y_\mu \mid \mu \in M\}$$

of continuous functions defined on the same space X is continuous.

EXERCISES

5A.   Let $\mathscr{F} = \{X_\mu \mid \mu \in M\}$ be an indexed family of spaces, where X_μ denotes the space obtained by topologizing a set X by a topology τ_μ.   Prove that the topological sum

$$\sum_{\mu \in M} X_\mu$$

is the space obtained by topologizing X with the topology

$$\tau = \mathrm{Inf}_{\mu \in M}\, \tau_\mu = \bigcap_{\mu \in M} \tau_\mu\,.$$

5B. Consider the topological product $\Phi = X_1 \times X_2$ of two spaces X_1 and X_2. Let $a_1 \in X_1$ and $a_2 \in X_2$. Define two functions

$$i_1 : X_1 \to \Phi, \qquad i_2 : X_2 \to \Phi$$

by taking $i_1(x_1) = (x_1, a_2) \in \Phi$ for each $x_1 \in X_1$ and $i_2(x_2) = (a_1, x_2) \in \Phi$ for each $x_2 \in X_2$. Prove that i_1 and i_2 are imbeddings and $p_1 \circ i_1$ and $p_2 \circ i_2$ are the identity maps on X_1 and X_2 respectively. Generalize these facts to arbitrary topological products.

5C. In the preceding exercise, let $E_1 \subset X_1$ and $E_2 \subset X_2$. Denote by $E_1 \times E_2$ the subset of the topological product $X_1 \times X_2$ which consists of the points (x_1, x_2) such that $x_1 \in E_1$ and $x_2 \in E_2$. Prove:
   (a) Cl $(E_1 \times E_2) = ($Cl $E_1) \times ($Cl $E_2)$;
   (b) Int $(E_1 \times E_2) = ($Int $E_1) \times ($Int $E_2)$;
   (c) $\partial(E_1 \times E_2) = (\partial E_1 \times$ Cl $E_2) \cup ($Cl $E_1 \times \partial E_2)$.

5D. Let $\mathscr{F} = \{X_\mu \mid \mu \in M\}$ be any indexed family of spaces. For each $\mu \in M$, we will also denote by μ the singleton space $\{\mu\}$. Let X_μ' denote the topological product $\mu \times X_\mu$. Show the family $\mathscr{F}' = \{X_\mu' \mid \mu \in M\}$ is disjoint. The topological sum of the family $\mathscr{F}'$ is called the *disjoint sum of $\mathscr{F}$*.

5E. Let E^n denote the *unit open n-cell* in the n-dimensional Euclidean space R^n which consists of all points $(x_1, \ldots, x_n)$ of R^n with $x_1^2 + \ldots + x_n^2 < 1$. Prove that E^n and R^n are homeomorphic.

5F. Let S^n denote the *unit n-sphere* in the $(n + 1)$-dimensional Euclidean space R^{n+1} which consists all points $(x_0, x_1, \ldots, x_n)$ of R^{n+1} satisfying the equation $x_0^2 + x_1^2 + \ldots + x_n^2 = 1$. Let p be a point in S^n. Prove that $S^n \setminus p$ is homeomorphic to the n-dimensional Euclidean space R^n.

5G. Let Δ^n denote the *unit n-simplex* in the Euclidean space R^{n+1} which consists of all points $(x_0, x_1, \ldots, x_n)$ in R^{n+1} such that $x_i \geqslant 0$ for each $i = 0, 1, \ldots, n$ and that $x_0 + x_1 + \ldots + x_n = 1$. Prove that Δ^n is homeomorphic to the unit n-cube I^n and to the *closed unit n-cell* Cl (E^n) in R^n.

5H. Prove that the subspace

$$T = [\text{Cl }(E^n) \times \{0\}] \cup [S^{n-1} \times I]$$

of the topological product $P = $ Cl $(E^n) \times I$ is a retract of P.

5I. Show that the projection $p : R^2 \to R$ of the Euclidean plane R^2 onto its first coordinate axis is not closed.

5J. Prove the assertion: If each space of a countable family satisfies the second axiom of countability, so does the topological product of the family. In particular, the spaces R^n, R^N satisfy the second axiom of countability.

6. IDENTIFICATION AND QUOTIENT SPACES

LEMMA 6.1. *For any map* $f: X \to Y$, *the following two statements are equivalent:*

(a) *A set* $E \subset Y$ *is open in* Y *iff* $f^{-1}(E)$ *is open in* X.

(b) *A set* $E \subset Y$ *is closed in* Y *iff* $f^{-1}(E)$ *is closed in* X.

Proof. The equivalence $(a) \Leftrightarrow (b)$ is an immediate consequence of the relation

$$f^{-1}(Y \setminus E) = X \setminus f^{-1}(E). \quad \|$$

A subjective map $f: X \to Y$ is said to be an *identification* iff it satisfies the equivalent conditions (a) and (b) in (6.1).

THEOREM 6.2. *If* $f: X \to Y$ *is a surjective open or closed map, then* f *is an identification.*

Proof. First, let us assume that f is open. Let E be a set in Y such that $f^{-1}(E)$ is open in X. Since f is surjective, we have

$$f[f^{-1}(E)] = E.$$

Since $f^{-1}(E)$ is open in X and f is open, it follows that E is open in Y. This proves that f satisfies the condition (a) in (6.1) and hence is an identification.

Similarly, one can prove that f is an identification if f is closed. $\|$

In particular, every homeomorphism is an identification.

THEOREM 6.3. *If* $f: X \to Y$ *is an identification and* $g: Y \to Z$ *is a function of* Y *into a space* Z, *then a necessary and sufficient condition for the continuity of* g *is that of the composition* $g \circ f$.

Proof. The necessity of the condition is obvious since the composition of two maps is a map.

To prove the sufficiency, let us assume that the composition

$$h = g \circ f: X \to Z$$

is continuous. Let W be an arbitrary open set in Z and let $V = g^{-1}(W)$ and $U = f^{-1}(V)$. Since $h = g \circ f$, we have

$$h^{-1}(W) = f^{-1}[g^{-1}(W)] = U.$$

Since W is open and h is continuous, it follows that U is open in X. By the definition of an identification, this implies that V is open in Y. Hence, g is continuous. $||$

Now, let $f: X \to Y$ be a surjective function from a space onto a set Y. According to §3, this function f induces a topology in Y as follows: a set $V \subset Y$ is open iff $f^{-1}(V)$ is open in X. This topology is usually called the *identification topology* in Y with respect to f. If Y is topologized by this topology, then f clearly becomes an identification.

Next, let X be any given space. By a *decomposition*, or *partition*, of X, we mean a disjoint family Q of nonempty subsets of X covering X; in other words, Q is a family of nonempty subsets of X such that each point of X belongs to one and only one member of Q. The function

$$p : X \to Q$$

which assigns to each point $x \in X$ the unique member $p(x)$ of Q containing x is called the *natural projection* of X onto Q. We give Q the identification topology with respect to p and obtain a space Q, which is usually called a *decomposition space* of X.

In particular, if, in a space X, there is given an equivalence relation, i.e. a reflexive, symmetric, and transitive relation $\sim$ defined between pairs of points of X, then the points of X are divided into disjoint subsets called the *equivalence classes*. Let Q denote the set of all equivalence classes. Then Q is a disjoint family of nonempty subsets of X which covers X and hence is a decomposition of X. The decomposition space Q so obtained is called the *quotient space* of X over the equivalence relation $\sim$, in symbols,

$$Q = X/\sim.$$

Conversely, let Q be any decomposition of X. Then we can define a relation $\sim$ in X as follows: For any two points a and b in X, $a \sim b$ iff there exists a member of Q which contains both a and b. One can easily verify that this relation $\sim$ is an equivalence relation and that Q consists of precisely all equivalence classes. Hence, every decomposition space of X is a quotient space over an equivalence relation.

Now, let us go back to study an arbitrary identification $f: X \to Y$. Define a relation $\sim$ in X as follows: For any two points a and b in X, $a \sim b$ iff $f(a) = f(b)$. It is easily verified that $\sim$ is an equivalence relation in X and hence defines a quotient space $Q = X/\sim$. The members of Q are precisely the inverse images $f^{-1}(y)$ for the points y of Y. The assignment $y \to f^{-1}(y)$ defines a bijective function

$$h : Y \to Q.$$

Since both $f : X \to Y$ and the natural projection $p : X \to Q$ are identifications and the triangle

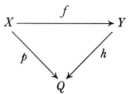

is commutative, it follows from (6.3) that h is a homeomorphism. This shows that every identification is essentially the natural projection of a space onto its quotient space.

EXAMPLES OF QUOTIENT SPACES.

(1) *The real projective space P^n.* Consider the $(n + 1)$-dimensional Euclidean space R^{n+1} and let

$$X = R^{n+1} \setminus O, \qquad O = (0, \ldots, 0).$$

Introduce an equivalence relation $\sim$ in X as follows: For any two points $a = (a_0, a_1, \ldots, a_n)$ and $b = (b_0, b_1, \ldots, b_n)$ in X, $a \sim b$ iff there exists a nonzero real number λ such that

$$b_i = \lambda a_i, \qquad (i = 0, 1, \ldots, n).$$

The quotient space $X/\sim$ thus obtained is called the *n-dimensional real projective space P^n.* Hence, the points of P^n are the straight lines in R^{n+1} passing through the origin O.

Let $p : X \to P^n$ denote the natural projection. Since the unit n-sphere S^n is a subspace of X, p defines a restriction

$$\pi = p \mid S^n : S^n \to P^n.$$

Since every point $x = (x_0, x_1, \ldots, x_n)$ in X can be normalized by multiplying X with the nonzero real number

$$\lambda = \frac{1}{|x|}, \qquad |x|^2 = x_0^2 + x_1^2 + \ldots + x_n^2,$$

the map π is surjective. One can easily see that π is an identification.

If $a = (a_0, a_1, \ldots, a_n)$ and $b = (b_0, b_1, \ldots, b_n)$ be any two points of S^n, then $\pi(a) = \pi(b)$ iff $a_i + b_i = 0$ for every $i = 0, 1, \ldots, n$; in other words, a and b are antipodal points. Hence P^n can be obtained from S^n by identifying the antipodal points.

(2) *Collapsing a subset to a point.* Consider a given space X and a

given nonempty subset A in X. The individual points of $X \setminus A$ together with the subset A form a decomposition of the space X. The quotient space Q thus defined is called the *space obtained from X by collapsing the subset A to a point*. We will give three special cases as examples.

First, let $X = \mathrm{Cl}\,(E^n)$ denote the closed unit n-cell in R^n and $A = S^{n-1}$ the unit $(n-1)$-sphere as defined in Exercises 5F and 5G. Then it is not difficult to show that the quotient space obtained from $\mathrm{Cl}\,(E^n)$ by collapsing its boundary S^{n-1} to a point is homeomorphic to the unit n-sphere S^n in R^{n+1}.

Second, let $X = E \times I$ denote the topological product of a space E and the closed unit interval I, and let $A = E \times \{1\}$. Then the quotient space obtained from $E \times I$ by collapsing its top $E \times \{1\}$ to a point is called the *cone* over the space E, denoted by $\mathrm{Con}\,(E)$. The point $v = E \times \{1\}$ of $\mathrm{Con}\,(E)$ is called the *vertex*. The given space E can be considered as a subspace of $\mathrm{Con}\,(E)$ by means of the imbedding $i : E \to \mathrm{Con}\,(E)$ defined by $i(e) = p(e, 0)$ for each $e \in E$, where p denotes the natural projection of $E \times I$ onto $\mathrm{Con}\,(E)$.

Third, let $X = U + V$ denote the topological sum of two disjoint nonempty spaces U and V, and let A denote the subspace of X which consists of a given point $u_0 \in U$ and a given point $v_0 \in V$. Then the quotient space obtained from $U + V$ by collapsing $\{u_0, v_0\}$ to a point is called the *one-point union* of the spaces U and V with base points $u_0 \in U$ and $v_0 \in V$, denoted by $U \vee V$. The given spaces U and V can be considered as subspaces of $U \vee V$ in the obvious way, and $U \vee V$ can be considered as a subspace of the topological product $U \times V$ by means of the imbedding $i : U \vee V \to U \times V$ defined by $i(u) = (u, v_0)$ for each $u \in U$ and $i(v) = (u_0, v)$ for each $v \in V$.

(3) *Mapping cylinder and mapping cone.* Let $f : X \to Y$ be any given map and consider the topological sum

$$E = (X \times I) + Y$$

of the topological product $X \times I$ and Y, where I denotes the unit interval. Then the individual points

$$\{(x, t) \in X \times I \mid x \in X, 0 \leqslant t < 1\}$$

together with the subsets

$$\{[f^{-1}(y) \times 1] \cup y \mid y \in Y\}$$

of E form a decomposition of E. The quotient space thus obtained is called the *mapping cylinder* of the map f, denoted by $\mathrm{Cyl}\,(f)$. Both X

and Y can be considered as subspaces of Cyl (f)) by means of the imbeddings

$$i : X \to \text{Cyl } (f), \quad j : Y \to \text{Cyl } (f).$$

defined by $i(x) = p(x, 0)$ for each $x \in X$ and $j(y) = p(y)$ for each $y \in Y$, where p denotes the natural projection of E onto Cyl (f). The quotient space obtained from the mapping cylinder Cyl (f) by collapsing its subspace X to a point v is called the *mapping cone* of f, denoted by Con (f). The point v is called the *vertex* of Con (f)). The space Y can be considered as a subspace of Con (f) in the obvious way.

EXERCISES

6A. Show that the natural projection p of a topological product $X \times Y$ onto X is an identification. Hence, by Exercise 5H, an identification may fail to be closed. Construct an example showing that an identification may fail to be open.

6B. Let Q be a quotient space of a space X with natural projection

$$p : X \to Q.$$

For each subset A of X, let
$$R(A) = \{x \in X \mid x \sim \text{some } a \in A\}.$$
$$S(A) = \{a \in A \mid x \sim a \text{ implies } x \in A\}.$$
Then prove that the following statements are equivalent:
  (a) p is an open map.
  (b) $R(A)$ is open for every open $A \subset X$.
  (c) $S(A)$ is closed for every closed $A \subset X$.
Show that the statements (a), (b), (c) remain equivalent if we interchange the words "open" and "closed."

6C. Consider the closed unit n-cell Cl (E^n) in R^n. Show that the quotient space obtained from Cl (E^n) by identifying the antipodal points on the boundary S^{n-1} is homeomorphic to the n-dimensional real projective space P^n.

6D. The points of the unit circle S^1 in R^2 can be considered as the complex numbers z with $|z| = 1$. Define a map $f : S^1 \to S^1$ by taking $f(z) = z^2$ for every $z \in S^1$. Prove that the mapping cone Con (f) is homeomorphic to the real projective plane P^2.

6E. Consider the unit square $I^2 = I \times I$. The quotient space obtained from I^2 by identifying $(0, t)$ with $(1, 1 - t)$ for every $t \in I$ is called the *Möbius strip*. Show by making a physical model that the

Möbius strip M can be imbedded in the 3-dimensional Euclidean space R^3. The subspace

$$E = p[(I \times 0) \cup (I \times 1)]$$

of M, where p denotes the natural projection from I^2 onto M, is called the *edge* of M. Prove that E is homeomorphic to S^1. Let $h : S^1 \to M$ be an imbedding which maps S^1 homeomorphically onto E. ⌈Show that the mapping cone Con (h) is homeomorphic to the real projective plane P^2. Then show that P^2 can be imbedded in the 4-dimensional Euclidean space R^4.⌋

6F. The quotient space obtained from I^2 by identifying $(0, t)$ with $(1, t)$, and $(t, 0)$ with $(t, 1)$, for every $t \in I$, is called the *torus* T^2. Prove that T^2 is homeomorphic to the topological product $S^1 \times S^1$.

6G. The quotient space obtained from I^2 by identifying $(0, t)$ with $(1, 1 - t)$, and $(t, 0)$ with $(t, 1)$, for every $t \in I$, is called the *Klein bottle* K^2. Prove that K^2 is homeomorphic to the quotient space obtained from the topological sum of two Möbius strips by identifying the corresponding points on their edges.

6H. The quotient space obtained from the cone Con (E) over a space E by collapsing E to a point u is called the *suspension* of the space E. The point u and the vertex v of Con (E) are called the *poles* of the suspension. Prove that the suspension of the unit n-sphere S^n is homeomorphic to S^{n+1}.

7. HOMOTOPY AND ISOTOPY

Let X and Y be given spaces and consider a family

$$\{h_t : X \to Y \mid t \in I\}$$

of maps indexed by the real numbers of the unit interval $I = [0, 1]$. The family $\{h_t\}$ is said to be *continuous* iff the function

$$H : X \times I \to Y,$$

defined by $H(x, t) = h_t(x)$ for each $x \in X$ and each $t \in I$, is continuous. A continuous family $\{h_t\}$ of maps, or equivalently the map H, is usually called a *homotopy*. Furthermore, if h_t is an imbedding for every $t \in I$, the continuous family $\{H_t\}$ is called an *isotopy*.

Now, let $f, g : X \to Y$ be two given maps. If there exists a homotopy $\{h_t : X \to Y \mid t \in I\}$ such that $h_0 = f$ and $h_1 = g$, f and g are said to be *homotopic*, in symbols, $f \simeq g$. Intuitively, $f, g : X \to Y$ are homotopic iff f can be continuously changed into g.

PROPOSITION 7.1.   *Any two maps*

$$f, g : X \to R^n$$

from a space X into the Euclidean space R^n are homotopic.

Proof. We will make use of the fact that R^n is a vector space over the real numbers.   Define a function

$$H : X \times I \to R^n$$

by taking

$$H(x, t) = (1 - t)f(x) + tg(x)$$

for each $x \in X$ and each $t \in I$.   Then we have $H(x, 0) = f(x)$ and $H(x, 1) = g(x)$ for every $x \in X$.

It remains to show the continuity of H.   For this purpose, it suffices to prove the continuity of the composed functions

$$p_i \circ H : X \times I \to R,$$

$(i = 1, . . ., n)$, because of (5.4).   Since the addition and the scalar multiplication in R^n are defined coordinate-wise, we have

$$(p_i \circ H)(x, t) = (1 - t)p_i[f(x)] + tp_i[g(x)]$$

for each $x \in X$ and $t \in I$. Since addition and multiplication of real numbers are continuous, this implies the continuity of $p_i \circ H$ for every $i = 1, . . ., n$. $\|$

PROPOSITION 7.2.   *Every map $f : X \to S^n$ from a space X into the n-sphere S^n which is not surjective is homotopic to a constant map.*

Proof. Since f is not surjective, there exists a point $p \in S^n$ such that

$$f(X) \subset S^n \setminus p.$$

According to Exercise 5F, the space $S^n \setminus p$ is homeomorphic to the Euclidean space R^n.   Let

$$h : R^n \to S^n \setminus p$$

be a homeomorphism and denote by q the image $h(O)$ of the origin O in R^n.

By (7.1), the map $\phi : X \to R^n$ defined by

$$\phi(x) = h^{-1}[f(x)]$$

for every $x \in X$ is homotopic to the constant map $\psi : X \to R^n$ defined by $\psi(X) = 0$. Hence, there exists a homotopy

$$\{\theta_t : X \to R^n \mid t \in I\}$$

such that $\theta_0 = \phi$ and $\theta_1 = \psi$.

Define a homotopy $\{f_t : X \to S^n \mid t \in I\}$ by taking

$$f_t(x) = h[\theta_t(x)]$$

for each $x \in X$ and each $t \in I$. Then $f_0 = f$ and $f_1(X) = q$. $\|$

PROPOSITION 7.3. *The relation $\simeq$ between the maps of X into Y is an equivalence relation.*

Proof. It suffices to verify that $\simeq$ is reflexive, symmetric, and transitive. Let $f : X \to Y$ be any map and define a family $\{h_t : X \to Y \mid t \in I\}$ of maps by taking $h_t = f$ for every $t \in I$. Then one can easily verify that $\{h_t\}$ is a homotopy with $h_0 = f$ and $h_1 = f$. Hence $f \simeq f$.

Next, let $f, g : X \to Y$ be two maps with $f \simeq g$. Then there exists a homotopy $\{h_t\}$ with $h_0 = f$ and $h_1 = g$. Define a family $\{k_t\}$ of maps by taking $k_t = h_{1-t}$ for each $t \in I$. Then one can easily verify that $\{k_t\}$ is a homotopy with $k_0 = g$ and $k_1 = f$. Hence $g \simeq f$.

Finally, let $f \simeq g$ and $g \simeq h$. Then there exist homotopies ξ_t, $\eta_t : X \to Y$, $(t \in I)$, such that $\xi_0 = f$, $\xi_1 = g = \eta_0$, and $\eta_1 = h$. Define a family $\{\zeta_t : X \to Y \mid t \in I\}$ of maps by taking

$$\zeta_t = \begin{cases} \xi_{2t}, & (0 \leqslant t \leqslant \tfrac{1}{2}), \\ \eta_{2t-1}, & (\tfrac{1}{2} \leqslant t \leqslant 1). \end{cases}$$

Using (4.3), one can verify that $\{\zeta_t\}$ is a homotopy. Since $\zeta_0 = \xi_0 = f$ and $\zeta_1 = \eta_1 = h$, we have $f \simeq h$. $\|$

It follows from (7.3) that the maps from X into Y are divided into disjoint equivalence classes, called the *homotopy classes*.

If $f, g : X \to Y$ are imbeddings, then we may define a stronger relation than $\simeq$ as follows: Two imbeddings $f, g : X \to Y$ are said to be *isotopic* iff there exists an isotopy $\{h_t : X \to Y \mid t \in I\}$ such that $h_0 = f$ and $h_1 = g$, in symbols, $f \cong g$. The proof of the following proposition is similar to that of (7.3).

PROPOSITION 7.4. *The relation $\cong$ between the imbeddings of X into Y is an equivalence relation.*

By (7.4), the imbeddings of X into Y are divided into disjoint equivalence classes, called the *isotopy classes*.

Now, let X be a subspace of a space Y. A homotopy

$$\{h_t : X \to Y \mid t \in I\}$$

is called a *deformation* iff h_0 is the inclusion map. Furthermore, if h_1 is a constant map, then the deformation $\{h_t\}$ is called a *contraction*. If a contraction $\{h_t : X \to Y \mid t \in I\}$ exists, we say that the subspace X is *contractible in the space Y*. In particular, if $X = Y$, then X is said to be *contractible*.

For example, it follows from (7.2) that every proper subspace of the n-sphere S^n is contractible in S^n. By (7.1), the Euclidean space R^n is contractible. In fact, this can be generalized to the following

PROPOSITION 7.5. *If every space X_μ in an indexed family*

$$\mathscr{F} = \{X_\mu \mid \mu \in M\}$$

of nonempty spaces is contractible, then so is the topological product

$$\Phi = \Pi_{\mu \in M} X_\mu.$$

Proof. Let $\mu \in M$. Since the space X_μ is contractible, there exists a map

$$h_\mu : X_\mu \times I \to X_\mu$$

such that $h_\mu(x, 0) = x$ for every $x \in X_\mu$ and that $h_\mu(X_\mu \times 1)$ is a single point $a_\mu \in X_\mu$. Consider the Cartesian product

$$H = \Pi_{\mu \in M} h_\mu : \Phi \times I^M \to \Phi$$

of the indexed family

$$\mathscr{H} = \{h_\mu \mid \mu \in M\}$$

of maps. By (5.7), H is continuous.

Next, form the Cartesian product

$$K = i \times d : \Phi \times I \to \Phi \times I^M$$

of the identity map $i : \Phi \to \Phi$ and the diagonal injection $d : I \to I^M$. By (5.5) and (5.7), K is continuous.

Finally, let us investigate the composed map

$$h = H \circ K : \Phi \times I \to \Phi.$$

One can easily verify that $h(f, 0) = f$ for every $f \in \Phi$ and that $h(\Phi \times 1)$ is the point $a \in \Phi$ defined by

$$a(\mu) = a_\mu, \qquad (\mu \in M).$$

Hence h defines a contraction of Φ. $\quad \|$

Next, let A be a subspace of a space X. If a deformation

$$\{h_t : X \to X \mid t \in I\}$$

exists such that h_1 is a retraction of X onto A, then the subspace A is called a *deformation retract* of X. If $h_t \mid A$ is the inclusion map for all $t \in I$, then A is said to be a *strong deformation retract* of X. As an example of deformation retracts, we have the following

PROPOSITION 7.6. *If X is a contractible space and if A is a subspace of X which consists of a single point $x_0 \in X$, then A is a deformation retract of X.*

Proof. Since X is contractible, there exists a deformation

$$\{d_t : X \to X \mid t \in I\}$$

such that $d_1(X)$ is a point $x_1 \in X$. Define a homotopy

$$\{h_t : X \to X \mid t \in I\}$$

by taking

$$h_t(x) = \begin{cases} d_{2t}(x), & (\text{if } 0 \leqslant t \leqslant \tfrac{1}{2}), \\ d_{2-2t}(x_0), & (\text{if } \tfrac{1}{2} \leqslant t \leqslant 1) \end{cases}$$

for every $x \in X$. Then $\{h_t\}$ is a deformation with $h_1(X) = x_0$. Hence the subspace $A = \{x_0\}$ is a deformation retract of X. ‖

A map $f : X \to Y$ is said to be a *homotopy equivalence* iff there exists a map $g : Y \to X$ such that the composed maps

$$g \circ f : X \to X, \qquad f \circ g : Y \to Y$$

are homotopic to the identity maps on X and Y respectively. In this case, the map $g : Y \to X$ is also a homotopy equivalence.

Obviously, every homeomorphism is a homotopy equivalence. As another example of homotopy equivalences, we have the following

PROPOSITION 7.7. *If a subspace A of a space X is a deformation retract of X, then the inclusion map $i : A \subset X$ is a homotopy equivalence.*

Proof. Since A is a deformation retract of X, there exists a deformation

$$\{d_t : X \to X \mid t \in I\}$$

such that d_1 is a retraction of X onto A. Hence, d_1 defines a map $r : X \to A$. Then, $r \circ i$ is the identity map on A. On the other hand, we have $d_1 = i \circ r$ and hence $i \circ r$ is homotopic to the identity map on X. This proves that $i : A \subset X$ is a homotopy equivalence. ‖

An imbedding $f: X \to Y$ is said to be an *isotopy equivalence* iff there exists an imbedding $g: Y \to X$ such that the composed imbeddings

$$g \circ f: X \to X, \qquad f \circ g: Y \to Y$$

are isotopic to the identity maps on X and Y respectively. In this case, the imbedding $g: Y \to X$ is also an isotopy equivalence.

Clearly, every isotopy equivalence is a homotopy equivalence, but the converse is false.

Obviously, every homeomorphism is an isotopy equivalence. As another example of isotopy equivalences, we have the following

PROPOSITION 7.8. *If J denotes the open unit interval defined by*

$$J = \{t \in I \mid 0 < t < 1\},$$

then the inclusion map $i: J \subset I$ is an isotopy equivalence.

Proof. Define an imbedding $j: I \to J$ by taking

$$j(x) = \tfrac{1}{3}(x + 1)$$

for every $x \in I$. It suffices to prove that the composed imbeddings

$$i \circ j: I \to I, \qquad j \circ i: J \to J$$

are isotopic to the identity maps on I and J respectively.

For this purpose, let us define an isotopy

$$\{f_t : I \to I \mid t \in I\}$$

by taking

$$f_t(x) = \tfrac{1}{3}(3x + t - 2tx)$$

for each $t \in I$ and each $x \in I$. Clearly, f_0 is the identity map on I and $f_1 = i \circ j$. This proves that $i \circ j$ is isotopic to the identity map on I.

On the other hand, we observe that

$$f_t(J) \subset J, \qquad (t \in I).$$

Hence, $\{f_t \mid t \in I\}$ defines an isotopy

$$\{g_t : J \to J \mid t \in I\}.$$

Since clearly g_0 is the identity map on J and $g_1 = j \circ i$, this proves that $j \circ i$ is isotopic to the identity map on J. ||

If a homotopy equivalence $h: X \to Y$ exists, we say that X is *homotopically equivalent* to Y, in symbols,

$$X \simeq Y.$$

Similarly, if an isotopy equivalence $i : X \to Y$ exists, X is said to be *isotopically equivalent* to Y, in symbols,

$$X \cong Y.$$

One can easily verify that the relations $\simeq$ and $\cong$ between spaces are both equivalence relations.

By (7.6) and (7.7), any two contractible spaces are homotopically equivalent; in particular, any two Euclidean spaces are homotopically equivalent. By (7.8), the closed interval I and the open interval J are isotopically equivalent.

A property of spaces is called a *homotopy property* iff it is preserved by every homotopy equivalence. In other words, a homotopy property is one which when possessed by a space X is also possessed by every space Y homotopically equivalent to X. Similarly, a property which is preserved by every isotopy equivalence will be called an *isotopy property*.

Since every homeomorphism is an isotopy equivalence and every isotopy equivalence is a homotopy equivalence, it follows that every homotopy property is an isotopy property and every isotopy property is a topological property.

As an example of homotopy properties, we have the following

PROPOSITION 7.9. *The contractibility of a space is a homotopy property.*

Proof. Assume that X is contractible and that $X \simeq Y$. We will prove that Y is also contractible.

Since X is contractible, there exists a contraction

$$\{c_t : X \to X \mid t \in I\}.$$

Next, since $X \simeq Y$, there exist maps $f : X \to Y$ and $g : Y \to X$ such that $f \circ g$ is homotopic to the identity map on Y. Let

$$\{d_t : Y \to Y \mid t \in I\}$$

be a deformation with $d_1 = f \circ g$. Define a homotopy

$$\{h_t : Y \to Y \mid t \in I\}$$

by taking

$$h_t = \begin{cases} d_{2t}, & (\text{if } 0 \leqslant t \leqslant \tfrac{1}{2}), \\ f \circ c_{2t-1} \circ g, & (\text{if } \tfrac{1}{2} \leqslant t \leqslant 1). \end{cases}$$

Since $h_0 = d_0$ is the identity map on Y and $h_1 = f \circ c_1 \circ g$ is a constant map, $\{h_t\}$ is a contraction. Hence Y is contractible. $\|$

In the next chapter, we shall study more homotopy properties, isotopy properties, and topological properties of spaces.

EXERCISES

7A. Prove that the unit n-sphere S^n in the Euclidean space R^{n+1} is a strong deformation retract of $R^{n+1} \setminus O$, where O denotes the origin of R^{n+1}.

7B. Prove that the cone Con (X) over an arbitrary space X is contractible.

7C. Prove that a map $f: X \to Y$ is homotopic to a constant map iff f has a continuous extension over Con (X).

7D. Prove that, for an arbitrary map $f: X \to Y$, the subspace Y of the mapping cylinder Cyl (f) is a strong deformation retract of Cyl (f).

7E. Prove that, for an arbitrary set M, the topological powers I^M and R^M are isotopically equivalent.

7F. Prove that every two indiscrete spaces are homotopically equivalent. Hence the cardinal number of the points in a space is not a homotopy property.

Chapter III: PROPERTIES OF
SPACES AND MAPS

As the title indicates, this chapter is devoted to the properties of spaces and maps usually studied in topology. Since there are too many of these properties to be all included in a book designed for our special purpose, we had to select the properties that would be important enough and could be treated in a desirably leisurely fashion. Among those thus excluded, some are not topological properties, such as completeness and completions of metric spaces, uniformities, etc.; others are topological properties, for example, the first and second category. These are either favorite subjects of standard analysis courses or can be found readily in more extensive existing books, in case of need.

1. SEPARATION AXIOMS

By a *Hausdorff space*, we mean a space X which satisfies the following *Hausdorff separation axiom*: Every two distinct points of X have disjoint neighborhoods in X; in other words, if a and b are distinct points of X, then there exist open sets U and V in X such that $a \in U$, $b \in V$, and $U \cap V = \square$.

For example, the real line R is a Hausdorff space. Every discrete space clearly satisfies the Hausdorff separation axiom, while an indiscrete space with more than one point can never be a Hausdorff space.

PROPOSITION 1.1. *Every subspace E of a Hausdorff space X is a Hausdorff space.*

Proof. Let a, b be any two distinct points in E. Since X is a Hausdorff space, there exist open sets U and V in X such that $a \in U$, $b \in V$ and $U \cap V = \square$. Let $U^* = E \cap U$ and $V^* = E \cap V$. Then U^* and V^* are open sets of the subspace E. Since $a \in U^*$, $b \in V^*$ and $U^* \cap V^* = \square$, it follows that E is a Hausdorff space. ‖

PROPOSITION 1.2. *The topological sum X of any disjoint collection $\{X_\mu \mid \mu \in M\}$ of Hausdorff spaces is a Hausdorff space.*

Proof. Let a, b be any two distinct points in X. Then there exist μ, $\nu \in M$ such that $a \in X_\mu$ and $b \in X_\nu$. If $\mu \neq \nu$, then take $U = X_\mu$ and $V = X_\nu$. If $\mu = \nu$, then a and b are two distinct points in a Hausdorff space X_μ and hence there are open sets U and V in X_μ such that $a \in U$, $b \in V$ and $U \cap V = \square$. In both cases, U and V are open sets of the topological sum X. This implies that X is a Hausdorff space. ‖

PROPOSITION 1.3. *The topological product X of any collection $\{X_\mu \mid \mu \in M\}$ of Hausdorff spaces is a Hausdorff space.*

Proof. Let a, b be any two distinct points in X. By definition of X, $a \neq b$ implies the existence of a $\nu \in M$ such that $a(\nu)$ and $b(\nu)$ are distinct points in X_ν. Since X_ν is a Hausdorff space, there exist open sets U and V in X_ν such that $a(\nu) \in U$, $b(\nu) \in V$, and $U \cap V = \square$. Let U^* and V^* denote the sub-basic open sets in X defined by

$$U^* = \{x \in X \mid x(\nu) \in U\},$$
$$V^* = \{x \in X \mid x(\nu) \in V\}.$$

Then, $a \in U^*$, $b \in V^*$, and $U^* \cap V^* = \square$. This implies that X is a Hausdorff space. ‖

As a consequence of (1.3), the n-dimensional Euclidean space R^n and the Hilbert space R^N are Hausdorff spaces. Hence, by (1.1), the unit n-simplex Δ^n and the unit n-sphere S^n are Hausdorff spaces.

PROPOSITION 1.4. *If E is a retract of a Hausdorff space X, then E is a closed set in X.*

Proof. Assume that E is a retract of a Hausdorff space X with a retraction $r : X \to E$. We are going to prove that $X \setminus E$ is an open set in X.

If $X \setminus E = \square$, the proposition is trivial. Thus, we assume that $X \setminus E \neq \square$. Let a be any point in $X \setminus E$. Then the point $b = r(a)$ is in E and hence $a \neq b$. Since X is a Hausdorff space, there exist open sets U and V of X such that $a \in U$, $b \in V$, and $U \cap V = \square$. Since r is continuous and $E \cap V$ is an open set in E, it follows that $r^{-1}(E \cap V)$ is an open set of X containing a. Let

$$W = U \cap r^{-1}(E \cap V).$$

Then W is an open set of X such that $a \in W$, $V \cap W = \square$, and $r(W) \subset V$. This implies that $r(x) \neq x$ for every $x \in W$ and hence $W \subset X \setminus E$. This proves that $X \setminus E$ is open and, therefore, E is closed. ‖

If we apply (1.4) to the special case where E consists of a single point, we deduce that a Hausdorff space X has the following property: *Every point of X forms a closed set in X.* A space X which has this property is called a *Fréchet space* or a *T_1-space.* It follows immediately that every Fréchet space X satisfies the following *Fréchet separation axiom:* For any pair of distinct points a and b in X, there exists an open set U of X such that $a \in U$ and $b \notin U$.

A space X is said to be *regular at a point p* of X iff every neighborhood of p contains a closed neighborhood of p. By a *regular space*, we mean a space X which is regular at each of its points.

PROPOSITION 1.5. *Every regular Fréchet space is a Hausdorff space.*

Proof. Let X be a regular Fréchet space and a, b be any two distinct points in X. Since X is a Fréchet space, $X \setminus b$ is an open set of X. From the regularity of X at the point a, there follows the existence of a closed neighborhood N of a with $N \subset X \setminus b$. Let

$$U = \text{Int } (N), \quad V = X \setminus N.$$

Then U and V are open sets of X such that $a \in U$, $b \in V$, and $U \cap V = \square$. ‖

A space X is said to be *completely regular at a point p* of X iff, for every neighborhood N of p in X, there exists a continuous function

$$\chi : X \to I$$

such that $\chi(p) = 0$ and $\chi(X \setminus N) = 1$. Since the set

$$M = \{x \in X \mid \chi(x) \leqslant \tfrac{1}{2}\}$$

is clearly a closed neighborhood of p contained in N, it follows that X is also regular at the point p. By a *completely regular space*, we mean a space X which is completely regular at each of its points. Hence, every completely regular space is regular. A completely regular Fréchet space is called a *Tychonoff space.*

A space X is said to be *normal* iff every disjoint pair of closed sets in X has disjoint neighborhoods; in other words, for any two disjoint closed sets A and B in X, there exist open sets U and V in X such that $A \subset U$, $B \subset V$, and $U \cap V = \square$.

Discrete spaces and indiscrete spaces are normal. Hence, a normal space may fail to satisfy the Fréchet axiom of separation or the first or second axiom of countability. On the other hand, since singletons are closed in a Fréchet space, it follows that every normal Fréchet space is regular and hence also a Hausdorff space.

THEOREM 1.6 (URYSOHN's LEMMA). *If A and B are two disjoint closed sets in a normal space X, then there exists a continuous function*

$$\chi : X \to I$$

such that $\chi(A) = 0$ *and* $\chi(B) = 1$.

Proof. Let D denote the set of all non-negative dyadic rational numbers, that is to say, the set of all numbers of the form $a/2^q$, where a and q are non-negative integers.

First of all, we will construct an indexed family $F = \{U_t \mid t \in D\}$ of open sets in X such that, for any two distinct $s, t \in D$, $s < t$ implies that

$$\text{Cl}\,(U_s) \subset U_t.$$

For this purpose, we define $U_t = X$ for every $t > 1$ in D and set $U_1 = X \setminus B$. Since X is normal and A, B are disjoint, there exist two open sets M and N of X such that $A \subset M$, $B \subset N$, and $M \cap N = \square$. Then we define $U_0 = M$. This implies that

$$\text{Cl}\,(U_0) \subset X \setminus N \subset X \setminus B = U_1.$$

Next, let $t \in D$ be satisfying $0 < t < 1$. Then t can be uniquely written in the form

$$t = (2m + 1)/2^n.$$

We will construct U_t by induction on n. Let

$$\alpha = 2m/2^n = m/2^{n-1},$$
$$\beta = (2m + 2)/2^n = (m + 1)/2^{n-1}.$$

Then $\alpha < t < \beta$ and, in accordance to the inductive hypothesis, the open sets U_α and U_β have already been constructed in such a way that $\text{Cl}\,(U_\alpha) \subset U_\beta$. Hence, $\text{Cl}\,(U_\alpha)$ and $X \setminus U_\beta$ are two disjoint closed sets in X. Since X is normal, there exist two open sets V and W of X such that

$$\text{Cl}\,(U_\alpha) \subset V, \quad X \setminus U_\beta \subset W, \quad V \cap W = \square.$$

Let $U_t = V$. Then we obtain

$$\text{Cl}\,(U_\alpha) \subset U_t, \quad \text{Cl}\,(U_t) \subset X \setminus W \subset U_\beta.$$

This completes the inductive construction of the indexed family $F = \{U_t \mid t \in D\}$ of open sets in X. From the construction, it is clear that F covers X.

Now, define a real function

$$\chi \; : \; X \to I$$

by taking $\chi(x) = \operatorname{Inf}\{t \mid x \in U_t\}$ for each $x \in X$. Then we have

$$\chi(A) = 0, \quad \chi(B) = 1.$$

Hence it remains to verify the continuity of this function χ.

For each real number $a \in I$, let

$$L_a = \{t \in I \mid t < a\}, \quad R_a = \{t \in I \mid t > a\}.$$

Then the collection $\{L_a, R_a \mid a \in I\}$ forms a sub-basis of the topology of I. It suffices to prove that, for each $a \in I$, $\chi^{-1}(L_a)$ and $\chi^{-1}(R_a)$ are open in X.

First, let us consider the set

$$\chi^{-1}(L_a) = \{x \in X \mid \chi(x) < a\}.$$

Since $\chi(x) = \operatorname{Inf}\{t \mid x \in U_t\}$ and since the infimum is less than a iff some member of $\{t \mid x \in U_t\}$ is less than a, the set $\chi^{-1}(L_a)$ consists of all points $x \in X$ such that $x \in U_t$ for some $t < a$. Hence

$$\chi^{-1}(L_a) = \bigcup \{U_t \mid t \in D \text{ and } t < a\}.$$

This implies that $\chi^{-1}(L_a)$ is an open set of X.

Finally, in order to show that $\chi^{-1}(R_a)$ is open, it suffices to prove that the set

$$\chi^{-1}(I \setminus R_a) = \{x \in X \mid \chi(x) \leqslant a\}$$

is closed. Since $\chi(x) = \operatorname{Inf}\{t \mid x \in U_t\}$, it follows that $\chi(x) \leqslant a$ iff $x \in U_t$ for every $t > a$ in D. Hence

$$\chi^{-1}(I \setminus R_a) = \bigcap \{U_t \mid t \in D \text{ and } t > a\}.$$

To complete the proof, it remains to prove that

$$\chi^{-1}(I \setminus R_a) = \bigcap \{\operatorname{Cl}(U_t) \mid t \in D \text{ and } t > a\}.$$

For this purpose, let r be any member of D with $r > a$. Since D is dense in I, there is an $s \in D$ such that $a < s < r$ and hence $\operatorname{Cl}(U_s) \subset U_r$. Since $s > a$, we deduce

$$\bigcap \{\operatorname{Cl}(U_t) \mid t \in D \text{ and } t > a\} \subset \operatorname{Cl}(U_s) \subset U_r.$$

Since r is an arbitrary member of D with $r > 0$, this implies that

$$\bigcap \{\operatorname{Cl}(U_t) \mid t \in D \text{ and } t > a\} \subset \chi^{-1}(I \setminus R_a).$$ *MAGNIFICENT MACHINERY !*

Since the inclusion

$$\chi^{-1}(I \setminus R_a) \subset \bigcap \{\text{Cl}\,(U_t) \mid t \in D \text{ and } t > a\}$$

is obvious, this completes the proof of (1.6). ||

COROLLARY 1.7.   *Every normal Fréchet space is a Tychonoff space.*

Proof.   Let X be a normal Fréchet space and p be an arbitrary point in X. It remains to prove that X is completely regular at p. For this purpose, let N be any neighborhood of p in X and let $U = \text{Int}\,(N)$. Then

$$A = \{p\}, \quad B = X \setminus U$$

are two disjoint closed sets in X. By (1.6), there exists a continuous function $\chi : X \to I$ such that

$$\chi(p) = \chi(A) = 0,$$

$$\chi(X \setminus N) \subset \chi(X \setminus U) = \chi(B) = 1.$$

Hence X is completely regular at p. ||

EXERCISES

1A. If X is a Hausdorff space and $x_1, \ldots, x_n$ are n distinct points in X, prove that there exist n disjoint open sets $U_1, \ldots, U_n$ in X such that $x_i \in U_i$ for every $i = 1, \ldots, n$. Hence, every finite Hausdorff space is discrete.

1B. Prove the following assertions:
 (a) Every subspace of a Fréchet space is a Fréchet space.
 (b) Every topological sum of a disjoint collection of Fréchet spaces is a Fréchet space.
 (c) Every topological product of Fréchet spaces is a Fréchet space. Establish similar assertions for regular spaces and completely regular spaces.

1C. Prove that a quotient space Q of a space X is a Fréchet space iff every member of Q is a closed set in X.

1D. Prove that every closed subspace of a normal space is normal.

1E. Prove that, for any space X, the following statements are equivalent:
 (a) X is a normal space.
 (b) If an open set G of X contains a closed set F of X, then there exists an open set H of X such that $F \subset H$ and $\text{Cl}\,(H) \subset G$.
 (c) For any two disjoint closed sets A and B in X, there are open

sets U and V of X such that $A \subset U$, $B \subset V$, and
$\text{Cl}\,(U) \cap \text{Cl}\,(V) = \square$.

(d) For any finite number of closed sets $F_1, \ldots, F_n$ of X such that
$F_1 \cap \cdots \cap F_n = \square$, there exist open sets $U_1, \ldots, U_n$ of X
such that $F_i \subset U_i$ for all $i = 1, \ldots, n$ and $U_1 \cap \cdots \cap U_n$
$= \square$.

(e) For any finite number of open sets $G_1, \ldots, G_n$ of X such that
$G_1 \cup \cdots \cup G_n = X$, there exist open sets $H_1, \ldots, H_n$ of X
such that $\text{Cl}\,(H_i) \subset G_i$ for all $i = 1, \ldots, n$ and $H_1 \cup \cdots$
$\cup H_n = X$.

1F. Let X denote the union of the set R of all real numbers and a
singleton set $\{\infty\}$. Give X the smallest topology which contains
every open set U of the real line R and every set $V \subset X$ such that
$X \setminus V$ is a finite set contained in R. Prove that the space X thus
obtained is a Fréchet space but not a Hausdorff space. *because of $\{\infty\}$.*

1G. Let X denote the set $\{t \in R \mid 0 \leqslant t \leqslant 1\}$ and D the subset
$\{1/n \mid n = 1, 2, \ldots\}$. Give X the smallest topology which contains
every open set of $X \setminus \{0\}$ as a subspace of the real line R and every
set B_a, $(0 < a \leqslant 1)$, defined by

$$B_a = \{t \in X \mid t < a \text{ and } t \notin D\}.$$

Prove that the space X thus obtained is a Hausdorff space but not
a regular space.

1H. Prove that every neighborhood of an accumulation point of a set
E in a Fréchet space X contains infinitely many points of E.

1I. Prove that the topological product of a family of Tychonoff spaces
is a Tychonoff space.

1J. A space X is said to be *completely normal* iff every subspace of X is
normal. Prove that a space X is completely normal iff, for any
two sets A and B such that $A \cap \text{Cl}\,(B) = \square = \text{Cl}\,(A) \cap B$, then
there exist two disjoint open sets U and V in X with $A \subset U$ and $B \subset V$.

2. COMPACTNESS

A space X is said to be *compact* iff every open cover of X has a finite
subcover. A set K in a space X is said to be *compact* iff, with the relative
topology, the subspace K is compact; equivalently, a set K in X is compact iff every cover of K by open sets in X has a finite subcover.

The definition of compactness given above was motivated by the
Heine-Borel theorem for bounded closed sets of the real line R as given

in any standard book on real analysis.   Hence, every bounded closed set of the real line R is compact; in particular, the unit interval I is compact.

A family $\mathscr{F}$ of sets is said to have the *finite intersection property* iff the intersection of the members of each finite subfamily of $\mathscr{F}$ is nonempty.

PROPOSITION 2.1.   *A space X is compact iff every family of closed sets in X which has the finite intersection property has a nonempty intersection.*

Proof: Necessity.   Let $\mathscr{F}$ be any family of closed sets in a compact space X and assume that the intersection of all members of $\mathscr{F}$ is empty. Since the complement of the intersection is equal to the union of the complements according to De Morgan formulae, it follows that the collection $\mathscr{G} = \{X \setminus A \mid A \in \mathscr{F}\}$ is an open cover of the compact space X.   By the definition of compactness, $\mathscr{G}$ has a finite subcover.   Hence, there are a finite number of sets $A_1, \ldots, A_n$ in $\mathscr{F}$ such that $\{X \setminus A_1, \ldots, X \setminus A_n\}$ covers X.   By De Morgan's formulae, this implies $A_1 \cap \cdots \cap A_n = \square$.   Hence $\mathscr{F}$ does not have the finite intersection property.

Sufficiency.   Let $\mathscr{C}$ be any open cover of X and consider the family $\mathscr{F} = \{X \setminus U \mid U \in \mathscr{C}\}$ of closed sets.   Since $\mathscr{C}$ is a cover of X, it follows from De Morgan formulae that the intersection of all members of $\mathscr{F}$ is empty.   Hence, $\mathscr{F}$ does not have the finite intersection property; in other words, there are a finite number of open sets $U_1, \ldots, U_n$ in $\mathscr{C}$ such that $(X \setminus U_1) \cap \cdots \cap (X \setminus U_n) = \square$.   By De Morgan formulae, this implies that $\{U_1, \ldots, U_n\}$ is a finite subcover of X in $\mathscr{C}$.   Hence X is compact. $\|$

PROPOSITION 2.2.   *Every closed set K in a compact space X is compact.*

Proof.   Let $\mathscr{C}$ be a cover of K by open sets of X.   Since K is closed, the complement $X \setminus K$ is open.   Hence, the members of $\mathscr{C}$ together with the open set $X \setminus K$ form an open cover of X.   Since X is compact, this open cover of X contains a finite subcover of X.   In other words, there are a finite number of open sets $U_1, \ldots, U_n$ in $\mathscr{C}$ such that

$$U_1 \cup \cdots \cup U_n \cup X \setminus K = X.$$

Hence $\{U_1, \ldots, U_n\}$ covers K and K is compact. $\|$

PROPOSITION 2.3.   *Every continuous image of a compact space is compact.*

Proof.   Let $f: X \to Y$ be a surjective map from a compact space X onto a space Y.   We will prove that Y is compact.   For this purpose, let $\mathscr{C}$ be any open cover of Y and consider

$$\mathscr{B} = \{f^{-1}(V) \mid V \in \mathscr{C}\}.$$

Since f is continuous, $\mathscr{B}$ is an open cover of X. Since X is compact, $\mathscr{B}$ has a finite subcover; in other words, there are a finite number of open sets $V_1, \ldots, V_n$ in $\mathscr{C}$ such that

$$X = f^{-1}(V_1) \cup \cdots \cup f^{-1}(V_n).$$

Since f is surjective, we have $f[f^{-1}(V_i)] = V_i$ for every $i = 1, \ldots, n$. Hence

$$Y = f(X) = V_1 \cup \cdots \cup V_n.$$

This implies that Y is compact. ||

PROPOSITION 2.4. *If K is a compact set in a Hausdorff space X and p is a point in $X \setminus K$, then there are disjoint open sets U and V of X such that $K \subset U$ and $p \in V$.*

Proof. For each point $a \in K$, there exist disjoint open sets U_a and V_a of X such that $a \in U_a$ and $p \in V_a$ since X is a Hausdorff space and $a \neq p$. Then the family $\mathscr{F} = \{U_a \mid a \in K\}$ is a cover of K by open sets of X. Since K is compact, $\mathscr{F}$ has a finite subcover of K. Hence, there are a finite number of points $a_1, \ldots, a_n$ of K such that K is contained in the union

$$U = U_{a_1} \cup \cdots \cup U_{a_n}.$$

On the other hand, let

$$V = V_{a_1} \cap \cdots \cap V_{a_n}.$$

Then U and V are open sets of X such that $K \subset U$, $p \in V$, and $U \cap V = \square$. ||

COROLLARY 2.5. *Every compact set K in a Hausdorff space X is closed.*

Proof. For each $p \in X \setminus K$, the open set V in (2.4) is contained in

$$X \setminus U \subset X \setminus K.$$

Hence, $X \setminus K$ is open and K is closed. ||

PROPOSITION 2.6. *Every bijective map $f : X \to Y$ from a compact space X onto a Hausdorff space Y is a homeomorphism.*

Proof. Since f is bijective and continuous, it remains to prove that f is closed. For this purpose, let E be any closed set in X. By (2.2), E is compact. By (2.3), $f(E)$ is compact. By (2.5), $f(E)$ is closed. Hence f is closed. ||

PROPOSITION 2.7. *Every compact Hausdorff space is normal.*

Proof. Let A and B be any two disjoint closed sets in a compact

Hausdorff space X. By (2.2), A and B are compact. According to (2.4), we may pick for each $b \in B$ two disjoint open sets U_b and V_b of X such that $A \subset U_b$ and $b \in V_b$. Then the collection

$$\mathscr{F} = \{V_b \mid b \in B\}$$

is a cover of B by open sets of X. Since B is compact, $\mathscr{F}$ has a finite subcover of B. In other words, there are a finite number of points $b_1, \ldots, b_n$ in B such that B is contained in the union

$$V = V_{b_1} \cup \cdots \cup V_{b_n}.$$

On the other hand, let

$$U = U_{b_1} \cap \cdots \cap U_{b_n}.$$

Then U and V are open sets of X such that $A \subset U$, $B \subset V$, and $U \cap V = \square$. Hence X is normal. $\|$

PROPOSITION 2.8. *If K is a compact set in a regular space X and if U is a neighborhood of K in X, then U contains a closed neighborhood V of K.*

Proof. For each point p in K, there exists an open neighborhood V_p of p in X such that $\mathrm{Cl}\,(V_p) \subset U$ since X is regular. Then the family

$$\mathscr{F} = \{V_p \mid p \in K\}$$

is a cover of K by open sets of X. Since K is compact, there exist a finite number of points $p_1, \ldots, p_n$ of K such that K is contained in the union of V_{p_i}, $i = 1, 2, \ldots, n$. Let

$$V = \mathrm{Cl}\,(V_{p_1}) \cup \cdots \cup \mathrm{Cl}\,(V_{p_n}).$$

Then V is a closed neighborhood of K contained in U. $\|$

COROLLARY 2.9. *Every compact regular space is normal.*

Proof. Let A and B be any two disjoint closed sets in a compact regular space X. By (2.2), A is compact. Since $X \setminus B$ is an open neighborhood of A in X, it follows from (2.8) that A has a closed neighborhood N contained in $X \setminus B$. Let

$$U = \mathrm{Int}\,(N), \qquad V = X \setminus N.$$

Then U and V are open sets of X such that

$$A \subset U, \qquad B \subset V, \qquad U \cap V = \square.$$

Hence X is normal. $\|$

THEOREM 2.10 (TYCHONOFF's THEOREM). *The topological product of a family of compact spaces is compact.*

In the proof of this theorem, we will make use of a set-theoretic notion as follows. A class $\mathscr{C}$ of sets is said to be of finite character iff the following condition is satisfied: a set E is a member of $\mathscr{C}$ iff every finite subset of E belongs to $\mathscr{C}$. An equivalent version of the Axiom of Choice is the Tukey Lemma: *For each member A of a class $\mathscr{C}$ of sets which is of finite character, there exists a maximal member M in $\mathscr{C}$ containing A.* [K, p. 33.]

Proof of (2.10). Let $\mathscr{F} = \{X_\mu \mid \mu \in M\}$ be a family of compact spaces and let X denote the topological product of the family $\mathscr{F}$. We are going to prove the compactness of X. Because of (2.1), it suffices to establish the assertion stated as follows: If $\mathscr{B}$ is a family of subsets of X having the finite intersection property, then

$$\bigcap\{\mathrm{Cl}\,(B) \mid B \in \mathscr{B}\} \neq \square.$$

For this purpose, let us consider the class $\mathscr{C}$ of all families of subsets of X which possess the finite intersection property. This class $\mathscr{C}$ clearly is of finite character. Hence it follows from the Tukey Lemma that there is a maximal member of $\mathscr{C}$ which contains the given family $\mathscr{B}$. Without loss of generality, we may assume that $\mathscr{B}$ itself is a maximal member of the class $\mathscr{C}$.

From the maximality of $\mathscr{B}$, it follows that the intersection of the members of every finite subfamily of $\mathscr{B}$ belongs to $\mathscr{B}$. Besides, if a subset E of X meets every member of $\mathscr{B}$, then E is also a member of $\mathscr{B}$.

Now, let $\mu \in M$ and consider the natural projection

$$p_\mu : X \to X_\mu.$$

Consider the family

$$\mathscr{B}_\mu = \{p_\mu(B) \mid B \in \mathscr{B}\}$$

of subsets of X_μ. Then $\mathscr{B}_\mu$ has the finite intersection property. Since X_μ is compact, it follows from (2.1) that the intersection

$$H_\mu = \bigcap\{\mathrm{Cl}\,[p_\mu(B)] \mid B \in \mathscr{B}\}$$

is nonempty. Pick a point $x_\mu \in H_\mu$ for each index $\mu \in M$.

Let x denote the point of the topological product X whose μ-th coordinate $x(\mu)$ is the point $x_\mu \in X_\mu$. It remains to prove that $x \in \mathrm{Cl}\,(B)$ for every $B \in \mathscr{B}$.

For this purpose, consider an arbitrary sub-basic open set $U_\mu{}^*$ of X which contains the point x, where $\mu \in M$ and U_μ is an open set of X_μ containing the point x_μ. Since $x_\mu \in \mathrm{Cl}\,[p_\mu(B)]$ for each $B \in \mathscr{B}$, it follows that U_μ meets $p_\mu(B)$ for each $B \in \mathscr{B}$. Hence, the set

$$U_\mu{}^* = p_\mu^{-1}(U_\mu)$$

meets every member B of $\mathscr{B}$. It follows from the maximality of $\mathscr{B}$ that $U_\mu{}^*$ belongs to $\mathscr{B}$ and, therefore, the intersection of any finite number of sub-basic open sets containing x is a member of $\mathscr{B}$. This implies that every neighborhood of x in X meets each member B of $\mathscr{B}$. Consequently, $x \in \mathrm{Cl}\,(B)$ for every $B \in \mathscr{B}$. ‖

COROLLARY 2.11. *Every topological power I^M of the closed unit interval I is a compact Hausdorff space.*

COROLLARY 2.12. *A set K in the n-dimensional Euclidean space R^n is compact iff it is bounded and closed.*

A space X is said to be *locally compact* at a point $p \in X$ iff p has at least one compact neighborhood in X. If X is locally compact at every point, it is called a *locally compact space*. Examples of locally compact spaces are compact spaces, discrete spaces, and the n-dimensional Euclidean space R^n.

PROPOSITION 2.13. *Every closed subspace of a locally compact space is locally compact.*

Proof. Let E be a closed subspace of a locally compact space X and let p be an arbitrary point in E. Since X is locally compact at p, there is a compact neighborhood K of p in X. Let $H = K \cap E$. As a closed subset of K, H is compact. Since K is a neighborhood of p in X, it follows that H is a neighborhood of p in E. This implies that E is locally compact at p. ‖

PROPOSITION 2.14. *If X is a locally compact space which is either Hausdorff or regular, then the family of closed compact neighborhoods of a point $p \in X$ is a local basis at p.*

Proof. Since X is locally compact, p has a compact neighborhood K in X. Let N be an arbitrary neighborhood of p in X; we are going to prove the existence of a closed compact neighborhood M of p contained in N.

First, assume that X is regular. There exists a closed neighborhood M in X contained in $K \cap N$. As a closed subset of a compact space K, M is also compact.

Next, assume X to be a Hausdorff space. By (2.7), K is a normal Hausdorff space and hence is also regular. Since $K \cap N$ is now a neighborhood of p in a regular space K, there is a closed neighborhood M of p in K contained in $K \cap N$. By (2.2), K is closed. Hence, M is both compact and closed in X. Since K itself is a neighborhood of p in X, it follows that M is also a neighborhood of p in X.

In both cases, M is a closed compact neighborhood of p in X contained in N. ||

COROLLARY 2.15. *Every locally compact Hausdorff space is regular.*

PROPOSITION 2.16. *If K is a closed compact set in a locally compact regular space X and if N is a neighborhood of K in X, then there exists a closed compact neighborhood M of K in X such that $K \subset M \subset N$. Furthermore, there exists a continuous function $f : X \to I$ such that*

$$f(x) = \begin{cases} 0, & (if \ x \in K), \\ 1, & (if \ x \in X \setminus M). \end{cases}$$

Proof. Let $p \in K$. By (2.14), there is a closed compact neighborhood M_p of p contained in N. Let U_p denote the interior of M_p. Then the family

$$\mathscr{F} = \{U_p \mid p \in K\}$$

is an open cover of K by open sets of X. Since K is compact, there are a finite number of points $p_1, \ldots, p_n$ in K such that K is contained in the union U of the open sets $U_{p_1}, \ldots, U_{p_n}$. Let

$$M = M_{p_1} \cup \cdots \cup M_{p_n}.$$

Then M is closed and compact, and

$$K \subset U \subset M \subset N.$$

Hence M is a closed compact neighborhood of K contained in N. This proves the first part of the proposition.

By (2.9), the subspace M of X is normal. Since K and $M \setminus U$ are two disjoint closed sets in a normal space M, it follows from the Urysohn Lemma that there exists a continuous function $g : M \to I$ which has the value 0 on K and 1 on $M \setminus U$. Define a function $f : X \to I$ by taking

$$f(x) = \begin{cases} g(x), & (if \ x \in M), \\ 1, & (if \ x \in X \setminus U). \end{cases}$$

By (II, 4.3), f is continuous. It is obvious that $f(x) = 0$ for $x \in K$ and $f(x) = 1$ for $x \in X \setminus M$. ||

COROLLARY 2.17. *Every locally compact regular space is completely regular.*

COROLLARY 2.18. *Every locally compact Hausdorff space is a Tychonoff space.*

A family $\mathscr{F}$ of sets in a space X is said to be *locally finite* iff every point of X has a neighborhood which meets at most a finite number of members of $\mathscr{F}$.

Let $\mathscr{F}$ and $\mathscr{G}$ be two covers of a space X. If every member of $\mathscr{F}$ is contained in some member of $\mathscr{G}$, then we say that $\mathscr{F}$ is a *refinement* of $\mathscr{G}$.

A space X is said to be *paracompact* iff every open cover of X has a locally finite open refinement, i.e. a refinement which is a locally finite open cover of X. Every compact space is paracompact. It will be seen in a later section that the converse is false. [Dieudonné 1.]

PROPOSITION 2.19.   *Every paracompact Hausdorff space is regular.*

Proof. Let X be a paracompact Hausdorff space and let U be an open neighborhood of a point $p \in X$. For each point $q \in X \setminus U$, choose open sets U_q and V_q of X such that

$$q \in U_q, \quad p \in V_q, \quad U_q \cap V_q = \square.$$

The open sets $\{U_q \mid q \in X \setminus U\}$ together with the given open set U form an open cover $\mathscr{C}$ of the paracompact space X. Hence, by definition, $\mathscr{C}$ has an open refinement $\mathscr{D}$ which is locally finite.

Since $\mathscr{D}$ is locally finite, there exists a neighborhood M of the point p which meets only the members of a finite subfamily $\mathscr{F}$ of $\mathscr{D}$. Let $W_1, \ldots, W_n$ denote the members of $\mathscr{F}$ which are not contained in U. Then there are n points $q_1, \ldots, q_n$ of $X \setminus U$ such that $W_i \subset U_{q_i}$ for each $i = 1, \ldots, n$. Let

$$N = M \cap V_{q_1} \cap \cdots \cap V_{q_n}, \quad V = \mathrm{Cl}\,(N).$$

It remains to prove that $V \subset U$.

For this purpose, let W denote the union of all members of $\mathscr{D}$ which are not contained in U. Then we have

$$N \cap W \subset M \cap V_{q_1} \cap \cdots \cap V_{q_n} \cap [U_{q_1} \cup \cdots \cup U_{q_n}] = \square$$

since $V_{q_i} \cap U_{q_i} = \square$ for every $i = 1, \ldots, n$. This implies that N is contained in the closed set $X \setminus W \subset U$. Hence

$$V = \mathrm{Cl}\,(N) \subset X \setminus W \subset U. \quad \|$$

PROPOSITION 2.20.   *Every paracompact regular space is normal.*

Proof. Let X be a paracompact regular space, and let A and B be any two disjoint closed sets in X. For each point $p \in A$, choose a closed neighborhood M_p of p in the space X contained in the open set $X \setminus B$. Let

$$U_p = \mathrm{Int}\,(M_p).$$

The open sets $\{U_p \mid p \in A\}$ together with the open set $X \setminus A$ form an open cover $\mathscr{C}$ of the paracompact space X. Hence, by definition, $\mathscr{C}$ has an open refinement $\mathscr{D}$ which is locally finite.

Let U denote the union of all members of $\mathscr{D}$ which are not contained in $X \setminus A$. Then U is an open set of X containing A.

Let q be an arbitrary point of B. Since $\mathscr{D}$ is locally finite, there exists a neighborhood N_q of q in the space X which meets only the members of a finite subfamily $\mathscr{F}_q$ of $\mathscr{D}$. Let $D_1, \ldots, D_n$ denote the members of $\mathscr{F}_q$ which are not contained in $X \setminus A$. Then, there are n points $p_1, \ldots, p_n$ of A such that $D_i \subset U_{p_i}$ for each $i = 1, \ldots, n$. Let

$$V_q = \mathrm{Int}\,(N_q) \cap (X \setminus M_{p_1}) \cap \cdots \cap (X \setminus M_{p_n}).$$

Then V_q is an open neighborhood of q such that $U \cap V_q = \square$.

Let V denote the union of the open sets V_q for all $q \in B$. Then V is an open set of X containing B such that

$$U \cap V = \square.$$

Hence X is a normal space. ||

EXERCISES

2A. Show that every indiscrete space is compact and normal, and that every indiscrete space of more than one point is not a Fréchet space.

2B. Prove that a space X is compact if its topology has a sub-basis σ such that every cover of X by members of σ has a finite subcover. Give a proof of (2.10) by using this fact.

2C. Let K be a compact set in a completely regular space X and let U be a neighborhood of K in X. Prove the existence of a map $f : X \to I$ such that

$$f(x) = \begin{cases} 0, & (\text{if } x \in K), \\ 1, & (\text{if } x \in X \setminus U). \end{cases}$$

2D. Consider spaces X, Y and compact sets $A \subset X$, $B \subset Y$. Let W be a neighborhood of $A \times B$ in the topological product $X \times Y$. Prove that there are neighborhoods U of A in X and V of B in Y with $U \times V \subset W$. In case $B = Y$, show that the compactness of A may be omitted from the hypothesis.

2E. Prove the assertion: if an infinite number of the coordinate spaces of a topological product X are noncompact, then every compact set K in X is *nowhere dense*, that is to say, Int (K) = $\square$.

2F. Prove that the closure of a compact set in a regular space is compact.

2G. Prove the assertion: if a topology τ in a set X makes X a compact Hausdorff space, then every topology in X which is strictly smaller than τ fails to make X a Hausdorff space.

2H. Show that the continuous image of a locally compact space may fail to be locally compact. However, if the map is open, then the image of a locally compact space is always locally compact.

2I. Prove the assertion: if a topological product is locally compact, then each coordinate space is locally compact and all except a finite number of coordinate spaces are compact. *(See 2E and 2 H*

2J. Prove the assertion: if X is a Hausdorff space and E is a dense, locally compact subspace of X, then E is open.

2K. By a *Cantor space*, we mean a topological power 2^M of the discrete space 2 which consists of two elements. Prove that every compact Hausdorff space is the continuous image of a closed subspace of some Cantor space.

2L. Let α and β be covers of a space X. We say that β is a *star-refinement* iff, for every $B \in \beta$, there exists an $A \in \alpha$ which contains every member of β meeting B. A space X is said to be *fully normal* iff every open cover of X has an open star-refinement. Prove that a regular space is fully normal iff it is paracompact. [Stone 1.]

3. CONVERGENCE

This section is devoted to a brief exposition of Moore-Smith convergence.

A binary relation $\geqslant$ in a set D is said to *direct* D iff D is nonempty and the following three conditions are satisfied:

(DS1)   If $a \in D$, then $a \geqslant a$.

(DS2)   If a, b, c are members of D such that $a \geqslant b$ and $b \geqslant c$, then $a \geqslant c$.

(DS3)   If a and b are members of D, then there exists a member $c \in D$ such that $c \geqslant a$ and $c \geqslant b$.

EXAMPLES. The set N of all natural numbers as well as the set R of all real numbers are directed by $\geqslant$ in the usual sense. Also, every local basis of a point in a space is directed by the inclusion $\subset$.

By a *directed set*, we mean a set D furnished with a binary relation $\geqslant$ which directs D. In particular, the set N of all natural numbers together with the usual relation $\geqslant$ is a directed set.

Let D be a given directed set and consider an arbitrary subset E of D. If there exists an element $d_0 \in D$ such that, for each $d \in D$, $d \geqslant d_0$ implies $d \in E$, then E is called a *residual subset* of D. If, for every $d \in D$, there exists an $e \in E$ such that $e \geqslant d$, then E is said to be a *cofinal subset* of D. It is easy to see that every residual subset of D is cofinal and that every cofinal subset of D is directed by $\geqslant$.

By a *net* in a space X, we mean a function

$$\phi : D \to X$$

from a directed set D into X. In particular, if the domain D is the set N of all natural numbers directed by $\geqslant$ in the usual sense, then ϕ is called a *sequence* in X.

Now, let $\phi : D \to X$ be a given net in a space X and let U be any subset of X. The net ϕ is said to be *in* U iff $\phi(D) \subset U$. The net ϕ is said to be *eventually in* U iff there exists a residual subset E of D such that $\phi(E) \subset U$. The net ϕ is said to be *frequently in* U iff there exists a cofinal subset C of D such that $\phi(C) \subset U$.

A net $\phi : D \to X$ in a space X is said to *converge* to a point $p \in X$ iff ϕ is eventually in every neighborhood of p. If X is indiscrete, then every net in X converges to every point of X. On the other hand, if X is discrete, then a net ϕ in X converges to a point $p \in X$ iff $\phi(d) = p$ for all $d \geqslant$ some $d_0 \in D$.

The convergence of nets in a space X characterizes the topology of the space X. Precisely, we have the following theorem.

THEOREM 3.1. *A set U in a space X is open iff no net in $X \setminus U$ can converge to a point of U.*

Proof: Necessity. Assume that U is open and that $\phi : D \to X$ is a net which converges to a point $p \in U$. Since U is a neighborhood of p, it follows from the definition of convergence that ϕ must be eventually in U. This implies that ϕ can never be in $X \setminus U$.

Sufficiency. Assume that U is not open. Then there exists a point $p \in U$ such that every neighborhood of p meets $X \setminus U$. Let D be a local basis at the point p in X. Then D is directed by the inclusion $\subset$. For each neighborhood $N \in D$, pick a point $\phi(N)$ in $N \cap (X \setminus U)$. The assignment $N \to \phi(N)$ defines a net $\phi : D \to X$ which converges to p and is in $X \setminus U$. Hence the condition cannot hold. ||

COROLLARY 3.2.   *A set* U *in a space* X *satisfying the first axiom of countability is open iff no sequence in* $X \setminus U$ *can converge to a point of* U.

This corollary follows from the proof of (3.1) and the following lemma.

LEMMA 3.3.   *Every point* p *of a space* X *satisfying the first axiom of countability has a local basis which consists of a decreasing sequence of open neighborhoods of* p.

Proof.   Let $\beta = \{U_1, U_2, \ldots, U_n, \ldots\}$ be a countable local basis of X at the point p.   For each $n = 1, 2, \ldots$, let

$$V_n = U_1 \cap U_2 \cap \cdots \cap U_n.$$

Then the sequence $\gamma = \{V_1, V_2, \ldots, V_n, \ldots\}$ is also a local basis of X at p.   Since $V_n \supset V_{n+1}$ for each $n = 1, 2, \ldots$, this completes the proof of (3.3). ||

Since, by (3.1), the notion of convergence determines the topology of the space, it should be able to characterize the features defined by the topology of a space, say for example, the closure and the accumulation points of a set E in a space X.

PROPOSITION 3.4.   *A point* p *of a space* X *belongs to the closure* Cl (E) *of a set* E *in* X *iff there exists a net* ϕ *in* E *which converges to* p.

Proof: Necessity.   Let D be any local basis at the point p.   Then D is directed by the inclusion $\subset$.   For each $U \in D$, the intersection $E \cap U$ is nonempty since p is a point of Cl (E).   Choose a point $\phi(U)$ in $E \cap U$ for each $U \in D$.   The assignment $U \rightarrow \phi(U)$ defines a net ϕ in E which obviously converges to p.

Sufficiency.   Let $\phi : D \rightarrow E$ be an arbitrary net in E which converges to a point p of X.   Let U be an arbitrary neighborhood of p.   Since ϕ converges to p there exists a residual subset R of D such that $\phi(R) \subset U$. In particular, $E \cap U \neq \square$.   Hence, $p \in$ Cl (E). ||

PROPOSITION 3.5.   *A point* p *of a space* X *is an accumulation point of a set* E *in* X *iff there exists a net* ϕ *in* $E \setminus \{p\}$ *which converges to* p.

Proof: Necessity.   Let p be any accumulation point of E and let D be a local basis at p.   Then D is directed by the inclusion $\subset$.   For each $U \in D$, the intersection $U \cap (E \setminus \{p\})$ is nonempty and hence we may pick a point $\phi(U)$ in $U \cap (E \setminus \{p\})$.   The assignment $U \rightarrow \phi(U)$ defines a net ϕ in $E \setminus \{p\}$ which obviously converges to p.

Sufficiency.   Let $\phi : D \rightarrow E \setminus \{p\}$ be a net in $E \setminus \{p\}$ which converges to p.   Let U be any neighborhood of p.   Since ϕ converges to p, there exists a residual subset R of D such that $\phi(R) \subset U$. In particular, $U \cap (E \setminus \{p\}) \neq \square$. Hence, p is an accumulation point of E in X. ||

As we have seen above, a net in a space may converge to several different points. However, in a Hausdorff space, convergence is unique. Precisely, we have the following theorem.

THEOREM 3.6. *A space X is a Hausdorff space iff every net in X can converge to at most one point.*

Proof: Necessity. Let X be a Hausdorff space and a, b be two distinct points of X. There are open sets U and V of X such that $a \in U$, $b \in V$, and $U \cap V = \square$. By the definition of residual subsets of a directed set, it is clear that no net can be eventually in both U and V. Hence, no net in X can converge to both a and b.

Sufficiency. Assume that a given space X is not a Hausdorff space. Then, there exist two distinct points a and b in X such that every neighborhood of a meets every neighborhood of b. Let A be a local basis at a and let B be a local basis at b. Both A and B are directed by the inclusion $\subset$. Consider the cartesian product

$$D = A \times B.$$

Introduce a binary relation $\geqslant$ as follows. Let (U_1, V_1) and (U_2, V_2) be two elements in D. We define

$$(U_1, V_1) \geqslant (U_2, V_2)$$

iff $U_1 \subset U_2$ and $V_1 \subset V_2$. Clearly, D is directed by $\geqslant$. For each $(U, V) \in D$, the intersection $U \cap V \neq \square$ and hence we may pick a point $\phi(U, V) \in U \cap V$. This assignment $(U, V) \to \phi(U, V)$ defines a net $\phi : D \to X$ which converges to both a and b. ||

If X is a Hausdorff space and a net $\phi : D \to X$ converges to a point $p \in X$, then the point p is said to be *the limit* of the net ϕ, in symbols,

$$\lim (\phi) = p.$$

A function $\lambda : E \to D$ from a directed set E into a directed set D is said to be *cofinal* iff, for every residual subset Q of D, there exists a residual subset R of E such that $\lambda(R) \subset Q$; in other words, for every $d \in D$, there exists an $e \in E$ such that $\lambda(x) \geqslant d$ for every $x \geqslant e$ in E.

By a *subnet* of a net $\phi : D \to X$, we mean a net $\psi : E \to X$ such that there exists a cofinal function $\lambda : E \to D$ with

$$\psi = \phi \circ \lambda.$$

In particular, if E is a cofinal subset of D and is directed by the same ordering in D, then the inclusion function $\lambda : E \subset D$ and the restriction

$$\phi \restriction E \ = \ \phi \circ \lambda$$

is a subnet of ϕ.

PROPOSITION 3.7. *If $\phi : D \to X$ is a net in a space X and if $\mathscr{F}$ is a family of sets in X such that the intersection of any two members of $\mathscr{F}$ contains a member of $\mathscr{F}$ and such that the net ϕ is frequently in each member of $\mathscr{F}$, then there exists a subnet of ϕ which is eventually in each member of $\mathscr{F}$.*

Proof. Since the intersection of any two members of $\mathscr{F}$ contains a member of $\mathscr{F}$, $\mathscr{F}$ is directed by the inclusion $\subset$. Consider the subset E of the cartesian product $D \times \mathscr{F}$ defined by

$$E \ = \ \{ (d, U) \ \in \ D \times \mathscr{F} \mid \phi(d) \ \in \ U \}.$$

Then E is directed by the binary order $\geqslant$ defined as follows. Let (d_1, U_1) and (d_2, U_2) be any two elements in E. Then $(d_1, U_1) \geqslant (d_2, U_2)$ iff $d_1 \geqslant d_2$ and $U_1 \subset U_2$.

Define a function $\lambda : E \to D$ by taking $\lambda(d, U) = d$ for each element (d, U) in E. Obviously, λ is cofinal and hence $\psi = \phi \circ \lambda : E \to X$ is a subnet of ϕ.

Finally, let U_0 be an arbitrary member of $\mathscr{F}$. Since ϕ is frequently in U_0, there exists a member d_0 of D such that $\phi(d_0) \in U_0$. Hence $e_0 = (d_0, U_0)$ is a member of E. Now, let $e = (d, U)$ be an arbitrary element of E such that $e \geqslant e_0$, in other words, $d \geqslant d_0$ and $U \subset U_0$. Then, we have

$$\psi(e) \ = \ \phi[\lambda(d, U)] \ = \ \phi(d) \ \in \ U \subset U_0.$$

Hence ψ is eventually in U_0. $\|$

Now, let us consider a given net

$$\phi : D \to X$$

in a space X. A point $p \in X$ is called a *cluster point* of the net ϕ iff ϕ is frequently in every neighborhood of p.

PROPOSITION 3.8. *A point p in a space X is a cluster point of a net $\phi : D \to X$ iff there exists a subnet $\psi : E \to X$ which converges to p.*

Proof: Necessity. Let p be a cluster point of a net $\phi : D \to X$ and let $\mathscr{F}$ be a local basis at the point p. Then the intersection of any two members of $\mathscr{F}$ contains a member of $\mathscr{F}$, and ϕ is frequently in each member of $\mathscr{F}$. Hence, by (3.7), there exists a subnet $\psi : E \to X$ of ϕ

which is eventually in each member of $\mathscr{F}$. Since $\mathscr{F}$ is a local basis at p, this implies that ψ converges to p.

Sufficiency. Assume that the net ϕ has a subnet ψ which converges to p. To prove that p is a cluster point of ϕ, let U be a neighborhood of p and d_0 any element in D. It suffices to find an element $d \in D$ such that $d \geqslant d_0$ and $\phi(d) \in U$. Since ψ is a subnet of ϕ, there exists a cofinal function $\lambda : E \rightarrow D$ such that $\psi = \phi \circ \lambda$. Since λ is cofinal, there is an element $e_0 \in E$ such that $\lambda(e) \geqslant d_0$ for every $e \geqslant e_0$. Since ψ converges to p, there exists an element $e \geqslant e_0$ with $\psi(e) \in U$. Now, let $d = \lambda(e)$. Then we have $d \geqslant d_0$ and $\phi(d) = \phi[\lambda(e)] = \psi(e) \in U$. ||

The compactness of a space X can be characterized by the convergence of nets as follows.

THEOREM 3.9. *A space X is compact iff every net in X has a subnet which converges to a point of X.*

Proof. According to (3.8), it suffices to prove that a space is compact iff every net in X has a cluster point.

Necessity. Let $\phi : D \rightarrow X$ be a net in a compact space X. For each $a \in D$, let M_a denote the subset of X which consists of the points $\phi(d)$ for all $d \geqslant a$ in D. Since D is directed by $\geqslant$, it follows that $\{M_a \mid a \in D\}$ has the finite intersection property and hence the family $\{\text{Cl}\,(M_a) \mid a \in D\}$ also has the finite intersection property. Since X is compact, it follows from (2.1) that there is a point $p \in X$ which belongs to $\text{Cl}\,(M_a)$ for every $a \in D$. We are going to prove that p is cluster point of ϕ. For this purpose, let U be a neighborhood of p and $a \in D$. Since $p \in \text{Cl}\,(M_a)$, it follows that $M_a \cap U \neq \square$. Hence there exists an element $d \in D$ such that $d \geqslant a$ and $\phi(d) \in U$. This implies that ϕ is frequently in any neighborhood of p and consequently p is a cluster point of ϕ.

Sufficiency. Assume that every net in a space X has a cluster point. We are going to prove that X is compact. For this purpose, consider a family $\mathscr{F}$ of closed sets in X with the finite intersection property. Let $\mathscr{G}$ denote the family of all finite intersections of members of $\mathscr{F}$; then $\mathscr{G}$ also has the finite intersection property. Since $\mathscr{F} \subset \mathscr{G}$, it suffices to prove that the intersection of all members of $\mathscr{G}$ is nonempty. Since the intersection of any two members of $\mathscr{G}$ is a member of $\mathscr{G}$, $\mathscr{G}$ is directed by the inclusion $\subset$. In each member B of $\mathscr{G}$, choose a point $\phi(B) \in B$. This assignment $B \rightarrow \phi(B)$ defines a net $\phi : \mathscr{G} \rightarrow X$. By our hypothesis, ϕ has a cluster point $p \in X$. It remains to prove that the point p belongs to every member B of $\mathscr{G}$. Let $B \in \mathscr{G}$ and let C be any member of $\mathscr{G}$

with $C \subset B$. Then $\phi(C) \in C \subset B$; hence, ϕ is eventually in the closed set B. By (3.1) and (3.8), p must belong to B. ∥

On the other hand, the continuity of a map $f: X \to Y$ can also be characterized by the convergence of nets as follows.

THEOREM 3.10. *A function $f: X \to Y$ from a space X into a space Y is continuous at a point $p \in X$ iff, for each net $\phi: D \to X$ which converges to p, the composition $\psi = f \circ \phi: D \to Y$ converges to $f(p)$.*

Proof: Necessity. Assume that $f: X \to Y$ is continuous at p and let V be any neighborhood of $f(p)$ in Y. By definition of continuity at p, there is a neighborhood U of p in X such that $f(U) \subset V$. Since ϕ converges to p, there exists a residual subset R of D such that $\phi(R) \subset U$. Then we have

$$\psi(R) \;=\; f[\phi(R)] \subset f(U) \subset V.$$

Hence ψ converges to $f(p)$.

Sufficiency. Assume that f is not continuous at p. Then there exists an open neighborhood V of $f(p)$ in Y such that every neighborhood of p in X meets $f^{-1}(Y \setminus V)$. Let D be a local basis at p directed by the inclusion $\subset$. In each $U \in D$, pick a point $\phi(U)$ in $U \cap f^{-1}(X \setminus V)$. The assignment $U \to \phi(U)$ defines a net $\phi: D \to X$ which converges to p. Now, the composition $\psi = f \circ \phi: D \to Y$ is a net in $Y \setminus V$. Since V is open and $f(p) \in V$, ψ can never converge to $f(p)$. ∥

EXERCISES

3A. Show that, for spaces satisfying the first axiom of countability, one can place "net" by "sequence" in the assertions in this section except Theorem 3.9.

3B. Prove that a net in a topological product converges to a point p iff its projection in each coordinate space converges to the projection of the point p.

3C. Prove that a Lindelöf T_1-space X is compact if every sequence in X has a cluster point.

4. CONNECTEDNESS

By a *separation* of a space X, we mean a pair of open sets U and V of X such that

$$U \cup V \;=\; X, \qquad U \cap V \;=\; \square;$$

in symbols, $X = U \mid V$. The separation $U \mid V$ of X is said to be *trivial* iff one of the open sets U, V is empty; otherwise, it is said to be *nontrivial*. If $U \mid V$ is a separation of a space X, then each of the sets U and V is both open and closed.

A space X is said to be *connected* iff it has no nontrivial separation; otherwise, it is said to be *disconnected*. In other words, a space X is connected iff it contains no nonempty proper subset which is both open and closed. For examples, every indiscrete space is connected and every discrete space containing more than one point is disconnected.

A set E in a space X is said to be *connected* iff, with the relative topology, the subspace E is connected. One can easily verify that a separation $U \mid V$ of the subspace E is a pair of subsets U and V of the space X such that

$$U \cup V = X, \quad \mathrm{Cl}\, U \cap V = \Box = U \cap \mathrm{Cl}\, V,$$

where the closure operation Cl is taken in the space X.

PROPOSITION 4.1. *The real line R is connected.*

Proof. Assume that $U \mid V$ were a nontrivial separation of R. Let $a \in U$ and $b \in V$. Without loss of generality, we may assume that $a < b$. Consider the closed interval $[a, b]$ of real numbers and the subset

$$A = U \cap [a, b], \quad B = V \cap [a, b].$$

As closed subsets of a compact set $[a, b]$, A and B are compact. Hence, the topological product $A \times B$ is compact. Define a continuous function $d : A \times B \to R$ by setting

$$d(x, y) = |x - y|, \quad (x \in A, y \in B).$$

The image $d(A \times B)$ is compact and therefore closed in R. Hence, $d(A \times B)$ contains its greatest lower bound δ; that is, there exist $u \in U$ and $v \in V$ such that $d(u, v) = \delta > 0$. Consider the point $w = \frac{1}{2}(u + v)$. Then

$$d(u, w) = \tfrac{1}{2}\delta, \quad d(w, v) = \tfrac{1}{2}\delta.$$

Hence w can belong to neither U nor V. This contradiction proves (4.1). $\parallel$

COROLLARY 4.2. *Every open interval of the real line is connected.*

PROPOSITION 4.3. *If C is a connected set in a space X and E is a set in X such that $C \subset E \subset \mathrm{Cl}\,(C)$, then E is connected.*

Proof. Let $U \mid V$ be an arbitrary separation of the subspace E of

X. Then $(U \cap C) \mid (V \cap C)$ is a separation of the separation of the subspace C. Since C is connected, one of the sets $U \cap C$ and $V \cap C$ must be empty. Without loss of generality, we may assume that $V \cap C = \square$. This implies that $C \subset U$ and hence $E \subset \mathrm{Cl}\,(C) \subset \mathrm{Cl}\,(U)$. Thus, we have

$$E \subset E \cap \mathrm{Cl}\,(U) = U$$

since U is closed in the subspace E. It follows that $V = \square$ and hence the separation $U \mid V$ of E is trivial. This implies that E is connected. $\ \| $

COROLLARY 4.4. *The closed unit interval I is connected.*

PROPOSITION 4.5. *Every continuous image of a connected set is connected.*

Proof. It suffices to prove that, if $f\colon X \to Y$ is a surjective map of a connected space X onto a space Y, then Y is also connected. For this purpose, let $U \mid V$ be an arbitrary separation of the space Y. Let $M = f^{-1}(U)$ and $N = f^{-1}(V)$. Then, M and N are open sets of X satisfying $X = M \cup N$ and $M \cap N = \square$. Hence $M \mid N$ is a separation of X. Since X is connected, one of the sets M and N must be empty. Without loss of generality, we may assume that $N = \square$. Since f is surjective and $N = f^{-1}(V)$, this implies that $V = \square$. Hence, Y is connected. $\ \| $

PROPOSITION 4.6. *If two connected sets A and B in a space X have a common point p, then $A \cup B$ is connected.*

Proof. Let $U \mid V$ be an arbitrary separation of the subspace $A \cup B$ with $p \in U$. Then it follows that $(A \cap U) \mid (A \cap V)$ is a separation of the subspace A. Since A is connected, one of the sets $A \cap U$ and $A \cap V$ must be empty. Since $p \in A \cap U$, we have $A \cap V = \square$. Hence, $A \subset U$. Similarly, one can prove $B \subset U$. Thus, $A \cup B \subset U$ and consequently $V = \square$. $\ \| $

Two points a and b of a space X are said to be *connected in X* iff there exists a connected set in X which contains both a and b.

PROPOSITION 4.7. *If every two points of a space X are connected in X, then X is connected.*

Proof. Assume that there were a nontrivial separation $U \mid V$ of the space X. Let $a \in U$ and $b \in V$. By hypothesis, there exists a connected set C in X which contains both a and b. Then $(U \cap C) \mid (V \cap C)$ is a nontrivial separation of C. This contradicts the connectedness of C and proves (4.7). $\ \| $

Cₒᵣₒₗₗₐᵣᵧ 4.8. *The union of any family of connected sets with a common point is connected.*

Define a binary relation $\sim$ in any given space X as follows: for any two points a and b of X, $a \sim b$ iff a and b are connected in X. By the aid of (4.6), one can easily verify that $\sim$ is an equivalence relation in X. Hence, the points of X are divided into disjoint equivalence classes called the *components* of the space X. We will denote by $C(p)$ the component of X which contains the point $p \in X$.

Pᵣₒₚₒₛᵢₜᵢₒₙ 4.9. *For each point p in a space X, the component $C(p)$ of X is the largest connected set in X which contains the point p.*

Proof. Let K be any connected set in X which contains p and let q be an arbitrary point in K. By definition, we have $p \sim q$ and hence $q \in C(p)$. This implies $K \subset C(p)$.

It remains to prove the connectedness of $C(p)$. For this purpose, let r denote an arbitrary point in $C(p)$. Since $p \sim r$, there exists a connected set K_r of X which contains both p and r. By the first half of the proof, $K_r \subset C(p)$. Hence, $C(p)$ is the union of the family $\{K_r \mid r \in C(p)\}$ of connected sets with a common point p. It follows from (4.8) that $C(p)$ is connected. ‖

Cₒᵣₒₗₗₐᵣᵧ 4.10. *For each point p in a space X, the component $C(p)$ of X is a closed set of X.*

Proof. By (4.9), $C(p)$ is the largest connected set of X containing the point p. By (4.3), the closure $\mathrm{Cl}\,[C(p)]$ of $C(p)$ is connected. Hence $\mathrm{Cl}\,[C(p)] = C(p)$ and $C(p)$ is closed. ‖

Pᵣₒₚₒₛᵢₜᵢₒₙ 4.11. *The topological product of an arbitrary family of connected spaces is connected.*

Proof. First, let us prove that the topological product $X \times Y$ of two connected spaces X and Y is connected. For this purpose, let (a, b) and (c, d) be any two points of $X \times Y$ and consider the point (a, d). Since the connected set $a \times Y$ contains both (a, b) and (a, d), we have $(a, b) \sim (a, d)$. On the other hand, since the connected set $X \times d$ contains both (a, d) and (c, d), we have $(a, d) \sim (c, d)$. Hence $(a, b) \sim (c, d)$ and $X \times Y$ is connected according to (4.7). It follows from a finite induction that the topological product of a finite family of connected spaces is connected.

Now, consider an arbitrary family

$$\mathscr{F} = \{X_\mu \mid \mu \in M\}$$

of connected spaces. Let X denote the topological product of this family and let p be a given point in X. Consider the component $C(p)$ of X which contains the point p. Let B denote an arbitrary basic open set of the topological product X. Then there are a finite number of elements of M, say, $\mu_1, \ldots, \mu_n$, and open sets

$$U_i \subset X_{\mu_i}, \qquad (i = 1, \ldots, n),$$

such that B consists of the points $x \in X$ satisfying $x(\mu_i) \in U_i$ for each $i = 1, \ldots, n$. In each U_i, $(i = 1, \ldots, n)$, pick a point a_i. Let q denote the point of X defined by

$$q(\mu) = \begin{cases} a_i, & \text{(if } \mu = \mu_i \text{ for some } i), \\ p(\mu), & \text{(if } \mu \neq \mu_i \text{ for all } i). \end{cases}$$

Then $q \in B$.

Consider the subset K of X which consists of all the points $x \in X$ such that $x(\mu) = p(\mu)$ for all $\mu \in M$ different from $\mu_1, \ldots, \mu_n$. Since K is homeomorphic to

$$X_{\mu_1} \times \cdots \times X_{\mu_n},$$

K is connected. Since K contains both p and q, it follows that $q \in C(p)$. Hence,

$$B \cap C(p) \neq \square.$$

Since B is an arbitrary basic open set of X, this implies that $C(p)$ is dense in X. Finally, since $C(p)$ is closed in X, we have $C(p) = X$. Hence, X is connected. ||

COROLLARY 4.12. *For every $n \geqslant 1$, the n-dimensional Euclidean space R^n, the unit n-cube I^n, and the n-sphere S^n are connected.*

Proof. That R^n and I^n are connected follows from (4.11) together with (4.1) and (4.4) respectively. To prove that S^n is connected, let $p \in S^n$. Since the subspace $S^n \setminus p$ is homeomorphic to R^n, it is connected. Hence, by (4.3), $\mathrm{Cl}\,(S^n \setminus p) = S^n$ is also connected. ||

Now, denote by $\Gamma(X)$ the set of all components of a space X. Consider an arbitrarily given map

$$f : X \to Y.$$

For each component α of X, the image $f(\alpha)$ is connected and hence is contained in a component β of Y. The assignment $\alpha \to \beta$ defines a function

$$\Gamma(f) : \Gamma(X) \to \Gamma(Y).$$

LEMMA 4.13. *If two maps $f, g : X \to Y$ are homotopic, then*

$$\Gamma(f) = \Gamma(g).$$

Proof. By definition of homotopic maps, there exists a map

$$H : X \times I \to Y$$

such that $H(x, 0) = f(x)$ and $H(x, 1) = g(x)$ for every $x \in X$. Let α be an arbitrary component of X. Then, as product of connected sets, $\alpha \times I$ is connected. It follows that $H(\alpha \times I)$ is connected and hence is contained in a component β of Y. Since $f(\alpha)$ and $g(\alpha)$ are both contained in $H(\alpha \times I)$, we have

$$[\Gamma(f)](\alpha) = \beta = [\Gamma(g)](\alpha).$$

Since α is an arbitrary element of $\Gamma(X)$, this proves $\Gamma(f)) = \Gamma(g)$. ‖

PROPOSITION 4.14. *If $f : X \to Y$ is a homotopy equivalence, then $\Gamma(f)$ is bijective.*

Proof. Let $g : Y \to X$ be a map such that the compositions $g \circ f$ and $f \circ g$ are homotopic to the identity maps i_X and i_Y on the spaces X and Y respectively. Hence, by (4.13),

$$\Gamma(g) \circ \Gamma(f) = \Gamma(g \circ f) = \Gamma(i_X),$$
$$\Gamma(f) \circ \Gamma(g) = \Gamma(f \circ g) = \Gamma(i_Y)$$

are identity functions on the sets $\Gamma(X)$ and $\Gamma(Y)$ respectively. This implies that $\Gamma(f)$ is bijective and $\Gamma(g)$ is the inverse of $\Gamma(f)$. ‖

COROLLARY 4.15. *Connectedness is a homotopy property of spaces.*

Now, let us turn to an application of connectedness. For this purpose, let X denote the closed interval $[a, b]$ as a subspace of the real line R and let A denote the subspace of X which consists of the two end points a and b.

LEMMA 4.16. *The subspace A is not a retract of X.*

Proof. Assume that there were a retraction $r : X \supset A$. Then r is surjective. Since X is connected, A should be also connected. However, A is obviously disconnected since the open sets $\{a\}$ and $\{b\}$ of the discrete space A form a nontrivial separation of A. This contradiction proves (4.16). ‖

PROPOSITION 4.17 (FIXED POINT THEOREM). *Every map*

$$f : [a, b] \to [a, b]$$

of the closed interval $[a, b]$ into itself has at least one fixed point, that is to say, there exists a real number $x \in [a, b]$ such that $f(x) = x$.

Proof. Without loss of generality, we may assume that $a = -1$ and $b = 1$.

To prove (4.17) by contradiction, let us assume $f(x) \neq x$ for every real number $x \in [-1, 1]$. Define a continuous function r on $[-1, 1]$ by taking

$$r(x) = \frac{x - f(x)}{|x - f(x)|}, \qquad (-1 \leqslant x \leqslant 1),$$

where $|x - f(x)|$ denotes the absolute value of the real number $x - f(x)$. The continuity of r follows from that of f and the assumption that $f(x) \neq x$ for all $x \in [-1, 1]$. One can easily verify that r is a retraction of $X = [-1, 1]$ onto its boundary 0-sphere $A = \{-1, 1\}$. This contradicts (4.16) and proves (4.17). ‖

The remainder of this section is devoted to local connectedness.

A space X is said to be *locally connected at a point* $p \in X$ iff, for every neighborhood U of p, there exists a neighborhood $V \subset U$ of p such that any two points of V are connected in U.

PROPOSITION 4.18.   *A space X is locally connected at a point p iff every neighborhood of p contains a connected neighborhood of p.*

Proof: Necessity. Assume X to be locally connected at p and let U be an arbitrary neighborhood of p. By definition, there exists a neighborhood $V \subset U$ of p such that any two points of V are connected in U. Let q be an arbitrary point of V. Then there exists a connected set C_q in U which contains both p and q. Let

$$C = \bigcup \{C_q \mid q \in V\} \subset U.$$

Since $V \subset C$, C is a neighborhood of p. By (4.8), C is connected. Therefore, C is a connected neighborhood of p contained in U.

Sufficiency. Assume that the condition holds. Let U be an arbitrary neighborhood of p in X. Then U contains a connected neighborhood V of p. Since V is connected, any two points of V are connected in V and hence also in U. Hence, X is locally connected at p. ‖

COROLLARY 4.19.   *If a space X is locally connected at a point $p \in X$, then p is an interior point of the component $C(p)$ of X.*

Proof. By (4.18), p has a connected neighborhood V. By (4.9), $V \subset C(p)$. Hence, p is an interior point of $C(p)$. ‖

A space X is said to be *locally connected* iff it is locally connected at each of its points. The following proposition is an immediate consequence of the definition.

PROPOSITION 4.20. *Every open subspace of a locally connected space is locally connected.*

On the other hand, the following proposition is an immediate consequence of (4.19).

PROPOSITION 4.21. *For each point p of a locally connected space X, the component $C(p)$ of X is an open set of X.*

PROPOSITION 4.22. *For a given space X, the following statements are equivalent:*

(a) *X is locally connected.*

(b) *The components of every open subspace of X are open.*

(c) *The connected open sets of X form a basis of the topology of X.*

Proof. (a) $\Rightarrow$ (b). Let X be a locally connected space and let U be an open subspace of X. By (4.20), U is a locally connected space. By (4.21), the components of U are open sets of U. Since U is open, these components are also open in X.

(b) $\Rightarrow$ (c). Assume that (b) holds and let U be any open set of X. By (b), the components of U are open in X. By (4.9), the components of U are connected. Hence, U is the union of a collection of connected open sets of X. This proves (c).

(c) $\Rightarrow$ (a). Assume that (c) holds and let U be any open neighborhood of an arbitrary point p in X. By (c), U is the union of a collection of connected open sets. Hence, there exists a connected open set V such that $p \in V \subset U$. By (4.18), X is locally connected at p. Since p is arbitrary, this implies that X is locally connected. ||

EXERCISES

4A. Prove that, if a connected set C in a space X meets a set $E \subset X$ and its complement $X \setminus E$, then C meets the boundary ∂E of E.

4B. Prove that, if $\{C_\mu \mid \mu \in M\}$ is a family of connected sets in a space X such that each C_μ meets a given connected set C in X, then the union of C and all C_μ, $\mu \in M$, is connected.

4C. Prove that, if $f: X \to Y$ is a closed map of a locally connected space X onto a space Y, then Y is locally connected. Hence every continuous image of the unit interval I in a Hausdorff space is locally connected.

5. PATHWISE CONNECTEDNESS

By a *path* in a space X, we mean a map

$$\sigma : I \to X$$

of the unit interval $I = [0, 1]$ into the space X. The points $\sigma(0)$ and $\sigma(1)$ in X are called the *initial point* and the *final point* of the path σ respectively.

In a given space X, let us define an equivalence relation $\sim$ as follows: for any two points a and b in X,

$$a \sim b$$

iff there exists a path $\sigma : I \to X$ such that $\sigma(0) = a$ and $\sigma(1) = b$. This equivalence relation $\sim$ divides X into disjoint equivalence classes called the *path-components* of the space X. If the space X has no more than one path-component, it is said to be *pathwise connected*. In other words, a space X is pathwise connected iff, for any two points a and b in X, there exists a path $\sigma : I \to X$ such that $\sigma(0) = a$ and $\sigma(1) = b$. A set E in a space X is said to be *pathwise connected* iff, with the relative topology, the subspace E is pathwise connected.

PROPOSITION 5.1.   *Every pathwise connected space is connected.*

Proof. Let X be an arbitrary pathwise connected space. Since (5.1) is trivial in case $X = \square$, we assume that X is nonempty. Pick a point $x_0 \in X$.

Since X is pathwise connected, we may choose for each point $x \in X$ a path

$$\sigma_x : I \to X$$

such that $\sigma_x(0) = x_0$ and $\sigma_x(1) = x$. As continuous image of a connected space I, $\sigma_x(I)$ is a connected set for every $x \in X$. Since $x_0 \in \sigma_x(I)$ and since

$$X = \bigcup_{x \in X} \sigma_x(I),$$

it follows from (4.8) that X is connected. $\|$

Thus, pathwise connectedness is a stronger form of connectedness. On the other hand, we have the following

PROPOSITION 5.2.   *Every contractible space is pathwise connected.*

Proof. Let X be an arbitrary contractible space. Then there exists a contraction

$$\{h_t : X \to X \mid t \in I\}.$$

Let a and b be any two points in X. Define a map $\sigma : I \rightarrow X$ by taking

$$\sigma(t) = \begin{cases} h_{2t}(a), & (\text{if } 0 \leqslant t \leqslant \tfrac{1}{2}), \\ h_{2-2t}(b), & (\text{if } \tfrac{1}{2} \leqslant t \leqslant 1). \end{cases}$$

This definition is justified by the fact that

$$h_1(a) = h_1(X) = h_1(b)$$

since $\{h_t\}$ is a contraction. Since

$$\sigma(0) = h_0(a) = a, \qquad \sigma(1) = h_0(b) = b,$$

the space X is pathwise connected. ‖

In particular, the real line R, the unit interval I, the unit n-simplex Δ^n, and the cone Con (X) over a space X are pathwise connected.

PROPOSITION 5.3. *Every continuous image of a pathwise connected set is pathwise connected.*

Proof. It suffices to prove that, if $f : X \rightarrow Y$ is a surjective map of a pathwise connected space X onto a space Y, then Y is also pathwise connected. For this purpose, let u and v be any two points in Y. Since the map $f : X \rightarrow Y$ is surjective, there exist two points a and b in X such that $f(a) = u$ and $f(b) = v$. Since X is pathwise connected, there exists a path

$$\sigma : I \rightarrow X$$

such that $\sigma(0) = a$ and $\sigma(1) = b$. Consider the composed map

$$\tau = f \circ \sigma : I \rightarrow Y.$$

Then τ is a path in Y with

$$\tau(0) = f(a) = u, \qquad \tau(1) = f(b) = v.$$

Hence Y is pathwise connected. ‖

PROPOSITION 5.4. *The topological product of an arbitrary family of pathwise connected spaces is pathwise connected.*

Proof. Consider an arbitrary family

$$\mathscr{F} = \{ X_\mu \mid \mu \in M \}$$

of pathwise connected spaces. Let Φ denote the topological product of this family and let f and g be any two points in Φ.

For each $\mu \in M$, $f(\mu)$ and $g(\mu)$ are points of a pathwise connected space X_μ. Hence, there exists a path

$$\sigma_\mu : I \to X_\mu$$

such that $\sigma_\mu(0) = f(\mu)$ and $\sigma_\mu(1) = g(\mu)$.

Then, the restricted cartesian product

$$\sigma : I \to \Phi$$

of the family $\{\sigma_\mu : I \to X_\mu \mid \mu \in M\}$ is a path in Φ with $\sigma(0) = f$ and $\sigma(1) = g$. Hence Φ is pathwise connected. $\|$

In particular, the topological powers R^M and I^M for any set M are pathwise connected.

Now, let us study the path-components of a given space X. . We will denote by $c(p)$ the path-component of X which contains the point $p \in X$.

PROPOSITION 5.5. *For each point p in a space X, the path-component $c(p)$ of X is the largest pathwise connected set in X which contains the point p.*

Proof. Let K be any pathwise connected set in X which contains the point p, and let q be an arbitrary point in K. Since K is pathwise connected, there exists a path $\sigma : I \to K$ with $\sigma(0) = p$ and $\sigma(1) = q$. Then the composed map

$$\tau = i \circ \sigma : I \to X$$

of $\sigma : I \to K$ and the inclusion map $i : K \subset X$ is a path in X with $\tau(0) = p$ and $\tau(1) = q$. Hence, $p \sim q$ and $q \in c(p)$. This proves that $K \subset c(p)$.

It remains to prove the pathwise connectedness of $c(p)$. For this purpose, let r denote an arbitrary point in $c(p)$. Since $p \sim r$, there exists a path $\sigma : I \to X$ with $\sigma(o) = p$ and $\sigma(1) = r$. For the pathwise connectedness of $c(p)$, it suffices to prove that

$$\sigma(I) \subset c(p).$$

Let $s \in I$ be arbitrarily given. Define a path $\tau : I \to X$ by taking

$$\tau(t) = \sigma(st)$$

for every $t \in I$. Then we have $\tau(0) = p$ and $\tau(1) = \sigma(s)$. Hence $p \sim \sigma(s)$ and $\sigma(s) \in c(p)$. This proves $\sigma(I) \subset c(p)$. $\|$

Now, denote by $\pi_0(X)$ the set of all path-components of a space X. Consider an arbitrarily given map

$$f : X \to Y.$$

For each path-component α of X, the image $f(\alpha)$ is pathwise connected and hence is contained in a path-component β of Y. The assignment $\alpha \rightarrow \beta$ defines a function

$$\pi_0(f) \;:\; \pi_0(X) \rightarrow \pi_0(Y).$$

LEMMA 5.6. *If two maps $f, g : X \rightarrow Y$ are homotopic, then*

$$\pi_0(f) = \pi_0(g).$$

PROPOSITION 5.7. *If $f : X \rightarrow Y$ is a homotopy equivalence, then $\pi_0(f)$ is bijective.*

COROLLARY 5.8. *Pathwise connectedness is a homotopy property of spaces.*

The proof of the preceding assertions (5.6)–(5.8) is similar to that of (4.13)–(4.15) and hence is left to the student.

A space X is said to be *locally pathwise connected at a point* $p \in X$ iff, for every neighborhood U of p, there exists a neighborhood $V \subset U$ of p such that every point $q \in V$ is the final point of a path

$$\sigma_q : I \rightarrow U$$

with initial point $\sigma_q(0) = p$.

PROPOSITION 5.9. *A space X is locally pathwise connected at a point p iff every neighborhood of p contains a pathwise connected neighborhood of p.*

Proof: Necessity. Assume X to be locally pathwise connected at p and let U be an arbitrary neighborhood of p. By definition, there exists a neighborhood $V \subset U$ of p such that, for each point $q \in V$, there exists a path

$$\sigma_q \;:\; I \rightarrow U$$

with $\sigma_q(0) = p$ and $\sigma_q(1) = q$. Hence, V is contained in the path-component $c_U(p)$ of U which contains p. By (5.5), it follows that $c_U(p)$ is a pathwise connected neighborhood of p contained in U.

Sufficiency. Assume that the condition holds. Let U be an arbitrary neighborhood of p in X. Then U contains a pathwise connected neighborhood V of p. Let q be an arbitrary point of V. Since V is pathwise connected, there is a path

$$\tau_q \;:\; I \rightarrow V$$

with $\tau_q(0) = p$ and $\tau_q(1) = q$. Then the composed map

$$\sigma_q \;=\; i \circ \tau_q \;:\; I \rightarrow U$$

of τ_q and the inclusion map $i : V \subset U$ is a path in U with $\sigma_q(0) = p$ and $\sigma_q(1) = q$. This proves that X is locally pathwise connected at p. ||

COROLLARY 5.10. *If a space X is locally pathwise connected at a point $p \in X$, then p is an interior point of the path-component $c(p)$ of X.*

COROLLARY 5.11. *If a space X is locally pathwise connected at a point $p \in X$, then X is locally connected at the point p.*

A space X is said to be *locally contractible at a point* $p \in X$ iff, for every neighborhood U of p in X, there exists a neighborhood $V \subset U$ of p which is contractible in U.

PROPOSITION 5.12. *If a space X is locally contractible at a point $p \in X$, then X is locally pathwise connected at the point p.*

Proof. Let U be an arbitrary neighborhood of p in X. Since X is locally contractible at the point p, there exists a neighborhood $V \subset U$ of p which is contractible in U. Let

$$\{h_t : V \to U \mid t \in I\}$$

be a contraction of V in U; then h_0 is the inclusion map and h_1 is a constant map. Let q be an arbitrary point in V and define a path $\sigma_q : I \to U$ by taking

$$\sigma_q(t) = \begin{cases} h_{2t}(p), & \text{(if } 0 \leqslant t \leqslant \tfrac{1}{2}), \\ h_{2-2t}(q), & \text{(if } \tfrac{1}{2} \leqslant t \leqslant 1). \end{cases}$$

Then $\sigma_q(0) = p$ and $\sigma_q(1) = q$. This proves that X is locally pathwise connected at the point p. ||

A space X is said to be *locally pathwise connected* iff it is locally pathwise connected at each of its points. Similarly, a space X is said to be *locally contractible* iff it is locally contractible at each of its points.

The following two propositions are immediate consequences of the definitions.

PROPOSITION 5.13. *Every open subspace of a locally pathwise connected space is locally pathwise connected.*

PROPOSITION 5.14. *Every open subspace of a locally contractible space is locally contractible.*

The following two propositions are immediate consequences of (5.11) and (5.12).

PROPOSITION 5.15. *Every locally pathwise connected space is locally connected.*

PROPOSITION 5.16. *Every locally contractible space is locally pathwise connected.*

THEOREM 5.17. *For each point p of a locally pathwise connected space X, the path-component $c(p)$ of X is both open and closed in X and hence $c(p)$ coincides with the component $C(p)$ of X.*

Proof. Let q be an arbitrary point in $c(p)$. Then $c(q) = c(p)$. Hence, q is an interior point of $c(p)$ by (5.10). This proves that $c(p)$ is open.

The union U of all path-components of X other than $c(p)$ is an open set of X. Since the path-components are disjoint, we have

$$c(p) = X \setminus U.$$

This proves that $c(p)$ is closed.

By (5.5) and (5.1), $c(p)$ is connected. It follows that $c(p)$ is the largest connected set in X containing the point p. Hence $c(p) = C(p)$. ||

COROLLARY 5.18. *If a space X is connected and locally pathwise connected, then X is pathwise connected.*

In the remainder of the present section, we will briefly investigate the classical notion of arcwise connectedness.

By an *arc* in a space X, we mean an imbedding

$$\alpha : I \to X$$

of the unit interval I into the space X. If we use arcs instead of paths, we can define the notions of arcwise connectedness and arc-components of spaces.

Since every arc in a space is also a path, the following proposition is trivial.

PROPOSITION 5.19. *Every arcwise connected space is pathwise connected.*

However, the converse of (5.19) is false. For example, let X denote the indiscrete space consisting of two points p and q. Then X is pathwise connected because p and q are connected by the path $\sigma : I \to X$ defined by

$$\sigma(t) = \begin{cases} p, & (\text{if } t = 0), \\ q, & (\text{if } t > 0). \end{cases}$$

Since X has only two points, there can be no arc in X and hence X is not arcwise connected.

Since X and the singleton space $Y = \{p\}$ are both indiscrete, they are homotopically equivalent by (II, Ex. 7F). Since Y is arcwise connected while X is not, we have the following

PROPOSITION 5.20.   *Arcwise connectedness is not a homotopy property.*

Because of (5.8) and (5.2), we prefer pathwise connectedness to arcwise connectedness, although the two notions coincide for Hausdorff spaces.   See [H–Y, pp. 115–130].

EXERCISES

5A. Prove that the union of any family of pathwise connected sets with a common point is connected.   Hence, the one point union of a family of pathwise connected spaces is pathwise connected.

5B. The *suspension* $S(X)$ of a space X is defined to be the quotient space obtained by collapsing the subset X of Con (X) to a point.   Prove that $S(X)$ is pathwise connected.   If X is homeomorphic to the unit n-sphere S^n, then the suspension $S(X)$ is homeomorphic to S^{n+1}.   Hence, S^n is pathwise connected for every $n > 0$.

5C. Prove that the mapping cylinder Cyl (f) of a map $f : X \rightarrow Y$ from a space X into a pathwise connected space Y is pathwise connected.

5D. Prove that the following statements are equivalent for a space X:
 (a) X is locally pathwise connected.
 (b) The path-components of every open subspace of X are open.
 (c) The pathwise connected open sets of X form a basis of the topology of X.

6. IMBEDDING THEOREMS

In the present section, we are concerned with the problem of imbedding a given space in a cube I^M.

Let us consider a given family

$$\mathscr{F} = \{ f_\mu : X \rightarrow Y_\mu \mid \mu \in M \}$$

of maps from a given space X into a space Y_μ which may be different for various indices $\mu \in M$.   Let Y denote the topological product of the family $\{ Y_\mu \mid \mu \in M \}$ of spaces and denote by

$$f : X \rightarrow Y$$

the (restricted) Cartesian product of the family $\mathscr{F}$ as defined in (I, § 3). Then we have $[f(x)](\mu) = f_\mu(x)$ for every $x \in X$ and every $\mu \in M$.   By (II, 5.8), f is continuous.

The family $\mathscr{F}$ is said to be *able to distinguish points of X* iff, for any two distinct points a and b of X, there exists a map $f_\mu \in \mathscr{F}$ such that

$$f_\mu(a) \neq f_\mu(b).$$

The family $\mathscr{F}$ is said to be *able to distinguish points from closed sets of X* iff, for any closed set A in X and any point p in $X \setminus A$, there exists a map $f_\mu \in \mathscr{F}$ such that $f_\mu(p)$ is not in the closure of $f_\mu(A)$.

LEMMA 6.1. *If the family $\mathscr{F}$ can distinguish points of X, then the Cartesian product $f : X \to Y$ is injective.*

Proof. Let a and b be any two distinct points of X. Then, there exists a map $f_\mu \in \mathscr{F}$ such that $f_\mu(a) \neq f_\mu(b)$. This implies $f(a) \neq f(b)$. ‖

LEMMA 6.2. *If the family $\mathscr{F}$ can distinguish points from closed sets of X, then the Cartesian product $f : X \to Y$ carries open sets of X onto those of the subspace $f(X)$ of Y.*

Proof. Let U be an arbitrary open set of X. We will prove that $f(U)$ is an open set of $f(X)$. For this purpose, let q be an arbitrary point of $f(U)$ and pick a point $p \in U$ such that $f(p) = q$. Since $X \setminus U$ is closed and $p \notin X \setminus U$, there exists a map $f_\mu \in \mathscr{F}$ such that $f_\mu(p)$ is not in the closure $\mathrm{Cl}[f_\mu(X \setminus U)]$ of $f_\mu(X \setminus U)$. Consider the basic open set

$$V = \{ y \in Y \mid y(\mu) \notin \mathrm{Cl}[f_\mu(X \setminus U)] \}$$

of the product space Y. Since $V \cap f(X)$ is an open set of $f(X)$ satisfying

$$q = f(p) \in V \cap f(X) \subset f(U),$$

it follows that $f(U)$ is an open set of $f(X)$. ‖

Combining (6.1) and (6.2), we obtain the following theorem.

THEOREM 6.3. *If the family $\mathscr{F}$ of maps can distinguish points of X and can also distinguish points from closed sets of X, then the Cartesian product $f : X \to Y$ of the family $\mathscr{F}$ is an imbedding.*

COROLLARY 6.4 (TYCHONOFF IMBEDDING THEOREM). *Every Tychonoff space X can be imbedded as a subspace of a cube.*

Proof. Let M denote the family of all continuous real functions $f_\mu : X \to I$ on the Tychonoff space X into the closed unit interval $I = [0, 1]$. By means of the complete regularity, one can easily verify that M can distinguish points from closed sets of X. On the other hand, since every singleton set of X is closed, M can also distinguish points of X. Therefore, the Cartesian product

$$f : X \to I^M$$

is an imbedding. ||

As a compact Hausdorff space, I^M is a Tychonoff space and so is every subspace of I^M. Hence, we have the following theorem.

THEOREM 6.5. *A space X is a Tychonoff space iff X is homeomorphic to a subspace of a cube.*

By (2.7), every cube I^M is a normal space. It follows from (6.4) that a subspace of a normal space may fail to be normal.

We recall that the cube I^N, where N denotes the set of all natural numbers, is called the *Hilbert cube*.

THEOREM 6.6 (URYSOHN IMBEDDING THEOREM). *Every regular Fréchet space X which satisfies the second axiom of countability can be imbedded as a subspace of the Hilbert cube I^N.*

Proof. In view of (6.3), it suffices to show that there exists a countable family $\mathscr{F}$ of continuous functions from X into I which distinguishes points from closed sets of X. For this purpose, let $\mathscr{B}$ denote a countable basis for the topology of X. Consider the Cartesian product $\mathscr{B} \times \mathscr{B}$ and its subcollection M which consists of the pairs (U, V) of basic open sets such that

$$\mathrm{Cl}(U) \subset V.$$

Then, M is countable.

By Exercise 1E, X is a normal space. Hence, it follows from Urysohn's lemma (1.6) that, for each $(U, V) \in M$, there exists a continuous real function $f_{(U, V)} : X \to I$ which carries $\mathrm{Cl}\,(U)$ into 0 and $X \setminus V$ into 1. Thus, we obtain a countable family

$$\mathscr{F} = \{f_{(U,V)} : X \to I \mid (U, V) \in M\}$$

of continuous functions. It remains to prove that $\mathscr{F}$ can distinguish points from closed sets of X.

For this purpose, let A be any closed set of X and p be an arbitrary point in the point set $X \setminus A$. Since $\mathscr{B}$ is a basis, there exists a $V \in \mathscr{B}$ such that $p \in V \subset X \setminus A$. Since X is regular, p has a closed neighborhood N contained in V. Again, since $\mathscr{B}$ is a basis there exists a

$U \in \mathscr{B}$ such that $p \in U \subset N$. Since N is closed and $N \subset V$, we have Cl $(U) \subset V$. Hence $(U, V) \in M$. Then, it is clear that

$$f_{(U, V)}(p) = 0, \qquad f_{(U, V)}(p) = 1.$$

Hence $\mathscr{F}$ can distinguish points from closed sets of X. ‖

According to Exercise 1B and (II, Ex. 5J), I^N is a regular Fréchet space satisfying the second axiom of countability. Hence, we have the following theorem.

THEOREM 6.7. *A space X is a regular Fréchet space satisfying the second axiom of countability iff X is homeomorphic to a subspace of the Hilbert cube I^N.*

EXERCISES

6A. Let X denote the set of all real numbers with the half-open interval topology, i.e. the smallest topology containing all half-open intervals (a, b). Prove:
  (a) X is regular and normal.
  (b) $X \times X$ is not normal.

6B. A set E in a space X is called a G_δ iff it is the intersection of the members of a countable family of open sets. Prove that if f is a continuous real function on a space X, then the inverse image $f^{-1}[a, b]$ of a closed interval $[a, b]$ is a G_δ in X.

6C. A set E in a space X is called an F_σ iff it is the union of the members of a countable family of closed sets. Prove that E is an F_σ iff $X \setminus E$ is a G_δ.

7. EXTENSION THEOREMS

Let X and Y be given spaces and let E be a given subspace of X. We recall the extension problem of any given map

$$g : E \to Y$$

over the space X formulated in (II, § 4) as follows: to determine whether or not g has an extension over X and to find an extension of g over X if such exists.

A few special cases of this important problem have been solved in the previous sections. As examples, we have the following results:

(1) Let X be a completely regular space and E be a subspace of X

which consists of a closed set F of X and a point $p \in X \setminus F$. If $g : E \to I$ denotes the map defined by

$$g(x) = \begin{cases} 0, & \text{(if } x = p), \\ 1, & \text{(if } x \in F), \end{cases}$$

then g has an extension $f : X \to I$.

(2) Let X be a normal space and E be the union of two disjoint closed subspaces A and B of X. If $g : E \to I$ denotes the map defined by

$$g(x) = \begin{cases} 0, & \text{(if } x \in A), \\ 1, & \text{(if } x \in B), \end{cases}$$

then g has an extension $f : X \to I$ according to Urysohn's lemma.

(3) Let X be a connected space and $E = Y$ be a disconnected subspace of X. Then the identity map $g : E \to Y$ has no extension over X by (4.5).

(4) Let X be a compact space and $E = Y$ be a non-compact subspace of X. Then the identity map $g : E \to Y$ has no extension over X by (2.3).

(5) Let X be a Hausdorff space and $E = Y$ be a subspace of X which is not closed. Then the identity map $g : E \to Y$ has no extension over X according to (1.4).

In the present section, we will study two cases where the extension problem is trivial, i.e. the answer is always affirmative.

THEOREM 7.1.   *The subspace E is a retract of the space X iff every map $g : E \to Y$ from E into any space Y has an extension over X.*

Proof: Necessity.   Assume that E is a retract of X. Then there exists a retraction $r : X \supset E$. Obviously, the composition $f = g \circ r$ is an extension of g over X.

Sufficiency.   Assume that the condition holds. Take $Y = E$ and consider the identity map $g : E \to Y$. According to the condition, g has an extension $r : X \to Y = E$ which is evidently a retraction of X onto E. ‖

THEOREM 7.2 (TIETZE'S EXTENSION THEOREM).   *If E is a closed subspace of a normal space X, then every map $g : E \to I$ has an extension over X.*

Proof.   For any two disjoint closed sets A and B in X, let us denote by $\chi_{A,B}$ a characteristic function whose existence follows from the normality of X according to Urysohn's lemma. $\chi_{A,B}$ is a map of X into I such that

$$\chi_{A,B}(x) = \begin{cases} 0, & \text{(if } x \in A), \\ 1, & \text{(if } x \in B). \end{cases}$$

Now let $g : E \to I$ be an arbitrarily given map. For each $n = 0, 1, 2,$ . . ., we shall define two maps

$$g_n : E \to I, \qquad f_n : X \to I$$

as follows. Let $g_0 = g$. Suppose that g_n has already been defined. Let

$$A_n = \{x \in E \mid g_n(x) \leqslant (1/3)(2/3)^n\},$$
$$B_n = \{x \in E \mid g_n(x) \geqslant (2/3)(2/3)^n\}.$$

Since E is closed in X, A_n and B_n are two disjoint closed sets of the normal space X. Pick a characteristic function χ_{A_n, B_n} and let

$$f_n = \frac{1}{3}\left(\frac{2}{3}\right)^n \chi_{A_n, B_n} : X \to I.$$

Next, define $g_{n+1} : E \to I$ by taking

$$g_{n+1}(x) = g_n(x) - f_n(x)$$

for every $x \in E$. To justify this definition, one must verify that

$$f_n(x) \leqslant g_n(x)$$

for every $x \in E$. For this purpose, let $x \in E$. If $x \in A_n$, then $f_n(x) = 0$ and hence $f_n(x) \leqslant g_n(x)$. If $x \notin A_n$, then

$$g_n(x) > (1/3)(2/3)^n.$$

Since $f_n(x) \leqslant (1/3)(2/3)^n$, we have $f_n(x) \leqslant g_n(x)$. This completes the inductive definition of the maps g_n and f_n.

Since, for each $x \in X$, we have

$$0 \leqslant f_n(x) \leqslant \frac{1}{3}\left(\frac{2}{3}\right)^n,$$

it follows that the series $\Sigma f_n(x)$ is uniformly convergent on X. Since f_n is a continuous function for each n, it follows from classical analysis that the limit

$$\lim_{n \to \infty} [f_0(x) + f_1(x) + \ldots + f_n(x)]$$

exists for every $x \in X$ and defines a continuous function

$$f : X \to I.$$

It remains to prove that $f \mid E = g$. For this purpose, let x be an arbitrary point of E and we will prove $f(x) = g(x)$. In order to do this, let us first prove by induction that

$$0 \leqslant g_n(x) \leqslant \left(\frac{2}{3}\right)^n.$$

First, the inequalities hold obviously for $n = 0$. Now assume the inequalities for n. By definition, we have

$$0 \leqslant g_{n+1}(x) = g_n(x) - f_n(x).$$

If $x \in B_n$, then $f_n(x) < (1/3)(2/3)^n$ and hence

$$g_{n+1}(x) \leqslant \left(\frac{2}{3}\right)^n - \frac{1}{3}\left(\frac{2}{3}\right)^n = \left(\frac{2}{3}\right)^{n+1}.$$

If $x \notin B_n$, then $g_n(x) < (2/3)(2/3)^n$ and hence

$$g_{n+1}(x) = g_n(x) - f_n(x) \leqslant g_n(x) < \left(\frac{2}{3}\right)^{n+1}.$$

This completes the inductive proof of the inequalities.

Finally, since $g_{r+1}(x) = g_r(x) - f_r(x)$ by definition, it follows that

$$f_r(x) = g_r(x) - g_{r+1}(x).$$

Summing for $r = 0, 1, \ldots, n$, we obtain

$$f_0(x) + f_1(x) + \ldots + f_n(x) = g(x) - g_{n+1}(x).$$

Now, let $n \to \infty$. The left member gives $f(x)$ while the right member approaches $g(x)$. Hence $f(x) = g(x)$. ‖

EXERCISES

7A. A closed subspace E of a space X is said to have the *extension property* in X with respect to a space Y iff every map $g : E \to Y$ has an extension over X. A space Y is said to be *solid* iff every closed subspace E of a normal space X has the extension property in X with respect to Y. By Tietze's extension theorem, every closed interval of real numbers is a solid space under the usual topology. Prove:
   (i) The topological product of any family of solid spaces is solid. Hence, the cubes are solid.
   (ii) Any retract of a solid space is solid.

7B. Let E denote the subspace of the unit interval $I = [0, 1]$ which consists of the two end points 0 and 1. Prove that a space X is pathwise connected iff E has the extension property in I with respect to X.

8. METRIZABILITY AND METRIC SPACES

By a *metric*, or a *distance function*, in a set X, we mean a non-negative real function

$$d : X \times X \to R$$

satisfying the following conditions:

(M1)   *The triangle inequality :* For any three points a, b, c in X, we have

$$d(a, c) + d(b, c) \geqslant d(a, b).$$

(M2)   For any two points a, b in X, $d(a, b) = 0$ iff $a = b$.

LEMMA 8.1.   *If $d : X^2 \to R$ is a metric in a set X, then we have*

(M3) $$d(a, b) = d(b, a)$$

for any two points a, b in X.

Proof.   Applying (M1) to the points a, b, a of X, we obtain

$$d(a, a) + d(b, a) \geqslant d(a, b).$$

By (M2), we have $d(a, a) = 0$. Hence, we get $d(b, a) \geqslant d(a, b)$. Similarly, we can prove $d(a, b) \geqslant d(b, a)$. Thus, we obtain (M3).   ‖

Now, assume that $d : X^2 \to R$ is a given metric in a set X. Define a family τ of subsets of X as follows. For an arbitrary subset U of X, U is in τ iff, for any point $p \in U$, there exists a positive real number r such that U contains every point $x \in X$ with $d(p, x) < r$. One can easily verify that the family τ is a topology in X. The topology τ in X is called the *topology defined by the metric d*.

A given space X is said to be *metrizable* iff there exists a metric

$$d : X^2 \to R$$

which defines the topology of the space X.

PROPOSITION 8.2.   *The real line R is metrizable.*

Proof.   Define a metric $d : R^2 \to R$ by taking

$$d(a, b) = |a - b|$$

for any two real numbers a, $b \in R$. The conditions (M1) and (M2) are easily verified by the properties of the absolute values of real numbers. Since, for each positive real number r and any $a \in R$, the open interval $(a - r, a + r)$ consists of the real numbers $x \in R$ such that $d(a, x) < r$, it is clear that d defines the usual topology in R.   ‖

PROPOSITION 8.3.   *Every subspace E of a metrizable space X is metrizable.*

Proof.   Let $D : X^2 \to R$ denote a metric in X which defines the topology of X.   Let $d : E^2 \to R$ be defined by taking $d = D|E^2$.   Then d is obviously a metric in E and defines the relative topology of E. ||

COROLLARY 8.4.   *The unit interval I is metrizable.*

THEOREM 8.5.   *The topological product of a countable family of metrizable spaces is metrizable.*

Proof.   First, let us prove that the topological product

$$X = X_1 \times X_2 \times \cdots \times X_n$$

of a finite number of metrizable spaces $X_1, X_2, \ldots, X_n$ is metrizable. For this purpose, let

$$d_i : X_i \times X_i \to R, \qquad (1 \leqslant i \leqslant n),$$

denote a metric in X_i which defines the topology of X_i.   Define a function

$$d : X \times X \to R$$

as follows.   Let $a = (a_1, \ldots, a_n)$ and $b = (b_1, \ldots, b_n)$ be any two points in X.   Then $d(a, b)$ is defined by

$$[d(a, b)]^2 = \sum_{i=1}^{n} [d_i(a_i, b_i)]^2.$$

One can easily verify that d is a metric in X and defines the product topology of X.

It remains to prove that the topological product X of a sequence $X_1, X_2, \ldots, X_n, \ldots$ of metrizable spaces is metrizable.   For this purpose, let d_i denote a metric in X_i for each $i = 1, 2, \ldots$.   Define a function

$$d : X \times X \to R$$

as follows.   Let $a = \{a_1, a_2, \ldots\}$ and $b = \{b_1\, b_2, \ldots\}$ be any two points in X.   Then $d(a, b)$ is defined by

$$d(a, b) = \sum_{i=1}^{\infty} 2^{-1} \min \{1, d_i(a_i, b_i)\}.$$

One can verify that d is a metric in X and defines the topology of X. ||

COROLLARY 8.6.   *The Euclidean n-space R^n, the unit n-cube I^n, and the Hilbert cube I^N are metrizable.*

The following theorem is an immediate consequence of (8.3), (8.6), and the Urysohn imbedding theorem.

THEOREM 8.7. *Every regular Fréchet space satisfying the second axiom of countability is metrizable.*

By a *metric space*, we mean a metrizable space X together with a given metric $d : X^2 \to R$ which defines the topology of X.

For an arbitrary point p in a metric space X and any positive real number r, the set

$$N_r(p) = \{x \in X \mid d(p, x) < r\}$$

is an open neighborhood of the point p called the r-neighborhood of p.

THEOREM 8.8. *The metric $d : X^2 \to R$ of a metric space X is continuous.*

Proof. Let r be any real number. It suffices to prove that the sets

$$A = \{(x, y) \in X^2 \mid d(x, y) < r\},$$
$$B = \{(x, y) \in X^2 \mid d(x, y) > r\}$$

are open in X^2.

To prove that A is open, let $(a, b) \in A$. Then $d(a, b) = q < r$. Take $p = \frac{1}{2}(r - q)$ and consider the open set

$$U = N_p(a) \times N_p(b)$$

of X^2. Then $(x, y) \in U$ implies that

$$d(x, y) \leqslant d(x, a) + d(a, b) + d(b, y)$$
$$< p + q + p = 2p + q = r.$$

Hence $(a, b) \in U \subset A$ and A is open.

To prove that B is open, let $(a, b) \in B$. Then $d(a, b) = q > r$. Take $p = \frac{1}{2}(q - r)$ and consider the open set

$$U = N_p(a) \times N_p(b)$$

of X^2. Then $(x, y) \in U$ implies that

$$d(a, b) \leqslant d(a, x) + d(x, y) + d(y, b).$$

Hence we obtain

$$d(x, y) \geqslant d(a, b) - d(a, x) - d(b, y)$$
$$> q - p - p = q - 2p = r.$$

This implies that $(a, b) \in U \subset B$ and hence B is open. $\|$

Let A and B be any two nonempty sets in a metric space X with metric $d: X^2 \to R$. Then the *distance* $d(A, B)$ between the sets A and B is defined by

$$d(A, B) = \inf \{d(x, y) \mid x \in A, y \in B\}.$$

In particular, if one of the two sets, say A, consists of a single point a, then $d(A, B)$ is simply denoted by $d(a, B)$ and is called the *distance from the point a to the set B*.

PROPOSITION 8.9. *For any given subset E in a metric space X, the function* $f: X \to R$ *defined by*

$$f(x) = d(x, E), \qquad (x \in X),$$

is continuous.

Proof. For arbitrary points x, y, z in X, we have by (M1) and (M3):

$$d(x, z) \leqslant d(x, y) + d(y, z).$$

Taking the greatest lower bounds over $z \in E$, we obtain

$$d(x, E) \leqslant d(x, y) + d(y, E).$$

Similarly, we also have

$$d(y, E) \leqslant d(x, y) + d(x, E).$$

It follows that

$$|f(y) - f(x)| = |d(y, E) - d(x, E)| \leqslant d(x, y).$$

This implies that f is continuous. ‖

PROPOSITION 8.10. *For any subset E of a metric space X, we have*

$$\mathrm{Cl}\,(E) = \{x \in X \mid d(x, E) = 0\}.$$

Proof. By (7.9), the set

$$F = \{x \in X \mid d(x, E) = 0\}$$

is a closed set of X. Since obviously $E \subset F$, it follows that $\mathrm{Cl}\,(E) \subset F$.

On the other hand, let $x \in F$. Let U denote an arbitrary neighborhood of x in X. Since d defines the topology of X, there exists a positive real number r such that $N_r(x) \subset U$. Since

$$d(x, E) = 0 < r,$$

there exists a point $y \in E$ such that $d(x, y) < r$ and hence $y \in U$. This implies that $y \in \mathrm{Cl}\,(E)$. Therefore, $F \subset \mathrm{Cl}\,(E)$. ‖

THEOREM 8.11. *Every metrizable space is a normal Fréchet space.*

Proof. Let X be a metrizable space and $d : X^2 \to R$ be a metric which defines the topology of X.

By (M2) and (8.10), X is a Fréchet space. It remains to prove that X is normal. For this purpose, let A and B be any two disjoint closed sets in X. Let

$$U = \{x \in X \mid d(x, A) < d(x, B)\},$$
$$V = \{x \in X \mid d(x, A) > d(x, B)\}.$$

By (8.9), U and V are open sets of X. One can easily verify that $A \subset U$, $B \subset V$, and $U \cap V = \square$. Hence, X is normal. $\|$

PROPOSITION 8.12. *Every metrizable space satisfies the first axiom of countability.*

Proof. Let p be an arbitrary point in a metrizable space X and $d : X^2 \to R$ be a metric which defines the topology of X. For each positive rational number r, consider the r-neighborhood $N_r(p)$ in X. This family $\mathscr{B} = \{N_r(p)\}$ is obviously a countable local basis at p. $\|$

PROPOSITION 8.13. *A metrizable space X satisfies the second axiom of countability iff X is separable.*

Proof: Necessity. Because of (II, 2.9), a space X which satisfies the second axiom of countability must be separable.

Sufficiency. Assume that X is a separable metric space with $d : X^2 \to R$ as metric. Let E be a countable dense set in X. Let Q denote the set of all positive rational numbers. Then, the family

$$\mathscr{B} = \{N_q(e) \mid e \in E, q \in Q\}$$

of open sets is countable. It remains to prove that $\mathscr{B}$ forms a basis of the topology of X. For this purpose, let U be any open set of X and $p \in U$. Since the metric e defines the topology of X, there exists a positive real number t such that

$$N_t(p) \subset U.$$

Let s be a rational number such that $0 < 3s < t$. Since E is dense in X, there exists a point

$$e \in E \cap N_s(p).$$

Let $V = N_{2s}(e)$. Then $p \in V$. It remains to prove that $V \subset U$. For this purpose, let $x \in V$. Then $d(e, x) < 2s$. Hence

$$d(p, x) \leqslant d(p, e) + d(e, x)$$
$$< s + 2s = 3s < t.$$

Hence $x \in N_t(p) \subset U$. It follows that

$$p \in V \subset U.$$

Since $V \in \mathscr{B}$, this proves that $\mathscr{B}$ is a basis of the topology of X. ||

EXERCISES

8A. Prove that every discrete space is metrizable and hence a metrizable space may fail to satisfy the second axiom of countability.

8B. Prove that the continuous image of a compact metrizable space in any Hausdorff space is metrizable.

8C. Prove that every metrizable space X has a bounded distance function

$$d : X^2 \to I$$

which defines its topology.   [Ku 1, I, p. 104.]

8D. Let X and Y be metric spaces with metrics d and e respectively. A function $f : X \to Y$ is said to be *isometric* iff

$$e[f(a), f(b)] \ = \ d(a, b)$$

for every pair a, b of points in X. Prove that every isometric function is an imbedding.

8E. Let $\mathscr{F} = \{U_1, \ldots, U_n\}$ be a finite open cover of a metric space X with metric d. Define, for each $i = 1, \ldots, n$, a continuous function $f_i : X \to I$ by

$$f_i(x) \ = \ \frac{d(x, X \setminus U_i)}{\sum_{j=1}^{n} d(x, X \setminus U_j)}$$

Justify this definition and prove that $f_i(x) = 0$ for every $x \in X \setminus U_i$ and that

$$\sum_{i=1}^{n} f_i(x) \ = \ 1$$

for every $x \in X$.

8F. Prove that a space X is metrizable iff at every point $p \in X$ there is a sequence $\beta(p) = \{W_n(p) \mid n = 1, 2, \ldots\}$ of open neighborhoods such that:
   (a) $W_{n+1}(p) \subset W_n(p)$ for each $n \geqslant 1$.
   (b) $\bigcap_n W_n(p) \ = \ \{p\}$.
   (c) $\beta(p)$ is a local basis at p.
   (d) For each $p \in X$ and each $n \geqslant 1$, there is an $m \geqslant 1$ such that $W_m(q) \subset W_n(p)$ whenever $W_m(q)$ meets $W_m(p)$.   [Frink 1.]

8G. Prove that the image Y of a closed identification $f: X \to Y$ of a metrizable space X is metrizable iff the inverse image $f^{-1}(y)$ has a compact boundary in X for every $y \in Y$. [Morita and Hanai 1, Stone 2.]

8H. Let X and Y be metric spaces with metrics $d: X^2 \to R$ and $e: Y^2 \to R$ respectively. A function $f: X \to Y$ is said to be *uniformly continuous* iff, for every positive real number t, there exists a positive real number s such that, for any two points a, b in X, we have

$$e[f(a), f(b)] < t$$

whenever $d(a, b) < s$. Prove that every uniformly continuous function is continuous and that the converse is also true in case X is compact.

9. COMPACTIFICATION

In studying a non-compact space X, it is often helpful to construct a compact space Y which contains X as a dense subspace. The device is called compactification. Precisely, by a *compactification* of a space X, we mean an imbedding

$$h : X \to Y$$

of the space X into a compact space Y such that $h(X)$ is dense in Y.

The simplest compactification of a non-compact space X is the *one-point compactification*

$$h : X \to X^*$$

obtained by adjoining a single point ∞ into the space X as follows. The points of X^* are those of X together with the point ∞ which may be any element not in X. The topology of X^* consists of the open sets of X and all subsets U of X^* such that $X^* \setminus U$ is a closed compact subset of X. One can easily verify that the axioms for open sets are satisfied.

THEOREM 9.1. *If X is non-compact, then the inclusion $h : X \subset X^*$ is a compactification of X.*

Proof. By the definition of the topology of X^*, it is clear that the inclusion function $h : X \subset X^*$ is an imbedding. It remains to prove that X^* is compact and that X is dense in X^*.

Let α be an arbitrary open cover of X^*. Then there is a member U_0 of α which contains the point ∞. This implies that $X^* \setminus U_0$ is a compact subset of X. Hence there exists a finite number of members of α, say $U_1, \ldots, U_n$, such that

$$X^* \setminus U_0 \subset (U_1 \cup \ldots \cup U_n).$$

This implies that $\{U_0, U_1, \ldots, U_n\}$ is a finite subcover of α. Therefore, X^* is compact.

To prove that X is dense in X^*, we have to use the hypothesis that X is non-compact. For this purpose, let U denote an arbitrary nonempty open set of X^*. If the point ∞ is not in U, then $U \subset X$. If the point ∞ is in U, then $X^* \setminus U$ is a compact subset of X. Since X is non-compact, this implies that U contains at least one point of X. Hence, X is dense in X^*. $\|$

Although the one-point compactification of a non-compact space X is simple and nice, it is unsatisfactory unless the given space X is locally compact. In fact, we have the following proposition.

PROPOSITION 9.2.   *The space X^* is a Hausdorff space iff X is a locally compact Hausdorff space.*

Proof: Necessity.   If X^* is a Hausdorff space, then $X = X^* \setminus \{\infty\}$ is an open subspace of X^* and hence is a locally compact Hausdorff space.

Sufficiency.   Assume that X is a locally compact Hausdorff space. We will see that X^* is a Hausdorff space. For this purpose, let a and b be any two distinct points of X^*. If none of the points a and b is ∞, then there are open sets U and V of X such that

$$a \in U, \quad b \in V, \quad U \cap V = \square.$$

By the definition of the topology of X^*, U and V are also open sets of X^*. On the other hand, if one of the points a and b is the point ∞, we may assume without loss of generality that $a = \infty$ and $b \in X$. Since X is locally compact, b has a compact neighborhood K in X. Let

$$U = X^* \setminus K, \quad V = \mathrm{Int}\,(K).$$

As a compact set in a Hausdorff space X, K is closed. Hence U and V are open sets of X^*. Obviously, we have

$$a \in U, \quad b \in V, \quad U \cap V = \square.$$

Hence, X^* is a Hausdorff space. $\|$

In the remainder of this section, we are concerned with another important compactification, namely, the *Stone-Čech compactification* of a Tychonoff space X.

Let X be any given Tychonoff space and consider the family M of all continuous real functions $f_\mu : X \to I$ of X into the closed unit interval I. According to the Tychonoff imbedding theorem (6.4), the Cartesian product

$$f : X \to I^M$$

of the family $M = \{f_\mu\}$ is an imbedding. By (2.11), I^M is compact. Let $\beta(X)$ denote the closure of the image $f(X)$ in I^M and let

$$h : X \to \beta(X)$$

denote the map defined by f. Then it is clear that $h : X \to \beta(X)$ is a compactification of X called the *Stone-Čech compactification* of X.

The Stone-Čech compactification has a crucial property given by the following theorem.

THEOREM 9.3. *If X is a Tychonoff space, then every map $\phi : X \to Y$ of X into a compact Hausdorff space Y has an extension over $\beta(X)$. Precisely, there exists a map $\psi : \beta(X) \to Y$ such that $\phi = \psi \circ h$ holds in the following triangle*

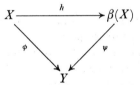

Proof. Consider the families of continuous real functions

$$M = \mathrm{Map}\,(X, I), \qquad N = \mathrm{Map}\,(Y, I).$$

Then the map $\phi : X \to Y$ induces a function

$$\phi^\# : N \to M$$

defined by $\phi^\#(\eta) = \eta \circ \phi$ for every $\eta : Y \to I$ in N.

Next, consider the topological products

$$f : X \to I^M, \qquad g : Y \to I^N$$

of the families M and N. Since both X and Y are Tychonoff spaces, f and g are imbeddings and define the Stone-Čech compactifications

$$h : X \to \beta(X), \qquad k : Y \to \beta(Y)$$

respectively. Since Y is compact, it follows that k is a homeomorphism.

Define a function

$$\phi_* : I^M \to I^N$$

by taking $\phi_*(\alpha) = \alpha \circ \phi^{\#} : N \to I$ for every $\alpha : M \to I$ in I^M. For each $\eta : Y \to I$ in N, let

$$p_\mu : I^N \to I$$

denote the natural projection of the product space I^N onto the η-th coordinate space. Then, the composed function

$$p_\mu \circ \phi_* : I^M \to I$$

gives $(p_\mu \circ \phi_*)(\alpha) = p_\eta(\alpha \circ \phi^{\#}) = \alpha[\phi^{\#}(\eta)] = \alpha(\eta \circ \phi)$ for each $\alpha \in I^M$. Hence, $p_\eta \circ \phi_*$ is the natural projection of I^M onto the $(\eta \circ \phi)$-th coordinate space. This implies that ϕ_* is continuous.

Consider the following rectangle of maps:

This rectangle is commutative, that is to say, $\phi_* \circ f = g \circ \phi$. To verify this, let x be an arbitrary point of X. We have to prove that the two points $\phi_*[f(x)]$ and $g[\phi(x)]$ of I^N are coincident. For this purpose, let $\eta : Y \to I$ be an arbitrary element in N. Then, the η-th coordinates of the points $\phi_*[f(x)]$ and $g[\phi(x)]$ are as follows:

$$p_\eta\{\phi_*[f(x)]\} = (p_\eta \circ \phi_*)[f(x)] = (\eta \circ \phi)(x),$$
$$p_\eta\{g[\phi(x)]\} = \eta[\phi(x)] = (\eta \circ \phi)(x).$$

Hence $\phi_*[f(x)] = g[\phi(x)]$. This proves the commutativity of the rectangle.

As a consequence of the commutativity $\phi_* \circ f = g \circ \phi$, the map ϕ_* sends $f(X)$ into $g(Y)$. By the continuity of ϕ_*, this implies that ϕ_* carries $\beta(X)$ into $\beta(Y)$ and hence defines a map

$$\beta(\phi) : \beta(X) \to \beta(Y).$$

Therefore, we obtain a commutative rectangle:

$$
\begin{array}{ccc}
X & \xrightarrow{\phi} & Y \\
{\scriptstyle h}\downarrow & & \downarrow{\scriptstyle k} \\
\beta(X) & \xrightarrow{\beta(\phi)} & \beta(Y)
\end{array}
$$

Since k is a homeomorphism, we may define a map

$$\psi \; : \; \beta(X) \to Y$$

by taking $\psi = k^{-1} \circ \beta(\phi)$. The commutativity of the rectangle gives $\phi = \psi \circ h$. ‖

By a *Hausdorff compactification* of a space X, we mean a compactification $j \; : \; X \to Y$ where Y is a Hausdorff space.

As an immediate consequence of (9.3), we have the following corollary.

COROLLARY 9.4. *If* $j : X \to Y$ *is any Hausdorff compactification of a Tychonoff space* X, *then there exists a map* $\psi : \beta(X) \to Y$ *such that* $j = \psi \circ h$, *where* $h : X \to \beta(X)$ *denotes the Stone-Čech compactification of* X.

Because of (9.4), the Stone-Čech compactification of X is sometimes referred to as the *maximal (Hausdorff) compactification* of X.

EXERCISES

9A. If X is a compact space, prove that the point ∞ is an *isolated point* of the space X^*, i.e. $\{\infty\}$ is both open and closed in X^*.

9B. Construct a compactification of the space R of real numbers by adjoining two new points $+\infty$ and $-\infty$. The compact obtained is called the *extended real line.*

9C. Prove that the one-point compactification of the n-space R^n is homeomorphic to the n-sphere S^n.

10. HEREDITARY PROPERTIES

In (II, § 3) we introduced topological equivalence and topological properties of spaces. In (II, § 7) we introduced the notions of homotopy properties and isotopy properties. We also observed that every homotopy property is an isotopy property and that every isotopy property is a topological property. As examples, we proved that contractibility and connectedness are homotopy properties of spaces.

To investigate the problem of whether or not the other properties studied in this chapter are homotopy properties or isotopy properties, let us first introduce the notion of hereditary properties and weakly hereditary properties.

A property P of spaces is said to be *hereditary* iff every subspace of a space with P also has P; it is said to be *weakly hereditary* iff every closed subspace of a space P also has P. As examples, the following topological properties of a space X are weakly hereditary:

(A) X is a Fréchet space.

(B) X is a Hausdorff space.

(C) X is a regular space.

(D) X is a completely regular space.

(E) X is a discrete space.

(F) X is an indiscrete space.

(G) X is a metrizable space.

(H) The first axiom of countability is satisfied in X.

(I) The second axiom of countability is satisfied in X.

(J) X can be imbedded in a given space Y.

(K) X is a normal space.

(L) X is a compact space.

(M) X is a paracompact space.

(N) X is a locally compact space.

The first ten properties (A)–(J) listed above are also hereditary.

THEOREM 10.1.   *If P is a weakly hereditary topological property such that every singleton space has P and that there exists a space X which does not have P, then P is not a homotopy property.*

Proof.   Let X be a space which does not have P. Consider the cone Con (X) over X which is the quotient space obtained by identifying the top $X \times 1$ of the cylinder $X \times I$ to a single point v, called the vertex of Con (X).   Since X is homeomorphic with the bottom $X \times 0$ of Con (X) which is a closed subspace of Con (X) and since P is a weakly hereditary topological property which X does not have, it follows that Con (X) cannot have P.   Since Con (X) is contractible by (II, Ex. 7B), the inclusion map

$$i \ : \ v \to \text{Con } (X)$$

is a homotopy equivalence by (II, 7.6 and 7.7).   Since the singleton space v has P while Con (X) does not have P, P is not a homotopy property.   ‖

Since every singleton space X has all of the properties (A)–(N) and since none of these properties prevails in all spaces, we have the following

COROLLARY 10.2. *None of the properties* (A)–(N) *is a homotopy property.*

The next question is whether or not these properties (A)–(N) are isotopy properties. For this purpose, we will establish the following

THEOREM 10.3. *Every hereditary topological property of spaces is an isotopy property.*

Proof. Let P be any hereditary topological property of spaces. Assume that $f: X \to Y$ is an isotopy equivalence and the space X has the property P. It suffices to prove that Y also has P.

By definition of an isotopy equivalence, there exists an imbedding $g: Y \to X$ such that the composed imbeddings $g \circ f$ and $f \circ g$ are isotopic to identity maps on X and Y respectively. The image $g(Y)$ is a subspace of X. Since P is hereditary, this implies that $g(Y)$ has P. As an imbedding, g is an homeomorphism of Y onto $g(Y)$. Since P is a topological property and $g(Y)$ has P, it follows that Y also has P. ||

Since the first ten properties (A)–(J) are hereditary, we have the following

COROLLARY 10.4. *Each of the properties* (A)–(J) *is an isotopy property.*

It remains to see if the properties (K)–(N) are isotopy properties.

PROPOSITION 10.5. *Compactness is not an isotopy property.*

Proof. By (II, 7.8), the closed unit interval I is isotopically equivalent to the open unit interval J. Since I is compact while J is noncompact, compactness cannot be an isotopy property. ||

PROPOSITION 10.6. *Local compactness is not an isotopy property.*

Proof. By (II, Ex. 7E), the topological powers I^M and R^M are isotopically equivalent for every M. If M is an infinite set, R^M is not locally compact by (Ex. 2E) while I^M is compact and hence locally compact. Therefore, local compactness cannot be an isotopy property. ||

For the remaining question of whether the properties (K) and (M) are isotopy properties, see the exercises 10D and 10E.

EXERCISES

10A. A space X is said to be a *Lindelöf space* iff every open cover of X has a countable subcover. Prove that being a Lindelöf space is a weakly hereditary topological property and hence not a homotopy property.

10B. The *inductive dimension* dim X of a space X is defined as follows: dim $X = -1$ iff X is empty, and dim $X \leqslant n$ iff for every point $p \in X$ and every neighborhood U of p there exists an open neighborhood $V \subset U$ of p such that dim $(\partial V) \leqslant n - 1$, where ∂V denotes the boundary $\overline{V} \setminus V$ of V in X, and finally

$$\dim X = \inf \{n \mid \dim X \leqslant n\}.$$

Prove that, for a given integer $n \geqslant 0$, dim $X \leqslant n$ is a hereditary topological property. Then, deduce that dim X is an isotopy property but not a homotopy property. [Hu 1.]

10C. A topological property of spaces is said to be an *open property* iff it is inherited by open subspaces and preserved by open maps. Verify that the following topological properties are open properties:
   (a) separability,
   (b) local connectedness,
   (c) local pathwise connectedness.
Prove that nontrivial open properties are not homotopy properties. [Gottlieb 1.]

10D. Prove that normality is not an isotopy property by the following method or otherwise. Consider the set Ω' of all ordinal numbers not greater than the first uncountable ordinal Ω. Give Ω' the order topology which is the smallest topology in Ω' containing all sets of the form $\{x \in \Omega' \mid x < a\}$ or $\{x \in \Omega' \mid a < x\}$ for some $a \in \Omega'$. Let

$$X = \Omega' \times I, \qquad Y = X \setminus \{(\Omega, 1)\}.$$

Then it remains to prove the following three assertions: [Gottlieb 1.]
   (a) $X \cong Y$,
   (b) X is normal,
   (c) Y is not normal.

10E. By using the spaces in the preceding exercise or otherwise, prove that a topological property P is not an isotopy property if it satisfies the following two conditions:
   (a) Every compact Hausdorff space has P.
   (b) Every regular space possessing P is normal.
In particular, paracompactness is not an isotopy property. Also, being a Lindelöf space is not an isotopy property. [Gottlieb 1.]

Chapter IV: POLYTOPES

In the present chapter, we will give an exposition of CW-complexes, the first of its kind to be given in a book. These polytopes were introduced by J. H. C. Whitehead about twenty-five years ago. Since then, so many useful applications have been developed that they deserve a reasonable account in elementary books such as this. Instead of defining CW-complexes as Hausdorff spaces with cellular structures as Whitehead did originally, we prefer the constructive definition as adjunction spaces obtained from unit simplexes and given characteristic maps, introduced also by Whitehead himself. CW-complexes will be named cellular polytopes from now on. We will define simplicial polytopes first and then prove them to be special cases of cellular polytopes.

1. SIMPLEXES

Let n be a given non-negative integer and consider a given set V of $n + 1$ distinct objects. By the *n-dimensional simplex spanned by* V, we mean the closed subspace σ_V of the topological power R^V of the real line R which consists of all functions

$$f : V \to R$$

satisfying the following two conditions:

(S1) $\qquad f(v) \geqslant 0$ for every $v \in V$.
(S2) $\qquad \sum_{v \in V} f(v) = 1$.

The $n + 1$ objects in V are called the *vertices* of the simplex σ_V. Frequently, V is called an *abstract simplex* and σ_V, the *topological realization* of V.

Since the topological power R^V is metrizable according to (III, 8.5), so is the simplex σ_V by (III, 8.3). The distance function d given by

$$d(f, g) = \sqrt{\sum_{v \in V} [g(v) - f(v)]^2}$$

for any two points f and g in σ_V defines the topology of σ_V.

As an example of an n-dimensional simplex, let us take V to be the first $n + 1$ non-negative integers

$$V = \{0, 1, \ldots, n\}.$$

In this case, the simplex σ_V reduces to the *unit n-simplex* Δ^n defined in (II, Ex. 5G) to be the closed subspace of the Euclidean space R^{n+1} consisting of all points $(x_0, x_1, \ldots, x_n)$ of R^{n+1} such that $x_i \geqslant 0$ for every $i = 0, 1, \ldots, n$ and that

$$\sum_{i=0}^{n} x_i = 1.$$

PROPOSITION 1.1. *Any two n-dimensional simplexes σ_V and σ_W are homeomorphic.*

Proof. Consider an arbitrary bijective function

$$\beta \; : \; V \to W$$

of V onto W. Then β induces a homeomorphism

$$h_\beta \; : \; R^W \to R^V$$

defined by taking

$$h_\beta(f) \; = \; f \circ \beta \; : \; V \to R$$

for every function $f: W \to R$ in R^W. One can easily see that h_β preserves the conditions (S1) and (S2) and hence sends σ_W homeomorphically onto σ_V. ||

Thus, every n-dimensional simplex is homeomorphic to the unit n-simplex Δ^n, and the latter will be used as the standard prototype of all n-dimensional simplexes.

For each vertex $v \in V$ of a given n-dimensional simplex σ_V, there is a unique point f_v in σ_V such that

$$f_v(v) \; = \; 1, \qquad f_v(V \setminus v) \; = \; 0.$$

The assignment $v \to f_v$ defines an injective function

$$i \; : \; V \to \sigma_V$$

of V into σ_V. We identify v with f_v for each $v \in V$; therefore, $V \subset \sigma_V$.

In general, let W be an arbitrary subset of V. If W consists of $q + 1$ objects, then it determines a q-dimensional simplex σ_W. For each point $g \in \sigma_W$, there is a unique point $f_g \in \sigma_V$ such that

$$f_g(v) \; = \; \begin{cases} g(v), & (\text{if } v \in W), \\ 0, & (\text{if } v \in V \setminus W). \end{cases}$$

The assignment $g \to f_g$ defines an imbedding

$$i \; : \; \sigma_W \to \sigma_V$$

of σ_W into σ_V. Identify g with f_g for every $g \in \sigma_W$ and obtain σ_W as the closed subspace of σ_V defined by

$$\sigma_W = \{ f \in \sigma_V \mid f(v) = 0 \text{ for each } v \in V \setminus W \}.$$

Such a simplex σ_W is called a *q-dimensional face of σ_V* or a *q-face of σ_V*. If the dimension q of σ_W is not emphasized, σ_W is called a *face of σ_V*; in symbols,

$$\sigma_W \; \leqslant \; \sigma_V.$$

In particular, σ_V has only one *n*-face, namely σ_V itself; this is called the *improper face* of σ_V. Other faces of σ_V are called *proper faces*. On the other hand, σ_V has $n + 1$ 0-faces, namely its vertices. If $0 < q < n$, then σ_V has

$$\binom{n+1}{q+1} = \frac{(n+1)!}{(n-q)! \, (q+1)!}$$

q-dimensional faces.

The union of all proper faces of σ_V as a subspace of σ_V is called the *boundary* of σ_V, denoted by $\partial \sigma_V$ or $\dot{\sigma}_V$. The residual space

$$\text{Int} \, (\sigma_V) \; = \; \sigma_V \setminus \partial \sigma_V$$

will be called the *interior* of σ_V; it is also called an *open n-simplex*. Thus, σ_V is the disjoint union of all of its open faces; in symbols,

$$\sigma_V \; = \; \bigcup\nolimits_{W \subset V} \text{Int} \, (\sigma_W).$$

The space R^V is a vector space over the field R of real numbers; in fact, if $f, g \in R^V$ and $\alpha, \beta \in R$, then

$$h \; = \; \alpha f + \beta g \in R^V$$

is the function $h : V \to R$ defined by

$$h(v) \; = \; \alpha f(v) + \beta g(v)$$

for every point $v \in V$. As a vector space over R, R^V is of dimension $n + 1$ and has a basis

$$\{ f_v \mid v \in V \},$$

which has been identified with V.

PROPOSITION 1.2. *The simplex σ_V is the convex hull of its vertices V in the vector space R^V. In other words, σ_V consists of all linear combinations*

$$\sum_{v \in V} \alpha_v f_v$$

where $\{\alpha_v \mid v \in V\}$ are non-negative real numbers satisfying

$$\sum_{v \in V} \alpha_v = 1.$$

Proof. First, consider such a linear combination,

$$f = \sum_{v \in V} \alpha_v f_v.$$

We will prove that $f \in \sigma_V$. For each $v \in V$, we have

$$f(v) = \alpha_v \geqslant 0$$

and hence

$$\sum_{v \in V} f(v) = \sum_{v \in V} \alpha_v = 1.$$

This verifies both (S1) and (S2). Therefore, $f \in \sigma_V$.

Conversely, let f be an arbitrary point in σ_V. For each $v \in V$, let

$$\alpha_v = f(v).$$

Then $\{\alpha_v \mid v \in V\}$ are non-negative real numbers satisfying

$$\sum_{v \in V} \alpha_v = 1$$

because of (S1) and (S2). Since $f(v) = \alpha_v$ for each $v \in V$, it follows that

$$f = \sum_{v \in V} \alpha_v f_v. \quad \|$$

The following corollary is a direct consequence of the convexity of σ_V.

COROLLARY 1.3. *If $x_0, \ldots, x_q$ are any $q + 1$ points in σ_V and if $\alpha_0, \ldots, \alpha_q$ are non-negative real numbers satisfying*

$$\sum_{i=0}^{q} \alpha_i = 1,$$

then we have

$$\sum_{i=0}^{q} \alpha_i x_i \in \sigma_V.$$

EXERCISES

1A. Prove that every simplex σ_V is contractible to any vertex $v_0 \in V$ by verifying that the system of functions $\{h_t : \sigma_V \to \sigma_V \mid t \in I\}$ defined by

$$[h_t(f)](v) = \begin{cases} t + (1 - t)f(v_0), & \text{(if } v = v_0\text{),} \\ (1 - t)f(v), & \text{(if } v \in V \setminus v_0\text{),} \end{cases}$$

is a contraction.

1B. Let σ_V be a given n-simplex and choose for each vertex $v \in V$ a point x_v in a given Euclidean space R^q of dimension q. Define a map

$$k \; : \; \sigma_V \to R^q$$

by taking

$$k(f) = \sum_{v \in V} f(v) x_v$$

for every $f \in \sigma_V$. Prove that, if $n \leqslant q$ and if the points $\{x_v \mid v \in V\}$ are linearly independent, then k is an imbedding. In particular, if $n = q$, then prove that

$$k \,(\text{Int } \sigma_V) = \text{Int } [k(\sigma_V)],$$

where Int $[k(\sigma_V)]$ denotes the interior of the set $k(\sigma_V)$ in the space R^n as defined in (II, § 2). Hence, σ_V is homeomorphic to a bounded closed convex set $k(\sigma_V)$ of R^n with interior points. On the other hand, prove that $k(\sigma_V)$ has no interior point in case $n < q$.

1C. Prove that any two bounded closed convex sets in R^n with interior points are homeomorphic. Hence, every n-dimensional simplex is homeomorphic to the unit n-cube I^n and to the unit n-cell $\text{Cl}(E^n)$ in R^n.

1D. Consider a given simplex σ_V and a bijective function

$$\pi \; : \; V \to V.$$

In view of $V \subset \sigma_V$, prove that π extends to a homeomorphism

$$h_\pi \; : \; \sigma_V \to \sigma_V$$

defined by

$$[h_\pi(f)](v) = f[\pi^{-1}(v)]$$

for every $f \in \sigma_V$ and every $v \in V$. Find a point $c \in \sigma_V$ such that $h_\pi(c) = c$ for every bijective function $\pi : V \to V$.

1E. Let $x_0, \ldots, x_q$ be any $q + 1$ linearly independent points in a simplex σ_V. Prove that the subspace S of σ_V which consists of all linear combinations $\alpha_0 x_0 + \cdots + \alpha_q x_q$, where $\alpha_0, \ldots, \alpha_q$ are non-negative real numbers satisfying $\alpha_0 + \ldots + \alpha_q = 1$, is homeomorphic to every q-simplex. This space S is called the q-simplex in σ_V spanned by the points $x_0, \ldots, x_q$.

2. SIMPLICIAL POLYTOPES

By an *abstract simplicial complex* with vertices in a set V, we mean a family K of finite subsets of V satisfying the condition that K is *hereditary*, i.e., every subset of any set in K is also in K.

As an example of abstract simplicial complexes, let us consider an open cover V of a space X. Then every member of V is a nonempty open set of X. Define a family K of finite sets of members of V as follows: A finite subset F of V is in the family K iff the intersection of all members of F is nonempty. Obviously, K is hereditary and hence K is an abstract simplicial complex with vertices in V. This complex K is called the *abstract nerve* of the open cover V of the space X. In fact, the abstract nerve is defined for every collection V of nonempty sets.

In the preceding example, we observe that every singleton subset of V is in K and hence $V \subset K$. In general, we may also assume $V \subset K$ by omitting those members of V which appear in none of the sets in K. Because of this assumption, the members of V will be called the *vertices* of K.

Let K and L be any two abstract simplicial complexes with vertices V and W respectively. If $L \subset K$, then L is said to be a *subcomplex* of K. On the other hand, K and L are said to be *isomorphic* iff there exists a bijective function $i : V \to W$ such that the induced function

$$i_* : 2^V \to 2^W$$

sends K bijectively onto L.

Now, let K be an arbitrarily given abstract simplicial complex. We will construct a space

$$P = |K|$$

called the *topological realization* of K as follows.

For each finite set $F \in K$, consider the simplex σ_F defined in the previous section. These simplexes $\{\sigma_F \mid F \in K\}$ (without the identification introduced in studying their faces) are by definition disjoint topological spaces. Form their topological sum

$$S = S(K) = \sum_{F \in K} \sigma_F$$

as defined in (II, § 5). Then S is clearly a metrizable space containing every simplex σ_F as an open and closed subspace.

Introduce a relation $\sim$ in S as follows. Let $f \in \sigma_F$ and $g \in \sigma_G$ be any two points in S. Then they are real functions $f : F \to R$ and $g : G \to R$. We define $f \sim g$ iff the following conditions are satisfied.

(R1) $f(v) = 0$ for every $v \in F \setminus G$;

(R2) $g(v) = 0$ for every $v \in G \setminus F$;

(R3) $f(v) = g(v)$ for every $v \in F \cap G$.

LEMMA 2.1.   *The relation $\sim$ in S is an equivalence relation.*

Proof. Since $\sim$ is obviously reflexive and symmetric, it remains to verify the transitivity of $\sim$. For this purpose, let

$$f \in \sigma_F, \qquad g \in \sigma_G, \qquad h \in \sigma_H$$

be three points in S and assume that

$$f \sim g, \qquad g \sim h.$$

We will prove that $f \sim h$.

First, let $v \in F \setminus H$. If $v \notin G$, we have $v \in F \setminus G$ and hence $f(v) = 0$. If $v \in G$, we have $v \in F \cap G$ as well as $v \in G \setminus H$ and hence $f(v) = g(v) = 0$. Therefore, $f(v) = 0$ in both cases. This verifies (R1) for $f \sim h$.

Similarly, we can verify (R2) for $f \sim h$, that is, $h(v) = 0$ for every $v \in H \setminus F$.

Next, let $v \in F \cap H$. If $v \in G$, we have $v \in F \cap G$ as well as $v \in G \cap H$ and hence $f(v) = g(v) = h(v)$. If $v \notin G$, we have $v \in F \setminus G$ as well as $v \in H \setminus G$ and hence $f(v) = 0 = h(v)$. Therefore, we have $f(v) = h(v)$ in both cases. This verifies (R3) for $f \sim h$. $\|$

The quotient space

$$P = |K| = S/\sim$$

of the space $S = S(K)$ over this equivalence relation $\sim$, as defined in (II, § 6), is called the *topological realization* of the abstract simplicial complex K. We will also call P a *simplicial polytope*. In mathematical literature, P is usually called a *simplicial complex* and is denoted by K instead of $|K|$.

Now, let us consider the *natural projection*

$$p : S \to P$$

of the space $S = S(K)$ onto the quotient space $P = |K|$ as defined in (II, § 6). Then, p is an identification and hence is continuous.

PROPOSITION 2.2. *For each $F \in K$, the restriction*

$$p_F = p \mid \sigma_F : \sigma_F \to P$$

is an imbedding.

Proof. First, let us prove that p sends σ_F bijectively onto the subspace $p(\sigma_F)$ of P. For this purpose, let f and g be any two points in σ_F such that $p(f) = p(g)$. Since p is the natural projection, this implies that $f \sim g$. Since f and g are both in σ_F, the condition (R3) implies that $f = g$. Hence, p_F is an injective map.

By (II, 3.2), it suffices to prove that the image $p(C)$ of any closed subset C of σ_F is closed in P and hence also in $p(\sigma_F)$. By (II, 6.1), it remains to prove that the inverse image

$$D = p^{-1}[p(C)]$$

is closed in the space S.

For an arbitrary $G \in K$, we will prove that $D \cap \sigma_G$ is a closed subset of the simplex σ_G. Let $H = F \cap G$. If $H = \square$, then the condition (R2) implies that $D \cap \sigma_G = \square$. If $H \neq \square$, then $H \in K$. The inclusions $H \subset F$ and $H \subset G$ determine imbeddings

$$i \ : \ \sigma_H \to \sigma_F, \qquad j \ : \ \sigma_H \to \sigma_G$$

as constructed in § 1. Then one can easily see that

$$D \cap \sigma_G = j[i^{-1}(C)].$$

Since i is continuous and j sends σ_H homeomorphically onto the closed subspace $j(\sigma_H)$ of σ_G, this implies that $D \cap \sigma_G$ is closed in σ_G. Since S is the topological sum of all σ_G, it follows that D is closed in S. ‖

If we take $C = \sigma_F$ in the preceding proof, we obtain the following

COROLLARY 2.3. *For each $F \in K$, $p(\sigma_F)$ is a closed subspace of P.*

Because of (2.2) and (2.3), we may identify σ_F with $p(\sigma_F)$ and consider each simplex σ_F as a closed subspace of the simplicial polytope P. Thus, each σ_F will be called a *(closed) simplex* of the simplicial polytope P. The image

$$\omega_F = p[\text{Int } (\sigma_F)]$$

will be called the corresponding *open simplex* of P. These open simplexes $\{\omega_F \mid F \in K\}$ are disjoint and cover P, i.e.

$$P = \bigcup_{F \in K} \omega_F.$$

Also, it is clear that $\text{Cl} (\omega_F) = \sigma_F$.

Now we can describe the topology τ of the simplicial polytope P precisely by the following

PROPOSITION 2.4. *A set $U \subset P$ is in τ iff the intersection $U \cap \sigma_F$ is an open subset of the simplex σ_F for every $F \in K$.*

Proof. Let U be any subset of P. Because of the identification of σ_F with $p(\sigma_F)$, we have

$$[p^{-1}(U)] \cap \sigma_F = U \cap p(\sigma_F) = U \cap \sigma_F.$$

Since $p : S \to P$ is an identification and S is the topological sum of all

σ_F, U is in τ iff $p^{-1}(U)$ is open in S and hence iff $U \cap \sigma_F$ is an open subset of the simplex σ_F for every $F \in K$. $\|$

This topology τ of the simplicial polytope P is what J. H. C. Whitehead called the *weak topology* and we will call the *Whitehead topology*. It is actually the largest topology of P such that the relative topology of each simplex σ_F of P is the same as that of σ_F defined in § 1. Naturally, there are other topologies of the set P; one of these will be given in Exercise 2F. However, the Whitehead topology is preferred in most applications. Perhaps the main reason for its usefulness is the following

PROPOSITION 2.5. *An arbitrary function $f : P \to X$ from a simplicial polytope P with Whitehead topology into a space X is continuous iff, for each simplex σ_F of P, the restriction*

$$f_F = f \mid \sigma_F \ : \ \sigma_F \to X$$

is continuous.

Proof. Since the necessity of the proposition is obvious, it remains to prove the sufficiency.

Assume that f_F is continuous for every $F \in K$. Let U be any open set in the space X. Since

$$[f^{-1}(U)] \cap \sigma_F = f_F^{-1}(U)$$

and since f_F is continuous, it follows by the Whitehead topology of P that $f^{-1}(U)$ is open in P. Hence, f is continuous. $\|$

Hereafter, all simplicial polytopes are assumed to have the Whitehead topology unless otherwise stated.

Now let P and Q be any two given simplicial polytopes defined as the topological realizations of two abstract simplicial complexes K and L with vertices V and W respectively.

If L is a subcomplex of K, then the inclusion $i : L \subset K$ induces an inclusion map

$$S(i) \ : \ S(L) \to S(K)$$

which preserves the equivalence relation $\sim$. Hence, $S(i)$ induces an imbedding

$$|i| \ : \ Q \to P.$$

Because of this imbedding $|i|$, Q can be considered as a subspace of P and will be called a *subpolytope* of P. In this case, $Q \cap \sigma_F$ is a union of faces of σ_F and hence is closed in σ_F for every $F \in K$. Therefore, we have the following

PROPOSITION 2.6. *Every subpolytope of a simplicial polytope P is closed in P.*

If K and L are isomorphic, then there exists a bijective function $i : V \to W$ which induces a bijective function

$$i_* \;:\; K \to L.$$

This bijective function i_* induces a homeomorphism

$$S(i_*) \;:\; S(K) \to S(L)$$

which preserves the equivalence relation $\sim$. Hence, $S(i_*)$ induces a homeomorphism

$$|i_*| \;:\; P \to Q.$$

Therefore, we have the following

PROPOSITION 2.7. *The topological realizations of isomorphic abstract simplicial complexes are homeomorphic.*

For each $F \in K$, let us define the *open star* st (F) and the *closed star* St (F) in the simplicial polytope P as follows:

$$\text{st } (F) \;=\; \bigcup \{ \omega_G \mid F \subset G \in K \},$$
$$\text{St } (F) \;=\; \bigcup \{ \sigma_G \mid F \subset G \in K \}.$$

Then one can easily see that St (F) and $P \setminus \text{st } (F)$ are subpolytopes of P. Hence, we have the following

PROPOSITION 2.8. *For each $F \in K$, the open star st (F) is open in P and the closed star St (F) is closed in P.*

In particular, if F consists of a single vertex $v \in V$, then we denote

$$\text{st } (v) = \text{st } (F), \qquad \text{St } (v) = \text{St } (F),$$

and call them the *open star* and the *closed star* of the vertex v in P. Since $\omega_F \subset \text{st } (v)$ for every $F \in K$ which contains v, we have the following

PROPOSITION 2.9. *The collection*

$$\Gamma = \{ \text{st } (v) \mid v \in V \}$$

is an open cover of P and its abstract nerve $\mathrm{N}(\Gamma)$ is isomorphic to K. Hence, the topological realization $|\mathrm{N}(\Gamma)|$ of $\mathrm{N}(\Gamma)$ is homeomorphic to P.

EXERCISES

2A. Prove that every finite simplicial polytope with no more than $n + 1$ vertices is isomorphic to a subpolytope of the unit n-simplex Δ^n.

2B. Let f, $g : X \to P$ be two maps from a space X into a simplicial polytope P such that, for each $x \in X$, there exists a simplex σ in P containing $f(x)$ and $g(x)$. Prove that f and g are homotopic.

2C. Let P be a given simplicial polytope. By dim $(P) \geqslant n$, we mean that P has at least one n-dimensional simplex. Then the *dimension* dim (P) of P is defined by

$$\dim (P) \;=\; \sup \{n \mid \dim (P) \geqslant n\}.$$

Prove that, if dim $(P) \geqslant 1$, then the natural projection $p : S \to P$ is not open.

2D. A simplicial polytope P is said to be *locally finite* iff every point in P has a neighborhood which meets only a finite number of simplexes of P. Prove that the following statements are equivalent:
   (a) P is locally finite.
   (b) For each vertex v of P, St (v) is finite.
   (c) For each $F \in K$, St (F) is finite.

Also, prove that, if there exists a non-singleton $F \in K$ such that St (F) is infinite, then the natural projection $p : S \to P$ is not closed.

2E. Prove that if a simplicial polytope P is not locally finite, then it fails to satisfy the first axiom of countability.

2F. Let P be a given simplicial polytope. Then the points of P can be considered as the real functions $f : V \to R$ defined on all vertices of P satisfying the three conditions
   (a) $f(v) \geqslant 0$ for every $v \in V$.
   (b) $f^{-1}(R \setminus 0) \in K$.
   (c) $\sum_{v \in V} f(v) = 1$.

Verify the distance function $d : P^2 \to R$ defined by

$$d(f, g) \;=\; \sqrt{\sum_{v \in V} [g(v) - f(v)]^2}$$

for any two points f and g of P. The topology in P defined by this distance function d is called the *metric topology* of P. Prove that the metric topology coincides with the Whitehead topology iff P is locally finite.

3. ADJUNCTION SPACES

In view of the application to the construction of the cellular polytopes in the following section, we will devote the present section to the study of the *adjunction space* for an arbitrarily given map

$$f : A \to Y$$

defined on a closed subspace A of a space X into another space Y as follows.

Without loss of generality, we may assume that X and Y are disjoint. Consider the topological sum

$$W \; = \; X + Y$$

of the spaces X and Y as defined in (II, § 5).

Introduce a relation $\sim$ in the space W as follows. Let u and v be any two points in the space W. Then we define $u \sim v$ iff at least one of the following four equations makes sense and is satisfied:

$$u = v, \quad f(u) = v, \quad u = f(v), \quad f(u) = f(v).$$

It is straightforward to verify that $\sim$ is an equivalence relation in the space W.

The quotient space

$$Z = W/\sim$$

of the space W over this equivalence relation $\sim$, as defined in (II, § 6), is called the *adjunction space* obtained by adjoining X to Y by means of the given map $f : A \to Y$.

Now, let us consider the *natural projection*

$$p \; : \; W \to Z$$

of the space W onto the quotient space Z as defined in (II, § 6). Then, p is an identification and hence is continuous.

PROPOSITION 3.1.   *The restriction*

$$i \; = \; p \mid Y : Y \to Z$$

is an imbedding.

Proof.   First, let us prove that p sends Y bijectively onto the subspace $p(Y)$. For this purpose, let u and v be any two points in Y such that $p(u) = p(v)$. Since p is the natural projection, this implies that $u \sim v$. Since u and v are both in Y, only the first of the four equations used in defining $u \sim v$ makes sense. Hence we get $u = v$. This proves that i is an injective map.

By (II, 3.2), it suffices to prove that the image $p(C)$ of any closed subset C of Y is closed in Z and hence also in $p(Y)$. By (II, 6.1), it remains to prove that the inverse image

$$D \; = \; p^{-1}[p(C)]$$

is closed in the space W. By the definition of $\sim$, we have

$$D \; = \; f^{-1}(C) \cup C.$$

Since A and C are closed in X and Y respectively and since f is continuous, it follows that D is closed in W. ‖

If we take $C = Y$ in the preceding proof, we obtain the following

COROLLARY 3.2. *The image $p(Y)$ is a closed subspace of the adjunction space Z.*

Because of (3.1) and (3.2), we may identify Y with $p(Y)$ and consider Y as a closed subspace of the adjunction space Z.

PROPOSITION 3.3. *The restriction*

$$ j = p \mid X \setminus A : X \setminus A \to Z $$

is an imbedding.

Proof. That j is an injective map can be proved exactly as in the proof of (3.1).

By (II, 3.2), it suffices to prove that the image $p(U)$ of any open subset U of $X \setminus A$ is open in Z and hence also in $p(X \setminus A)$. By (II, 6.1), it remains to prove that the inverse image

$$ V = p^{-1}[p(U)] $$

is open in the space W. By the definition of $\sim$, we have $V = U$. Since U is open in $X \setminus A$ and $X \setminus A$ is open in X, it follows that V is open in X and hence in W. ‖

If we take $U = X \setminus A$ in the preceding proof, we obtain the following

COROLLARY 3.4. *The image $p(X \setminus A)$ is an open subspace of the adjunction space Z.*

Because of (3.3) and (3.4), we may identify $X \setminus A$ with $p(X \setminus A)$ and consider $X \setminus A$ as an open subspace of the adjunction space Z.

Furthermore, the following proposition is obvious.

PROPOSITION 3.5. *$p(Y)$ and $p(X \setminus A)$ are disjoint and*

$$ Z = p(Y) \cup p(X \setminus A). $$

Hence, the adjunction space Z can be considered as the disjoint union of Y and $X \setminus A$ sewn together by a special topology defined by means of the given map f. In case A is also open in X, then Z becomes the topological sum of Y and $X \setminus A$.

For examples of adjunction spaces, let us take $X = \mathrm{Cl}\,(E^n)$ the closed unit n-cell in R^n and $A = S^{n-1}$ the unit $(n-1)$-sphere as defined in (II, Ex. 5F and 5G).   Consider a map $f: S^{n-1} \to Y$ and the adjunction space Z obtained by adjoining Cl (E^n) to Y by means of f.   Then the pair (Z, Y) is called a *relative n-cell*.   In particular, if $Y = P^{n-1}$ is the real projective $(n - 1)$-space and if $f: S^{n-1} \to P^{n-1}$ is the map obtained by identifying antipodal points, then the adjunction space Z is the real projective n-space P^n.   Hence, the pair (P^n, P^{n-1}) is a relative n-cell.

As another example, let us take $n = 2$, i.e. $X = $ Cl (E^2) and $A = S^1$.   Let Y be a subspace of R^2 consisting of two circles α and β tangent at a point v.   If $f: S^1 \to Y$ denotes a map starting at v and wrapping around the circles in the order and direction $\alpha\beta\alpha^{-1}\beta^{-1}$, then the adjunction space Z is homeomorphic to the *torus surface*.   On the other hand, if the order and direction is $\alpha\beta\alpha^{-1}\beta$, then the adjunction space Z is the *Klein bottle*.   In both cases, the pair (Z, Y) is a relative 2-cell.

The usefulness of adjunction spaces is illustrated by the following

PROPOSITION 3.6.   *The given map* $f: A \to Y$ *has an extension over* X *iff the space* Y *is a retract of the adjunction space* Z.

Proof: Necessity.   Let $g: X \to Y$ be a map with $g \mid A = f$.   Define a function $r: Z \to Y$ as follows.   Let $z \in Z$.   If $z \in Y$, we define $r(z) = z$.   If $z \notin Y$, it follows from (3.5) that $z \in X \setminus A$.   In this case, we define $r(z) = g(z)$.   Then the composed function

$$h = r \circ p: W \to Y$$

is given by

$$h(w) = \begin{cases} g(w), & (\text{if } w \in X), \\ w, & (\text{if } w \in Y). \end{cases}$$

By (II, 4.3), h is continuous.   Therefore, it follows from (II, 6.3) that r is continuous.   Since $r \mid Y$ is the identity map, r is a retraction.

Sufficiency.   Let $r: Z \supset Y$ be a retraction.   Define a map $g: X \to Y$ by taking

$$g(x) = r[p(x)]$$

for every point $x \in X \subset W$.   If $x \in A$, then we have

$$g(x) = r[p(x)] = r[f(x)] = f(x).$$

Hence g is an extension of f over X.   ‖

In the remainder of the present section, we are concerned with the topological properties of the adjunction space Z.   Let π be any topological property of spaces.   We say that the adjunction space Z *preserves* the property π iff Z has the property π whenever both X and Y have the property π.

Since Z reduces to the topological sum of X and Y in case $A = \square$, we will assume hereafter that $A \neq \square$.

THEOREM 3.7. *The adjunction space Z preserves each of the following topological properties:*
   (a) *being a compact space,*
   (b) *being a connected space,*
   (c) *being a pathwise connected space,*
   (d) *being a Fréchet space,*
   (e) *being a normal space,* [Hanner 1].

Proof of (a). As the union of two compact sets X and Y, the space W is clearly compact. Hence, by (III, 2.3), $Z = p(W)$ is compact. ∥

Proof of (b) *and* (c). Pick a point $x_0 \in A$ and let $y_0 = f(x_0)$. Then we have $p(x_0) = p(y_0)$. Since X and Y are (pathwise) connected, so are their continuous images $p(X)$ and $p(Y)$. Since Z is the union of $p(X)$ and $p(Y)$ with a common point $p(x_0) = p(y_0)$, it follows that Z is (pathwise) connected. ∥

Proof of (d). Let z be any point of Z. If $z \in Y$, then $\{z\}$ is closed in Y since Y is a Fréchet space. Since Y is closed in Z, it follows that $\{z\}$ is also closed in Z. If $z \notin Y$, then the inverse image $p^{-1}(z)$ is a single point in $X \setminus A$ and is closed in X since X is a Fréchet space. Since X is closed in W, $p^{-1}(z)$ is also closed in W. By (II, 6.1), $\{z\}$ is closed in Z. ∥

Proof of (e). Let F_1 and F_2 be any two disjoint closed sets in Z. Then $F_1 \cap Y$ and $F_2 \cap Y$ are disjoint closed sets in Y. Since Y is normal, it follows from (III, Ex. 1F(c)) that there exist two open sets U_1 and U_2 of Y such that

$$F_1 \cap Y \subset U_1, \qquad F_2 \cap Y \subset U_2$$

and that their closures $\text{Cl}(U_1)$ and $\text{Cl}(U_2)$ in Y are disjoint. Since Y is closed in Z, these are also their closures in Z.

Next, consider the closed sets

$$K_1 = F_1 \cup \text{Cl}(U_1), \qquad K_2 = F_2 \cup \text{Cl}(U_2)$$

of Z. By the choice of the sets U_1 and U_2, one can easily verify that K_1 and K_2 are disjoint. Therefore,

$$J_1 = p^{-1}(K_1) \cap X, \qquad J_2 = p^{-1}(K_2) \cap X$$

are disjoint closed sets of X. Since X is normal, there exist two disjoint open sets V_1 and V_2 of X such that

$$J_1 \subset V_1, \qquad J_2 \subset V_2.$$

Now let us investigate the two sets

$$G_1 = p(V_1 \setminus A) \cup U_1, \qquad G_2 = p(V_2 \setminus A) \cup U_2$$

in the adjunction space Z.

We will first prove $F_1 \subset G_1$. For this purpose, let $z \in F_1$. If $z \in Y$, then we have $z \in U_1 \subset G_1$. If $z \notin Y$, then there is a unique point $x \in X \setminus A$ such that $z = p(x)$. Since $z \in F_1 \subset K_1$, it follows that $x \in J_1 \subset V_1$. This implies that $x \in V_1 \setminus A$ and hence $z \in p(V_1 \setminus A) \subset G_1$. Similarly, we can prove that $F_2 \subset G_2$.

Next, we will prove $G_1 \cap G_2 = \square$. For this purpose, we first observe that $U_1 \cap U_2 = \square$. Second, since $V_1 \cap V_2 = \square$ and since p sends $X \setminus A$ homeomorphically onto $Z \setminus Y$, we have $p(V_1 \setminus A) \cap p(V_2 \setminus A) = \square$. Third, since $U_1 \subset Y$ and $p(V_2 \setminus A) \subset Z \setminus Y$, we have $U_1 \cap p(V_2 \setminus A) = \square$. Finally, we have

$$U_2 \cap p(V_1 \setminus A) = \square$$

by the same reason. This proves $G_1 \cap G_2 = \square$.

Consequently, for the normality of the adjunction space Z, it remains to prove that the sets G_1 and G_2 are open in Z.

To prove that G_1 is open in Z, we have to show that $p^{-1}(G_1)$ is an open set of the topological sum W. Now,

$$p^{-1}(G_1) \cap Y = G_1 \cap Y = U_1;$$

hence $p^{-1}(G_1) \cap Y$ is open in Y. On the other hand, we have

$$p^{-1}(G_1) \cap X = (V_1 \setminus A) \cup f^{-1}(U_1)$$

since $p^{-1}(U_1) \cap X = f^{-1}(U_1)$. Since $f^{-1}(U_1)$ is an open set of A, there exists an open set H_1 of X such that

$$f^{-1}(U_1) = A \cap H_1.$$

Since $p^{-1}(U_1) \cap X \subset J_1 \subset V_1$, we also have

$$f^{-1}(U_1) = A \cap H_1 \cap V_1.$$

Therefore, we obtain

$$\begin{aligned} p^{-1}(G_1) \cap X &= (V_1 \setminus A) \cup (A \cap H_1 \cap V_1), \\ &= (V_1 \setminus A) \cup (H_1 \cap V_1). \end{aligned}$$

Since $V_1 \setminus A$ and $H_1 \cap V_1$ are open sets of X, this proves that $p^{-1}(G_1) \cap X$ is open in X. Hence, G_1 is open in Z.
Similarly, one can prove that G_2 is open in Z. $\quad ||$

EXERCISES

3A. Prove that the adjunction space Z obtained by adjoining X to Y by means of a map $f : A \to Y$ defined on a closed subspace A of X is connected if Y is connected and if A meets every component of X.

3B. Prove that the adjunction space Z obtained by adjoining X to Y by means of a map $f : A \to Y$ defined on a closed subspace A of X is pathwise connected if Y is pathwise connected and if A meets every path-component of X.

3C. Prove that the adjunction space Z does not always preserve the following topological properties:
   (a) being a Hausdorff space,
   (b) being a regular space,
   (c) being a completely regular space.

3D. Prove that the adjunction space Z does not always preserve contractibility by showing that the n-sphere S^n is the adjunction space obtained by adjoining the closed unit n-cell $\mathrm{Cl}\,(E^n)$ to a singleton space Y by means of the constant map $f : S^{n-1} \to Y$.

3E. Let $f : A \to Y$ be a closed map defined on a closed subspace A of a metrizable space X into a metrizable space Y. Prove that the adjunction space Z obtained by adjoining X to Y by means of the map f is metrizable iff, for each $y \in Y$, the boundary $\partial[f^{-1}(y)]$ in the space X of the inverse image $f^{-1}(y)$ is either empty or compact. (Apply III, Ex. 8G.)

3F. Take X to be the real line R, A to be the subspace of R consisting of all integers, and Y to be a singleton space. Deduce from 3G below that the adjunction space Z obtained by adjoining X to Y by means of the constant map $f : A \to Y$ is not metrizable. Check this by proving directly that Z fails to satisfy the first axiom of countability.

3G. Prove that the adjunction space Z preserves full normality and complete normality. [Hanner 2 and Iséki 1.]

3H. Let Y be a space in which every two distinct points have disjoint closed neighborhoods. Prove that the adjunction space Z obtained by adjoining a normal Hausdorff space X to Y by means of a map $f : A \to Y$ defined on a closed subspace A of X is a Hausdorff space. [Whitehead 1.]

4. CELLULAR POLYTOPES

To introduce the notion of a *cellular polytope*, let us first consider a given sequence

$$S = \{S_n \mid n = 0, 1, 2, \ldots\}$$

of disjoint sets, where the leading set S_0 is nonempty. The members of the set S_n will be called the *abstract n-cells*.

Give each S_n the discrete topology. We will construct a sequence

$$\{P_n \mid n = 0, 1, 2, \ldots\}$$

of spaces as follows. First, we take

$$P_0 = S_0$$

a discrete space. Next, assume that $n > 0$ and P_{n-1} has already been constructed. If $S_n = \square$, we define $P_n = P_{n-1}$. Otherwise, assume that there is a given family

$$\{\phi_\xi : \partial \Delta^n \to P_{n-1} \mid \xi \in S_n\}$$

of maps indexed by the abstract n-cells. Here, $\partial \Delta^n$ denotes the boundary sphere of the unit n-simplex Δ^n. The map ϕ_ξ will be called the *characteristic map* of the abstract n-cell ξ. Consider the topological products

$$X_n = S_n \times \Delta^n, \qquad A_n = S_n \times \partial \Delta^n.$$

Then, A_n is a closed subspace of X_n. Define a function

$$f_n : A_n \to P_{n-1}$$

by taking $f_n(\xi, t) = \phi_\xi(t)$ for every $\xi \in S_n$ and every $t \in \partial \Delta^n$. Since S_n is discrete, each $\xi \times \partial \Delta^n$ is open in A_n and hence f_n is continuous by (II, 4.5). Then we define P_n to be the adjunction space obtained by adjoining X_n to P_{n-1} by means of the map f_n. This completes the inductive construction of the sequence of spaces $\{P_n \mid n = 0, 1, 2, \ldots\}$.

By (3.1) and (3.2), we will imbed each P_{n-1} as a closed subspace of P_n. Thus, we obtain an expanding sequence

$$P_0 \subset P_1 \subset \ldots \subset P_{n-1} \subset P_n \subset \ldots$$

of spaces. The topological sum

$$P = \sum_{n=0}^{\infty} P_n$$

will be called the *cellular polytope* determined by the given abstract cells and the given characteristic maps.

For each $n \geqslant 0$, P_n will be called the *n-dimensional skeleton* of the cellular polytope P. Let $n > 0$ and consider the natural projection

$$p_n : W_n \rightarrow P_n$$

from the (disjoint) topological sum

$$W_n = X_n + P_{n-1}$$

onto its quotient space P_n. By (3.3) and (3.4), p_n sends $X_n \setminus A_n$ homeomorphically onto the open subspace $P_n \setminus P_{n-1}$. Since

$$X_n \setminus A_n = S_n \times \text{Int}\,(\Delta^n)$$

where $\text{Int}\,(\Delta^n)$ denotes the open unit n-simplex $\Delta^n \setminus \partial(\Delta^n)$, p_n sends $\xi \times \text{Int}\,(\Delta^n)$ homeomorphically onto an open set e_ξ of $P_n \setminus P_{n-1}$ which will be called the *open n-cell* corresponding to ξ for each $\xi \in S_n$. Thus, $P_n \setminus P_{n-1}$ decomposes into a disjoint union

$$P_n \setminus P_{n-1} = \bigcup_{\xi \in S_n} e_\xi.$$

If $\xi \in S_0$, we define the corresponding *open 0-cell* $e_\xi = \{\xi\} \in P_0$. Hence, we obtain the following

PROPOSITION 4.1. *Every cellular polytope is the disjoint union of all of its open cells.*

In order to prove that every cellular polytope is a normal Hausdorff space, we will need the following lemma.

LEMMA 4.2. *If every space Y_n in a given expanding sequence*

$$Y_0 \subset Y_1 \subset \ldots \subset Y_n \subset Y_{n+1} \subset \ldots$$

is normal and closed in Y_{n+1}, then the topological sum

$$Y = \sum_{n=0}^{\infty} Y_n$$

is a normal space.

Proof. Let A and B be any two disjoint closed sets in Y. We will construct two open sets U and V in Y such that $A \subset U$, $B \subset V$, and $U \cap V = \square$.

For each $n \geqslant 0$, the intersections

$$A_n = A \cap Y_n, \qquad B_n = B \cap Y_n$$

are disjoint closed sets in Y_n. Since Y_0 is a normal space, it follows from (III, Ex. 1F (c)) that there exist two open sets U_0 and V_0 of Y_0 such that

$$A_0 \subset U_0, \qquad B_0 \subset V_0, \qquad \mathrm{Cl}\,(U_0) \cap \mathrm{Cl}\,(V_0) = \square.$$

Now we will construct for each $n > 0$ two open sets U_n and V_n of Y_n such that

$$A_n \subset U_n, \qquad B_n \subset V_n, \qquad \mathrm{Cl}\,(U_n) \cap \mathrm{Cl}\,(V_n) = \square,$$
$$U_n \cap Y_{n-1} = U_{n-1}, \qquad V_n \cap Y_{n-1} = V_{n-1}.$$

For this purpose, let $n > 0$ and assume that U_i and V_i have been constructed for every $i > n$. Then

$$C_n = A_n \cup \mathrm{Cl}\,(U_{n-1}), \qquad D_n = B_n \cup \mathrm{Cl}\,(V_{n-1})$$

are disjoint closed sets in a normal space Y_n; therefore, there exist two open sets G_n and H_n in Y_n such that

$$C_n \subset G_n, \qquad D_n \subset H_n, \qquad \mathrm{Cl}\,(G_n) \cap \mathrm{Cl}\,(H_n) = \square.$$

Since U_{n-1} and V_{n-1} are open in Y_{n-1} which is closed in Y_n, the sets

$$L_n = U_{n-1} \cup (Y_n \setminus Y_{n-1}), \qquad M_n = V_{n-1} \cup (Y_n \setminus Y_{n-1})$$

are open in Y_n. Let

$$U_n = G_n \cap L_n, \qquad V_n = H_n \cap M_n.$$

Then one can easily verify that U_n and V_n are open sets of Y_n satisfying the required conditions. This completes the inductive construction of the open sets U_n and V_n for all $n \geqslant 0$.

Now let us consider the two sets

$$U = \bigcup_{n=0}^{\infty} U_n, \qquad V = \bigcup_{n=0}^{\infty} V_n$$

in the space Y. Since

$$U \cap Y_n = U_n, \qquad V \cap Y_n = V_n$$

are open in Y_n for every $n \geqslant 0$, it follows that U and V are open in Y. Furthermore, it is obvious that

$$A \subset U, \qquad B \subset V, \qquad U \cap V = \square.$$

Hence Y is a normal space. $\ \|$

THEOREM 4.3. *Every cellular polytope is a normal Hausdorff space.*

Proof. Let P be an arbitrary cellular polytope as constructed at the beginning of this section. As a discrete space, the 0-dimensional skeleton P_0 is a normal Fréchet space. By applying (3.7) and an induction on n, we deduce that the n-dimensional skeleton P_n of P is a normal Fréchet space for every $n \geqslant 0$.

By (4.1), P is a normal space. Let x be an arbitrary point in P. Then there exists an $n \geqslant 0$ such that $x \in P_n$. Since P_n is a Fréchet space, $\{x\}$ is closed in P_n. Since P_n is closed in P, this implies that $\{x\}$ is closed in P and hence P is a Fréchet space. Hence, P is a normal Hausdorff space. ||

Now let us return to study the cells of the cellular polytope P.

For each $\xi \in S_n$ with $n > 0$, the characteristic map $\phi_\xi : \partial \Delta^n \to P_{n-1}$ extends to a map

$$\phi_\xi{}^* : \Delta^n \to P_n$$

given by $\phi_\xi{}^*(t) = p_n(\xi, t)$ for every $t \in \Delta^n$, where p_n denotes the natural projection. This map $\phi_\xi{}^*$ sends the interior Int (Δ^n) of Δ^n homeomorphically onto the open cell e_ξ. The image

$$s_\xi = \phi_\xi{}^*(\Delta^n)$$

in P_n will be called the *closed n-cell* corresponding to ξ.

PROPOSITION 4.4. *The closed n-cell s_ξ is the closure of the open n-cell e_ξ in P, in symbols, $s_\xi = $ Cl (e_ξ).*

Proof. Since $\Delta^n = $ Cl (Int Δ^n), it follows from (II, 3.1 (vi)) that

$$s_\xi \subset \text{Cl } (e_\xi).$$

As a continuous image of a compact set Δ^n, s_ξ is compact by (III, 2.3). Since P is a Hausdorff space by (4.3), it follows from (III, 2.5) that s_ξ is closed in P. Therefore,

$$\text{Cl } (e_\xi) \subset s_\xi.$$

Thus, we obtain $s_\xi = $ Cl (e_ξ). ||

COROLLARY 4.5. $\partial e_\xi = \phi_\xi(\partial \Delta^n)$.

Now we can describe the topology τ of the cellular polytope P precisely by the following

PROPOSITION 4.6. *A set $U \subset P$ is in τ iff the intersection $U \cap s_\xi$ is an open subset of the closed cell s_ξ for every ξ.*

Proof. Since s_ξ is a subspace of P, the necessity of the condition is obvious. It remains to prove the sufficiency.

Let U be a set in P such that $U \cap s_\xi$ is open in s_ξ for every closed cell s_ξ of P. To prove that $U \in \tau$, we have to show that $U \cap P_n$ is open in P_n for every $n \geqslant 0$.

For $n = 0$, $U \cap P_0$ is always open in P_0 since the latter is a discrete space. Let $n > 0$ and assume that $U \cap P_{n-1}$ is open in P_{n-1}. Consider the inverse image

$$V = p_n^{-1}(U \cap P_n)$$

under the natural projection $p_n : W_n \to P_n$. To prove that $U \cap P_n$ is open in P_n, it suffices to show that $V \cap P_{n-1}$ is open in P_{n-1} and $V \cap X_n$ is open in X_n.

Since $V \cap P_{n-1} = U \cap P_{n-1}$, it is open in P_{n-1} by our inductive hypothesis. On the other hand, since

$$X_n = S_n \times \Delta^n$$

with a discrete S_n, it remains to show that $V \cap (\xi \times \Delta^n)$ is open in $\xi \times \Delta^n$ for every $\xi \in S_n$. Since

$$s_\xi = \phi_\xi{}^*(\Delta^n) = p_n(\xi \times \Delta^n),$$

it follows that

$$V \cap (\xi \times \Delta^n) = [p^{-1}(U \cap s_\xi)] \cap (\xi \times \Delta^n).$$

Since $U \cap s_\xi$ is open in s_ξ, this implies that $V \cap (\xi \times \Delta^n)$ is open in $\xi \times \Delta^n$. $\|$

This topology τ of the cellular polytope P is what J. H. C. Whitehead called the *weak topology* and we will call the *Whitehead topology*.

As an immediate consequence of the Whitehead topology, we have the following

COROLLARY 4.7. *An arbitrary function $f : P \to X$ from a cellular polytope P into a space X is continuous iff, for each closed cell s_ξ of P, the restriction*

$$f_\xi = f \,|\, s_\xi \,:\, s_\xi \to X$$

is continuous.

In constructing the cellular polytope P, obviously the unit n-simplex Δ^n can be replaced by any of its homeomorphic images such as the unit n-cube I^n, the closed unit n-cell $\mathrm{Cl}(E^n)$, etc., whichever might be convenient in the particular cases. In the remainder of the present section, we will give a few examples of cellular polytopes of which the simplicial polytopes are certainly the most important ones.

PROPOSITION 4.8.   *Every simplicial polytope is a cellular polytope.*

Proof.   Let P be any given simplicial polytope which is the topological realization of an abstract simplicial complex K. We will reconstruct P as a cellular polytope.

For each $n \geqslant 0$, let S_n denote the subset of K defined by $F \in S_n$ iff F consists of $n + 1$ vertices. With these as abstract cells, we will construct a cellular polytope as follows.

The 0-dimensional skeleton $P_0 = S_0$ is obviously the subspace of the simplicial polytope P consisting of all of its vertices.

Now let $n > 0$ and assume that P_{n-1} is the subspace of the simplicial polytope P which is the union all simplexes in P of dimension $< n$. To construct the n-dimensional skeleton P_n of the cellular polytope, we must first give the characteristic maps for the n-cells. For this purpose, let $F \in S_n$ and give F an arbitrary order, say,

$$F = \{v_0, v_1, \ldots, v_n\}.$$

Then let the characteristic map $\phi_F : \partial \Delta^n \to P_{n-1}$ be defined by

$$\phi_F(t) = \sum_{i=0}^{n} t_i v_i \in P_{n-1}$$

for every $t = (t_0, t_1, \ldots, t_n) \in \partial \Delta^n$. These having been given, P_n can be constructed as described at the beginning of this section.

To identify P_n with a subspace of the simplicial polytope P, let us define a function

$$h : P_n \to P$$

as follows. Let x be an arbitrary point in P_n. If $x \in P_{n-1}$, we define $h(x) = x$. If $x \notin P_{n-1}$, then there exists a unique point $(F, t) \in X_n \setminus A_n$ with

$$F \in S_n, \qquad t = (t_0, t_1, \ldots, t_n) \in \text{Int}\,(\Delta^n),$$

such that $p_n(F, t) = x$. In this case, we define

$$h(x) = \sum_{i=0}^{n} t_i v_i \in P.$$

To prove that h is continuous, let us consider the composed function

$$k = h \circ p_n : W_n \to P$$

where $p_n : W_n \to P_n$ denotes the natural projection. Since $k \mid P_{n-1}$ is the inclusion map and since

$$k(F, t) = \sum_{i=0}^{n} t_i v_i$$

for every $F = \{v_0, v_1, \ldots, v_n\} \in S_n$ and every $t = (t_0, t_1, \ldots, t_n) \in \Delta^n$, k is continuous by (II, 4.5). Hence, by (II, 6.3), h is also continuous.

Obviously, this map h sends P_n bijectively onto the subspace Q_n of P which is the union of all simplexes of P of dimension $\leqslant n$. To prove the continuity of the inverse function

$$h^{-1} : Q_n \to P_n$$

it suffices to show that the restriction

$$j_F = h^{-1} \mid \sigma_F : \sigma_F \to P_n$$

is continuous for every $F \in S_n$. For this purpose, let

$$F = \{v_0, v_1, \ldots, v_n\} \in S_n$$

and consider the homeomorphism $g_F : \sigma_F \to \Delta^n$ defined by

$$g_F(f) = (f(v_0), f(v_1), \ldots, f(v_n))$$

for every $f \in \sigma_F$. Then we have

$$j_F(f) = p_n(F, g_F(f))$$

for each $f \in \sigma_F$. This proves the continuity of j_F. Hence, h is an imbedding.

By means of this imbedding h, we identify P_n with the subspace Q_n of P which is the union of all simplexes of P of dimension $\leqslant n$. This completes the inductive construction and identification of the n-dimensional skeletons for every $n \geqslant 0$. Since the given simplicial polytope P is the topological sum

$$P = \sum_{n=0}^{\infty} P_n,$$

we have reconstructed P as a cellular polytope. ‖

In the preceding proof, we have seen that the characteristic maps of the cells of a simplicial polytope are imbeddings. In a general cellular polytope, this is usually false.

For other examples of cellular polytopes, we observe that the examples of adjunction spaces given in the previous section are cellular polytopes. As an example of infinite cellular polytopes, we will give the *infinite-dimensional real projective space* P^∞ as follows.

For each $n \geqslant 0$, let S_n be a singleton set. Then the 0-dimensional skeleton P_0 is a singleton space. For the lone 1-dimensional abstract cell S_1, we have the characteristic map

$$\phi_1 \; : \; \partial \Delta^1 \rightarrow P_0$$

which is uniquely defined. The 1-dimensional skeleton P_1 thus obtained can be identified with the unit sphere S^1 in the space R^2 of all complex numbers. To construct P_2, we will use the closed unit 2-cell Cl (E^2) in R^2 instead of the unit 2-simplex Δ^2. For the lone 2-dimensional cell S_2, let us define its characteristic map

$$\phi_2 \; : \; S^1 \rightarrow S^1$$

by taking $\phi_2(z) = z^2$ for every complex number $z \in S^1$. The 2-dimensional skeleton P_2 thus obtained is the real projective plane P^2. Next, let $n > 2$ and assume that P_{n-1} has been constructed and identified with the real projective $(n - 1)$-space P^{n-1}. To construct P_n, we will use the closed unit n-cell Cl (E^n) instead of Δ^n. For the lone n-dimensional cell S_n, let its characteristic map

$$\phi_n \; : \; S^{n-1} \rightarrow P^{n-1}$$

be obtained by identifying antipodal points of S^{n-1}. The P_n thus obtained is the real projective n-space P^n. This completes the inductive construction of the n-dimensional skeleton P_n for each $n \geqslant 0$. The cellular polytope thus obtained is called the *infinite-dimensional real projective space* P^∞. Also, note that S^1 is homeomorphic to the real projective line P^1 and that the singleton space P_0 can be considered as the 0-dimensional real projective space P^0.

EXERCISES

4A. Represent the n-sphere S^n, $n > 0$, as a cellular polytope with one 0-cell and one n-cell.

4B. Represent the Möbius strip as a cellular polytope with two 0-cells, three 1-cells, and one 2-cell.

4C. Represent the torus surface and the Klein bottle both as cellular polytopes with one 0-cell, two 1-cells, and one 2-cell, but with different characteristic maps for the 2-cell.

4D. Show by examples that two different cellular polytopes may be homeomorphic.

5. PROPERTIES OF CELLULAR POLYTOPES

Let P be an arbitrary cellular polytope constructed as in the preceding section. We will use the notations introduced there.

By a *subpolytope* of the cellular polytope P, we mean a subspace Q of P such that, for every ξ, the closed cell s_ξ is contained in Q iff the open cell e_ξ meets Q. Hence, Q is a union of open cells and is also the union of the corresponding closed cells.

The following two propositions are obvious.

PROPOSITION 5.1. *Every subpolytope Q of a cellular polytope P is a cellular polytope, with those $\xi \in S_n$ such that $s_\xi \subset Q$ as its abstract n-cells, with $Q_{n-1} = Q \cap P_{n-1}$, and with essentially the same characteristic maps as in P.*

PROPOSITION 5.2. *Both the union and the intersection of any given family of subpolytopes of P are subpolytopes of P.*

For examples, both $\square$ and P are subpolytopes of P. Besides, for each $n \geqslant 0$, the n-dimensional skeleton P_n of P is a subpolytope of P.

Let X be any set in P. By (5.2), the intersection of all subpolytopes of P containing X is a subpolytope $C(X)$ of P which will be called the *cellular carrier* of X in P. In fact, $C(X)$ is the smallest subpolytope of P containing X.

A subpolytope Q of P is said to be *finite* iff it is the union of a finite number of open cells of P; otherwise, it is said to be *infinite*. By a *countable subpolytope* of P, we mean one which is either finite or countably infinite.

THEOREM 5.3. *The cellular carrier $C(X)$ of a compact set X in a cellular polytope P is finite.*

Proof. Let us prove inductively that $C(X)$ is finite if $X \subset P_n$. For $n = 0$, this assertion is obvious since P_0 is discrete. Now let $q > 0$ and assume our assertion for $n = q - 1$. Let X be any compact set in P_q. For every open cell e_ξ in P_q which meets X, choose a point $x_\xi \in X \cap e_\xi$. Let A denote the subset of X which consists of these x_ξ's. Let B be any subset of A. Let e_η be any open cell in P_q. Then its boundary ∂e_η is a compact set in P_{q-1} and hence, by our inductive hypothesis, $C(\partial e_\eta)$ is finite. Since

$$C(s_\eta) = C(\partial e_\eta) \cup e_\eta$$

for the closed cell s_η, $C(s_\eta)$ is also finite. This implies that $B \cap s_\eta$

contains at most a finite number of points and hence is closed in s_η. Because of the Whitehead topology in P_q, B is closed in P_q and also in A. Since B is an arbitrary subset of A, this implies that A is discrete. On the other hand, if we take $B = A$, we deduce that A is closed in P_q and also in X. Since X is compact, this implies that A is compact. Since A is both discrete and compact, it follows that A is finite. Hence X meets only a finite number of open cells e_ξ of P_q. Now $C(X)$ is clearly the union of the following finite family

$$\{C(e_\xi) \mid X \cap e_\xi \neq \Box\}$$

of finite subpolytopes $C(e_\xi) = C(s_\xi)$. Hence $C(X)$ is finite. This completes our inductive proof.

Now, let us prove the theorem. Let X be any compact set in P. For every open cell e_ξ of P which meets X, choose a point $x_\xi \in X \cap e_\xi$. By using the auxiliary assertion proved above, one can prove by a similar method that the set

$$A = \{x_\xi \mid X \cap e_\xi \neq \Box\}$$

is finite and therefore $C(X)$ is a finite subpolytope of P. $\|$

COROLLARY 5.4. *A cellular polytope P is compact iff P is finite.*

COROLLARY 5.5. *For every open cell e_ξ of a cellular polytope P, the carrier $C(e_\xi)$ is finite.*

Because of (5.5), cellular polytopes are said to be *closure-finite*. In fact, cellular polytopes are usually called CW-*complexes*, where C stands for closure-finiteness and W stands for Whitehead (or weak) topology.

COROLLARY 5.6. *Every subpolytope Q of a cellular polytope P is a closed subspace of P.*

Proof. Let s_ξ be any closed cell in P. Since $s_\xi \subset C(e_\xi)$, we have

$$Q \cap s_\xi = Q \cap C(e_\xi) \cap s_\xi.$$

Since $Q \cap C(e_\xi)$ is finite by (5.5), it is compact by (5.4). Hence $Q \cap s_\xi$ is closed in s_ξ. By the Whitehead topology in P, this implies that Q is closed in P. $\|$

COROLLARY 5.7. *A set U of a cellular polytope P is open iff $U \cap Q$ is open in Q for every finite subpolytope Q of P.*

Proof. The necessity is obvious. To prove the sufficiency, assume that the condition holds for a set $U \subset P$. Let s_ξ be any closed cell of P. Then $C(e_\xi)$ is a finite subpolytope of P and hence $U \cap C(e_\xi)$ is open in $C(e_\xi)$. Since $s_\xi \subset C(e_\xi)$, this implies that $U \cap s_\xi$ is open in s_ξ. Therefore, U is open in P by (4.6). ||

A cellular polytope P is said to be *locally finite* iff every point $x \in P$ has a neighborhood U which meets only a finite number of open cells of P. In this case, the cellular carrier $C(U)$ of U is a finite subpolytope of P and is also a neighborhood of x in P. Hence, P is locally finite iff every point of P has a neighborhood which is a finite subpolytope of P.

PROPOSITION 5.8. *A cellular polytope P is locally compact iff it is locally finite.*

Proof: Necessity. Assume P to be locally compact and let $x \in P$. Then x has a compact neighborhood X in P. By (5.3), X meets only a finite number of open cells of P. Hence, P is locally finite.

Sufficiency. Assume P to be locally finite and let $x \in P$. Then x has a neighborhood Q in P which is a finite subpolytope of P. By (5.4), Q is compact. Hence, P is locally compact. ||

The points of the 0-dimensional skeleton P_0 of a cellular polytope P are called the *vertices* of P. We define an equivalence relation W in P_0 as follows. Let u and v be any two vertices of P. We define $u \sim v$ iff there is a finite sequence of vertices

$$u = x_0, x_1, \ldots, x_n = v$$

in P such that, for each $i = 1, \ldots, n$, there is a closed 1-cell s_i of P which contains both x_{i-1} and x_i. Let

$$M = P_0/\sim$$

denote the quotient set of all equivalence classes.

THEOREM 5.9. *The components of any cellular polytope P are pathwise connected subpolytopes and are in a 1–1 correspondence with the equivalence classes M of the vertices of P given by the inclusion $\mu \subset C_\mu$ for each $\mu \in M$.*

Proof. By the definition of $\sim$, the vertices in any closed 1-cell s_ξ of P are contained in an equivalence class. Hence, for each $\mu \in M$, we may define a subspace C_μ^1 of P_1 which is the union of the set μ of vertices and the open 1-cells e_ξ such that $\phi_\xi(\partial \Delta^1)$ is contained in μ. Hence

$$\gamma_1 = \{C_\mu^1 \mid \mu \in M\}$$

is a disjoint family of nonempty subpolytopes of P_1 covering P_1. Hence, each C_μ^1 is both open and closed in P_1.

Next, let $n > 1$ and assume that we have constructed a disjoint family

$$\gamma_{n-1} = \{C_\mu^{n-1} \mid \mu \in M\}$$

of nonempty subpolytopes of P_{n-1} covering P_{n-1}. Then, each C_μ^{n-1} is both open and closed in P_{n-1}. For each open n-cell e_ξ of P, the boundary $\partial e_\xi = \phi_\xi(\partial \Delta^n)$ is a connected set in P_{n-1} and hence must be contained in some C_μ^{n-1}. For each $\mu \in M$, we define C_μ^n to be the union of C_μ^{n-1} and the open n-cells e_ξ such that ∂e_ξ is contained in C_μ^{n-1}. Hence,

$$\gamma_n = \{C_\mu^n \mid \mu \in M\}$$

is a disjoint family of nonempty subpolytopes of P_n covering P_n. Therefore, each C_μ^n is both open and closed in P_n.

Thus, we have completed the inductive construction of the sequence

$$\gamma_1, \gamma_2, \cdots, \gamma_{n-1}, \gamma_n, \cdots.$$

By definition, we have

$$\mu \subset C_\mu^1 \subset C_\mu^2 \subset \cdots \subset C_\mu^{n-1} \subset C_\mu^n \subset \cdots$$

for every $\mu \in M$. Now, let

$$C_\mu = \bigcup_{n=1}^{\infty} C_\mu^n$$

for each $\mu \in M$. By (5.2), each C_μ is a subpolytope of P. Since each γ_n is disjoint, it is obvious that the family

$$\gamma = \{C_\mu \mid \mu \in M\}$$

is also disjoint. This implies that each C_μ is both open and closed in P. Besides, we have $\mu \subset C_\mu$ for every $\mu \in M$.

It remains to prove that each member C_μ in the family γ is pathwise connected.

For this purpose, let us first prove by induction that C_μ^n is pathwise connected for every $n \geq 1$. For $n = 1$, this is obvious from the definition of the equivalence relation $\sim$ in P_0. Now, let $n > 1$ and assume that C_μ^{n-1} is pathwise connected. Let x be any point of C_μ^n which is not in C_μ^{n-1}. Then x must belong to an open n-cell e_ξ in C_μ^n. Hence, there is a unique point $t = (t_0, t_1, \ldots, t_n)$ in Int (Δ^n) such that

$$x = \phi_\xi^*(t) = p_n(\xi, t).$$

Define a path $\pi : I \to C_\mu^n$ by taking

$$\pi(s) = \phi_\xi^*[s + (1-s)t_0, (1-s)t_1, \ldots, (1-s)t_n]$$

for every $s \in I$. Then $\pi(0) = x$ and $\pi(1) \in \partial e_\xi \subset C_\mu{}^{n-1}$. This implies that $C_\mu{}^n$ is pathwise connected.

Finally, let x and y be any two points in C_μ. Then there exists an n such that $C_\mu{}^n$ contains both x and y. Since $C_\mu{}^n$ is pathwise connected, x and y can be connected by a path in $C_\mu{}^n$ and hence in C_μ. This proves that each C_μ is pathwise connected. $\|$

COROLLARY 5.10. *For an arbitrary cellular polytope P, the following statements are equivalent:*

(a) *P is connected.*

(b) *P_1 is connected.*

(c) *For any two vertices u and v of P, we have $u \sim v$.*

(d) *P_1 is pathwise connected.*

(e) *P is pathwise connected.*

COROLLARY 5.11. *The cellular carrier $C(X)$ of a connected set X in a cellular polytope P is connected.*

Now let us consider the topological sum

$$X = \sum_{n=0}^{\infty} X_n$$

of the disjoint spaces $X_n = S_n \times \Delta^n$. Define a map

$$p : X \to P$$

by taking $p(x) = p_n(x)$ for each $x \in X_n$ and every $n \geq 0$. Since each P_n sends X_n onto P_n, it follows that p is surjective. This map p will be called the *natural projection* of X onto P.

PROPOSITION 5.12. *The natural projection $p : X \to P$ is an identification.*

Proof. Let U be any set in P such that the inverse image

$$V = p^{-1}(U)$$

is open in X. Since

$$p_n{}^{-1}(U \cap P_n) = V \cap X_n$$

is open in X_n, it follows that $U \cap P_n$ is open in P_n for every $n \geq 0$. Since P is the topological sum of all P_n, this implies that U is open in P. By the definition of identifications in (II, §6), p is an identification. $\|$

Define an equivalence relation $\sim$ in X as follows. Let a and b be any two points in X. Then $a \sim b$ iff $p(a) = p(b)$. The equivalence classes in X are precisely the inverse image $p^{-1}(y)$ for all $y \in P$. Let

$$Q = X/\sim$$

denote the quotient space of X over this equivalence relation $\sim$. Since $p : X \to P$ is an identification, the assignment $y \to p^{-1}(y)$ defines a homeomorphism

$$h : P \to Q$$

of the given cellular polytope P onto the quotient space Q. Because of this, P can be identified with Q as a quotient space of X.

PROPOSITION 5.13. *If the cellular polytope P is locally finite, then the natural projection $p : X \to P$ is closed and the inverse image $p^{-1}(y)$ is compact for every point $y \in P$.*

Proof. Let y be an arbitrary point in P. Since P is locally finite, there exists an open neighborhood V of y in P which meets only a finite number of open cells of P. By the continuity of p, the inverse image $U = p^{-1}(V)$ is an open set of X. For each $n \geqslant 0$ and every $\xi \in S_n$, the intersection

$$U_\xi = U \cap (\xi \times \Delta^n)$$

is open in $\xi \times \Delta^n$. Hence, either U_ξ is empty or U_ξ meets $\xi \times \text{Int} (\Delta^n)$. Since p sends $\xi \times \text{Int} (\Delta^n)$ onto the open cell e_ξ, it follows that $U_\xi = \square$ unless V meets e_ξ. This implies that only a finite number of the U_ξ's are nonempty.

Next, let us consider the inverse image $J = p^{-1}(y)$ in X. Then J is a closed set in X. For each $n \geqslant 0$ and each $\xi \in S_n$, the intersection

$$J_\xi = J \cap (\xi \times \Delta^n)$$

is a closed set of the compact space $\xi \times \Delta^n$ and hence is compact. Since $y \in V$, we have $J_\xi \subset U_\xi$. Hence, only a finite number of the J_ξ's are nonempty. This implies that

$$p^{-1}(y) = J = \bigcup_\xi J_\xi$$

is compact.

It remains to prove that p is a closed map. For this purpose, let F be any closed set in X and assume that y is a point of the closure $\text{Cl} (G)$ of the image $G = p(F)$ in P. Since P is a normal Hausdorff space by (4.3), P is regular and hence there is a closed neighborhood M of y contained in V. Let

$$H = G \cap M \subset V.$$

Since M is a neighborhood of y in P, it follows that

$$y \in \mathrm{Cl}\,(H).$$

For each $n \geqslant 0$ and every $\xi \in S_n$, let

$$F_\xi \;=\; F \cap (\xi \times \Delta^n), \qquad G_\xi \;=\; p(F_\xi).$$

Since F is closed and $\xi \times \Delta^n$ is compact, F_ξ and G_ξ are both compact. Since $U_\xi \neq \square$ for only a finite number of the ξ's, it follows that only a finite number of the G_ξ's meet V. Let E denote the union of all sets G_ξ meeting V. Then E is compact and

$$H \;=\; G \cap M \;=\; E \cap M.$$

Since M is closed, this implies that H is compact and hence is closed in the Hausdorff space P. Therefore, we have

$$y \in \mathrm{Cl}\,(H) \;=\; H \subset G.$$

This proves that G is closed and so is the natural projection p. ||

THEOREM 5.14. *Every locally finite cellular polytope is metrizable.*

Proof. Let P be any locally finite cellular polytope. Then, by (5.13), the natural projection $p : X \to P$ is a closed identification and the inverse image $p^{-1}(y)$ in X is compact for every $y \in P$. As topological sum of the disjoint metrizable spaces $\xi \times \Delta^n$, the space X is a metrizable space. Hence, by (III, Ex. 8G), P is metrizable. ||

EXERCISES

5A. Prove that every cellular polytope is paracompact and completely normal. [Morita 1 and Tsuda 1.]

5B. Prove that every component of a locally finite cellular polytope is a countable subpolytope. Hence, every locally finite connected cellular polytope is a separable metrizable space.

5C. Prove that a cellular polytope P is not metrizable if there exists a point $y \in P$ such that the inverse image $p^{-1}(y)$ under the natural projection $p : X \to P$ meets infinitely many of the sets $\xi \times \Delta^n$.

5D. Prove that the quotient space M obtained from a cellular polytope P by collapsing a subpolytope Q to a point is a cellular polytope.

5E. A cellular polytope P is said to be *finite-dimensional* iff there exists an $n \geqslant 0$ such that $P_n = P$. In this case, the *dimension* dim (P)

of P is defined to be the smallest integer n with $P_n = P$. Prove that $\dim (P_n) \leqslant n$. Deduce paracompactness and complete normality of a finite-dimensional cellular polytope P from Exercise 3G.

6. PRODUCT OF CELLULAR POLYTOPES

In the present section we are concerned with the topological product of two cellular polytopes with application to homotopy. The following lemma will be needed in the proof of the basic theorem.

Let us consider any two identifications

$$f \ : \ X \to P, \qquad g \ : \ Y \to Q$$

of the spaces X and Y onto the spaces P and Q respectively, as defined in (II, § 6). Then the topological product

$$h \ = \ f \times g \ : \ X \times Y \to P \times Q$$

is defined in (II, § 5) by $h(x, y) = (f(x), g(y))$ for every $x \in X$ and every $y \in Y$. This map h is obviously surjective.

LEMMA 6.1. *The topological product $h = f \times g$ of two identifications $f : X \to P$ and $g : Y \to Q$ is an identification if, for every open set W in Q and every $y \in g^{-1}(W)$, there exists an open set V in Q such that $y \in g^{-1}(V)$ and that $\mathrm{Cl}\,[g^{-1}(V)]$ is compact and is contained in $g^{-1}(W)$.*

Proof. Let M be any set in $P \times Q$ such that $h^{-1}(M)$ is open in $X \times Y$. It suffices to prove that M is open in $P \times Q$.

For this purpose, let (p_0, q_0) be an arbitrary point in M. Choose arbitrary points $x_0 \in f^{-1}(p_0)$ and $y_0 \in g^{-1}(q_0)$. Since $h^{-1}(M)$ is open in $X \times Y$, there is an open set G in Y such that

$$x_0 \times G \ = \ (x_0 \times Y) \cap h^{-1}(M).$$

Let $W = g(G)$ and $y_1 \in g^{-1}(W)$. Then $g(y_1)$ is in $g(G)$ and hence there exists a point $y_2 \in G$ such that $g(y_1) = g(y_2)$. Thus, we have

$$h(x_0, y_1) \ = \ (f(x_0), g(y_1)) \ = \ (f(x_0), g(y_2)) \ = \ h(x_0, y_2) \ \in \ M.$$

This implies that $G = g^{-1}(W)$ and hence W is an open set of Q.

By our assumption about the map g, there exists an open set V in Q such that $y_0 \in g^{-1}(V)$ and that the set

$$C \ = \ \mathrm{Cl}\,[g^{-1}(V)]$$

is compact and is contained in G. Let F denote the set in X consisting of all points $x \in X$ such that $x \times C$ is contained in $h^{-1}(M)$. Then we have

$$x_0 \in F, \quad F \times C \subset h^{-1}(M).$$

To prove that F is open in X, let $x \in F$. Then we have $x \times C \subset h^{-1}(M)$. Since C is compact and $h^{-1}(M)$ is open, it follows from (III, Ex. 2D) that there exists an open neighborhood H of x in X with $H \times C \subset h^{-1}(M)$. Hence $H \subset F$. This proves that F is open.

Now let $U = f(F)$ and $x_1 \in f^{-1}(U)$. Then $f(x_1)$ is in $U = f(F)$ and hence there exists a point $x_2 \in F$ such that $f(x_1) = f(x_2)$. For every $y \in C$, we have

$$h(x_1, y) = (f(x_1), g(y)) = (f(x_2), g(y)) = h(x_2, y) \in M.$$

This implies that $x_1 \in F$. Therefore, $f^{-1}(U) = F$. Since f is an identification and F is open in X, it follows that U is an open set in P.

Since $p_0 = f(x_0) \in U$ and $q_0 = g(y_0) \in V$, we have

$$(p_0, q_0) \in U \times V.$$

On the other hand, since $F \times C \subset h^{-1}(M)$, we obtain

$$U \times V \subset f(F) \times g(C) = h(F \times C) \subset M.$$

This proves that M is an open set of the topological product $P \times Q$. $\|$

Obviously, (6.1) still holds if the roles played by the identifications f and g are interchanged.

Now let us consider two cellular polytopes P and Q with abstract cells

$$\{S_m \mid m = 0, 1, \ldots\}, \quad \{T_n \mid n = 0, 1, \ldots\}$$

respectively and with natural projections

$$p : X \to P, \quad q : Y \to Q$$

where X is the topological sum of the disjoint spaces $X_m = S_m \times \Delta^m$ and Y is the topological sum of the disjoint spaces $Y_n = T_n \times \Delta^n$. By (5.12), p and q are identifications.

LEMMA 6.2. *If at least one of the cellular polytopes P and Q is locally finite, then the topological product*

$$r = p \times q : X \times Y \to P \times Q$$

is an identification.

Proof. Without loss of generality, let us assume that Q is locally finite.

Let W be any open set in Q and let y be any point in $q^{-1}(W)$. Denote $z = q(y) \in W$. Since Q is locally finite, there exists an open neighborhood $U \subset W$ of z in Q which meets only a finite number of open cells of Q. As a normal Hausdorff space, Q is regular. Hence, there exists an open neighborhood V of z in Q such that $\text{Cl}(V) \subset U$.

As in the proof of (5.13), the inverse image $q^{-1}(U)$ in Y meets only a finite number of the sets $\eta \times \Delta^n$. Hence, as the union of a finite number of compact sets, the set $q^{-1}[\text{Cl}(V)]$ in Y is compact. Since

$$\text{Cl}\,[q^{-1}(V)] \subset q^{-1}\,[\text{Cl}\,(V)],$$

it follows that $\text{Cl}\,[q^{-1}(V)]$ is compact.

Since $\text{Cl}(V) \subset U \subset W$, we obtain that $\text{Cl}\,[q^{-1}(V)]$ is contained in $q^{-1}(W)$.

Therefore, by (6.1), $r = p \times q$ is an identification. $||$

THEOREM 6.3. *If at least one of the cellular polytopes P and Q is locally finite, then the topological product $P \times Q$ is a cellular polytope which has the following structure:*

(a) *The open k-cells of $P \times Q$ are the topological products $e_\xi \times e_\eta$ with $\xi \in S_m$, $\eta \in S_n$, and $m + n = k$ for each $k \geqslant 0$.*

(b) *The closed cell corresponding to the open cell $e_\xi \times e_\eta$ is the topological product $s_\xi \times s_\eta$ of closed cells.*

(c) *The boundary of the open cell $e_\xi \times e_\eta$ is the set*

$$\partial(e_\xi \times e_\eta) = (\partial e_\xi \times e_\eta) \cup (e_\xi \times \partial e_\eta).$$

Proof. Let us construct a cellular polytope R as follows.

For each $k \geqslant 0$, the set U_k of all abstract k-cells of R is defined to be the union of all $S_m \times T_n$ with $m + n = k$. Then we have

$$R_0 = U_0 = S_0 \times T_0 = P_0 \times Q_0 \subset P \times Q.$$

Let $k > 1$ and assume that R_{k-1} has been constructed and identified with the subspace of $P \times Q$ which is the union of all $P_m \times Q_n$ with $m + n \leqslant k - 1$. Hence, R_{k-1} is the union of all $e_\xi \times e_\eta$ such that

$$\xi \in S_m, \qquad \eta \in T_n, \qquad m + n < k.$$

To construct R_k, let us consider any abstract k-cell $\xi \times \eta \in U_k$, where $\xi \in S_m$, $\eta \in T_n$, with $m + n = k$. Choose an arbitrary homeomorphism

$$h_{\xi \times \eta} : \Delta^k \to (\xi \times \Delta^m) \times (\eta \times \Delta^n) \subset X_m \times Y_n.$$

Then let the characteristic map

$$\phi_{\xi \times \eta} \ : \ \partial \Delta^k \to R_{k-1}$$

for the abstract k-cell $\xi \times \eta$ be defined by

$$\phi_{\xi \times \eta}(t) \ = \ r[h_{\xi \times \eta}(t)]$$

for every $t \in \partial \Delta^k$. Let

$$Z_k \ = \ U_k \times \Delta^k, \qquad C_k \ = \ U_k \times (\partial \Delta^k);$$

and define a map $g_k : C_k \to R_{k-1}$ by taking

$$g_k(\xi \times \eta, t) \ = \ \phi_{\xi \times \eta}(t)$$

for every $\xi \times \eta \in U_k$ and each $t \in \partial \Delta^k$. Then R_k is the adjunction space obtained by adjoining Z_k to R_{k-1} by means of the map g_k. Since r is an identification and since each $h_{\xi \times \eta}$ is a homeomorphism, one can easily see that R_k can be identified with the subspace of $P \times Q$ which is the union of all $P_m \times Q_n$ with $m + n \leqslant k$. This completes the inductive construction of the k-dimensional skeleton R_k for all $k \geqslant 0$.

From the preceding construction of R_k, we observe that (a), (b), and (c) hold.

Finally, since $P \times Q$ is the union of all R_k with $k \geqslant 0$ and since $r = p \times q$ is an identification, it follows easily that $P \times Q$ is the topological sum

$$P \times Q \ = \ \sum_{k=0}^{\infty} R_k.$$

Hence, $P \times Q$ is a cellular polytope with cells described by (a)–(c) and with $\phi_{\xi \times \eta}$'s as characteristic maps. ||

In particular, if we consider the unit interval $I = [0, 1]$ as a cellular polytope with closed cells $s_0 = \{0\}$, $s_1 = \{1\}$, and $s_I = I$, we have the following

COROLLARY 6.4.   *The topological product $P \times I$ of a cellular polytope P and the closed unit interval I is a cellular polytope. For each $n \geqslant 0$, the closed n-cells of $P \times I$ are:*

$$s_\xi \times \{0\}, \qquad s_\xi \times \{1\}, \qquad (\xi \in S_n);$$

and

$$s_\eta \times I, \qquad (\eta \in S_{n-1} \text{ in case } n > 0).$$

Now let us turn to the application of (6.4) to homotopy.

THEOREM 6.5.   *A family $\{h_t : P \to Y \mid t \in I\}$ of maps of a cellular polytope P*

into a space Y is a homotopy iff, for every closed cell s_ξ of P, the restricted family $\{h_t \mid s_\xi\}$ is a homotopy from s_ξ into Y.

Proof. Since the necessity of the condition is obvious, it remains to establish the sufficiency.

Define a function $H : P \times I \to Y$ by taking

$$H(x, t) = h_t(x)$$

for every $x \in P$ and each $t \in I$. Then it remains to prove the continuity of H.

Consider a closed cell of $P \times I$. If it is of the form $s_\xi \times I$, where s_ξ is a closed cell of P, the restriction

$$H \mid s_\xi \times I$$

is continuous because of the condition that $\{h_t \mid s_\xi\}$ is a homotopy. If it is of the form $s_\xi \times \{0\}$ or $s_\xi \times \{1\}$, the restriction of H to this closed cell is also continuous since it is a subspace of $s_\xi \times I$. Hence, by (4.7), H is continuous. ‖

The properties (4.7) and (6.5) show the usefulness of cellular polytopes. In fact, the problem of continuity and homotopy is localized to closed cells.

We will conclude this chapter by the following theorem on the *homotopy extension property* of cellular polytopes. Other properties can be found in the exercises.

THEOREM 6.6. *Let $f : P \to Y$ be a given map of a cellular polytope P into a space Y and let $\{g_t : Q \to Y \mid t \in I\}$ be any homotopy defined on a sub-polytope Q of P satisfying the condition $g_0 = f \mid Q$. Then there exists a homotopy $\{h_t : P \to Y \mid t \in I\}$ such that $h_0 = f$ and*

$$h_t \mid Q = g_t, \qquad (t \in I).$$

Proof. For each $n \geqslant 0$, consider the subpolytope

$$K_n = Q \cup P_n$$

of P, where P_n denotes the n-dimensional skeleton of P. We will construct by induction on n a sequence

$$\{h_t^n : K_n \to Y \mid t \in I\}, \qquad (n = 0, 1, 2, \ldots)$$

of homotopies satisfying the conditions:

(a) $h_0^n = f \mid K_n$ for every $n \geqslant 0$,

(b) $h_t^n \mid Q = g_t$ for every $n \geqslant 0$ and each $t \in I$,

(c) $h_t^n \mid K_{n-1} = h_t^{n-1}$ for every $n > 0$ and each $t \in I$.

For $n = 0$, we simply define $h_t{}^0$ by taking

$$h_t{}^0(x) = \begin{cases} g_t(x), & (\text{if } x \in Q), \\ f(x), & (\text{if } x \in K_0 \setminus Q), \end{cases}$$

for every $t \in I$. Then the conditions (a) and (b) are satisfied. By (6.5), the family $\{h_t{}^0 \mid t \in I\}$ is a homotopy.

Now, let $n > 0$ and assume that the homotopy $\{h_t{}^{n-1} \mid t \in I\}$ has been constructed. We will construct $h_t{}^n$ as follows.

Consider an arbitrary open n-cell of P not in the subpolytope Q. By (II, Ex. 5H), the subspace

$$T_\xi = (\xi \times \Delta^n \times \{0\}) \cup (\xi \times \partial\Delta^n \times I)$$

of the topological product $S_\xi = \xi \times \Delta^n \times I$ is a retract of S_ξ. Let $r_\xi : S_\xi \supset T_\xi$ be any retraction of S_ξ onto T_ξ.

Define a map $\psi_\xi : T_\xi \to Y$ by taking

$$\psi_\xi(\xi, x, t) = \begin{cases} h_t{}^{n-1}[p(\xi, x)], & (\text{if } x \in \partial\Delta^n, t \in I), \\ f[p(\xi, x)], & (\text{if } x \in \Delta^n, t = 0), \end{cases}$$

where $p : X \to P$ stands for the natural projection. The continuity of ψ_ξ can be verified by (II, 4.3). Then ψ_ξ has an extension

$$\psi_\xi{}^* = \psi_\xi \circ r_\xi : S_\xi \to Y.$$

Next, define a function $\theta_\xi : s_\xi \times I \to Y$, where s_ξ denotes the closed n-cell Cl (e_ξ) in P as follows. Let $x \in s_\xi$ and $t \in I$. If $x \in \partial s_\xi$, we define $\theta_\xi(x, t) = h_t{}^{n-1}(x)$. If $x \in e_\xi$, there exists a unique point w in Int (Δ^n) such that $p(\xi, w) = x$; in this case, we define

$$\theta_\xi(x, t) = \psi_\xi{}^*(\xi, w, t).$$

To establish the continuity of θ_ξ, let us consider the topological product

$$\rho_\xi = (p \mid \xi \times \Delta^n) \times i : \xi \times \Delta^n \times I \to s_\xi \times I,$$

where $i : I \to I$ denotes the identity map. By (6.1), ρ_ξ is an identification. Since

$$\theta_\xi \circ \rho_\xi = \psi_\xi{}^* : \xi \times \Delta^n \times I \to Y$$

and $\psi_\xi{}^*$ is continuous, it follows from (II, 6.3) that θ_ξ is continuous.

Assume that θ_ξ has been constructed for every closed n-cell s_ξ of P not in Q. Then we may define $h_t{}^n$ by taking

$$h_t{}^n(x) = \begin{cases} h_t{}^{n-1}(x), & (\text{if } x \in K_{n-1}, t \in I), \\ \theta_\xi(x, t), & (\text{if } x \in s_\xi, t \in I). \end{cases}$$

By the construction of θ_ξ, we have

$$\theta_\xi(x, t) = h_t^{n-1}(x), \qquad (x \in \partial s_\xi).$$

Hence h_t^n is well-defined. By (6.5), $\{h_t \mid t \in I\}$ is a homotopy. From our construction, it is clear that the conditions (a)–(c) are satisfied. This completes the inductive construction of the sequence

$$\{h_t^n : K_n \to Y \mid t \in I\}, \qquad (n = 0, 1, 2, \ldots).$$

Finally, define $\{h_t : P \to Y \mid t \in I\}$ by taking $h_t(x) = h_t^n(x)$ if $x \in K_n$. It is well-defined since P is the union of all K_n and since the condition (c) holds for all $n > 0$. According to (6.5), $\{h_t \mid t \in I\}$ is a homotopy. By the conditions (a) and (b), we have $h_0 = f$ and $h_t \mid Q = g_t$ for every $t \in I$. $\ \| $

EXERCISES

6A. Prove that the cone Con (P) over a cellular polytope P is a cellular polytope.

6B. Prove that the suspension $S(P)$ of a cellular polytope P as defined in (II, Ex. 6H) is a cellular polytope.

6C. By a *cellular map*, we mean a map $f : P \to Q$ from a cellular polytope P into a cellular polytope Q such that $f(P_n) \subset Q_n$ for every $n \geqslant 0$. Prove that every map $f : P \to Q$ is homotopic to a cellular map. [Whitehead 1.]

6D. By a *cellular homotopy*, we mean a homotopy $\{h_t : P \to Q \mid t \in I\}$ from a cellular polytope P into a cellular polytope Q such that the map $H : P \times I \to Q$ is cellular. Prove that, if two cellular maps $f, g : P \to Q$ are homotopic, then there exists a cellular homotopy $\{h_t : P \to Q \mid t \in I\}$ such that $h_0 = f$ and $h_1 = g$. [Whitehead 1.]

6E. Prove that the mapping cylinder Cyl (f) and the mapping cone Con (f) of a cellular map $f : P \to Q$ are cellular polytopes.

6F. Prove that the adjunction space Z obtained by adjoining a cellular polytope X to a cellular polytope Y by means of a cellular map $f : A \to Y$ defined on a subpolytope A of X is a cellular polytope.

6G. Prove that every cellular polytope P is locally contractible. In fact, every neighborhood U of any point $x \in P$ contains a contractible neighborhood V of x. [Whitehead 1.]

Chapter V: SPACES OF MAPS

Various spaces of maps have been playing increasingly important roles in modern topology. The present chapter is devoted to an expository account of these spaces. The compact-open topology is predominantly preferred, although other topologies will be also defined and compared with it. Our effort will be mostly centered on two questions frequently confronted in topological applications, namely, the continuity of the evaluation and maps on topological products. Finally, we will specialize to the important particular case where the domain of the maps is the closed unit interval.

1. THE SPACE Map (X, Y)

Let X and Y be arbitrarily given spaces and consider the set

$$\Omega = \text{Map } (X, Y)$$

of all maps $f: X \to Y$ from X into Y. There are various ways of topologizing this set Ω. In this section, we will mention only two of these.

First, since every map is also a function, the set Map (X, Y) is contained in the Cartesian power

$$\Phi = Y^X$$

which is defined in (I, § 3) to be the set of all functions from X into Y. Since Y is given as a space, the set Φ is topologized in (II, § 5) and becomes a space called the topological power. The relative topology of Ω inherited from Φ as a subspace of Φ is called the *pointwise topology* π *in* Ω.

The pointwise topology π in Ω can be precisely described as follows. For each point $x \in X$ and every open set $U \subset Y$, let

$$E(x, U) = \{f \in \Phi \mid f(x) \in U\},$$
$$M(x, U) = \{f \in \Omega \mid f(x) \in U\}.$$

By the definition of the topological power Φ, the totality of the sets $E(x, U)$ form a sub-basis of the topology in Φ. Since

$$M(x, U) \;=\; \Omega \cap E(x, U),$$

the totality of the sets $M(x, U)$ form a sub-basis of the pointwise topology π in Ω.

Now, for each finite set F in X and every open set U in Y, consider the set

$$M(F, U) \;=\; \{f \in \Omega \,|\, f(F) \subset U\}$$
$$=\; \bigcap_{x \in F} M(x, U).$$

Since F is finite, $M(F, U) \in \pi$. Thus, the collection of all of these sets $M(F, U)$ is a larger sub-basis of the topology π. Because of this, the topology π of Ω can also be called the *finite-open topology* of Ω.

We observe that, in the definition of the pointwise topology π of Ω, the topology in the space X is not used. Because of this, we will not be surprised if this topology turns out to be unsatisfactory in case X is not discrete. In fact, π contains too few open sets to assure the continuity of some important function, as will be shown in the sequel.

Let us now introduce the more satisfactory *compact-open topology* κ of

$$\Omega \;=\; \text{Map } (X, Y).$$

For any two sets $K \subset X$ and $U \subset Y$, let $M(K, U)$ denote the subset of Ω defined by

$$M(K, U) \;=\; \{f \in \Omega \,|\, f(K) \subset U\}.$$

This set $M(K, U)$ will be called a *sub-basic set* of Ω iff K is compact and U is open. The compact-open topology κ of Ω is defined to be the smallest topology in Ω containing all sub-basic sets. Then the sub-basic sets of Ω form a sub-basis of κ and every set in κ is the union of a collection of finite intersections of sub-basic sets.

Since every finite set is compact, it follows that κ contains π. If X is a discrete space, then $\kappa = \pi$.

Throughout the present chapter, we will denote by Ω_τ the space obtained by topologizing Ω with a topology τ.

In the remainder of this section, we are concerned with a few elementary properties of the space Ω_κ.

PROPOSITION 1.1. *If Y is a Fréchet, Hausdorff, or regular space, then so is Ω_κ.*

Proof. Let f and g be any two distinct maps in Ω; then there exists a point $x \in X$ such that

$$f(x) \neq g(x).$$

If Y is a Fréchet space, then there is an open neighborhood W of $f(x)$ which excludes $g(x)$. The sub-basic open set $M(x, W)$ contains f but excludes g. Hence Ω_κ is a Fréchet space. If Y is a Hausdorff space, then there are two disjoint open sets U and V in Y such that $f(x) \in U$ and $g(x) \in V$. The sub-basic open sets $M(x, U)$ and $M(x, V)$ are disjoint with $f \in M(x, U)$ and $g \in M(x, V)$. Hence Ω_κ is a Hausdorff space.

Now suppose that Y is a regular space. Let $f \in \Omega_\kappa$ and assume G to be a given neighborhood of f in Ω_κ. By definition of the topology κ, there are a finite number of sub-basic sets $M(K_i, U_i), i = 1, \ldots, n$, such that

$$f \in M(K_1, U_1) \cap \cdots \cap M(K_n, U_n) \subset G.$$

As continuous image of a compact set K_i, the set $f(K_i)$ is compact for every $i = 1, \ldots, n$. Hence, by (III, 2.8), we can find open sets V_i, $i = 1, \ldots, n$, of Y such that

$$f(K_i) \subset V_i, \qquad \mathrm{Cl}\,(V_i) \subset U_i$$

for every $i = 1, \ldots, n$. Let H denote the open neighborhood of f defined by

$$H = M(K_1, V_1) \cap \cdots \cap M(K_n, V_n).$$

We will prove $\mathrm{Cl}\,(H) \subset G$. For this purpose, let $g \in \Omega_\kappa \setminus G$. Then g is not in $M(K_i, U_i)$ for some i. This implies that there is a point $x \in K_i$ such that $g(x) \notin U_i$. Let $W_i = Y \setminus \mathrm{Cl}\,(V_i)$. Then $M(x, W_i)$ is an open neighborhood of g which does not meet H. This implies that $g \notin \mathrm{Cl}\,(H)$. Hence $\mathrm{Cl}\,(H) \subset G$ and Ω_κ is regular. $||$

PROPOSITION 1.2. *Let X be a locally compact Hausdorff space. If both X and Y satisfy the second axiom of countability, so does Ω_κ.*

Proof. By hypothesis, there is a countable basis α for the open sets of X and a countable basis β for those of Y. Since X is locally compact, we may assume that, for each $U \in \alpha$, the closure $\overline{U} = \mathrm{Cl}\,(U)$ is compact. Consider the family

$$\gamma = \{M(\overline{U}, V) \mid U \in \alpha, V \in \beta\}$$

of sub-basic open sets in Ω_κ. Then γ is countable. Hence, it remains to prove that γ is a sub-basis of κ.

Assume that a sub-basic open set $M(K, W)$ of Ω_κ and a map $f \in M(K, W)$ be given. For each $x \in K$, choose a set $V_x \in \beta$ such that $f(x) \in V_x \subset W$. By (III, 2.15), X is a regular space. Hence, there is a set $U_x \in \alpha$ such that $x \in U_x$ and $f(\bar{U}_x) \subset V_x$. Since K is compact, there are a finite number of points $x_1, \ldots, x_n$ in K such that

$$K \subset U_{x_1} \cup \cdots \cup U_{x_n}.$$

Hence we have

$$f \in M(\bar{U}_{x_1}, V_{x_1}) \cap \cdots \cap M(\bar{U}_{x_n}, V_{x_n}) \subset M(K, W).$$

Since the sub-basic sets form a sub-basis of κ, this implies that γ is also a sub-basis of κ. ‖

PROPOSITION 1.3. *If X is a Hausdorff space and σ is a sub-basis for the topology of Y, then the totality of the sets $M(K, U)$, where K is a compact set in X and $U \in \sigma$, form a sub-basis for the compact-open topology κ of Ω.* [Jackson 2.]

Proof. It suffices to prove that if K is a compact set in X and U an open set in Y, and if $f \in M(K, U)$, then there exist compact sets $K_1, \ldots, K_m$ in X and members $U_1, \ldots, U_m$ of σ such that

$$f \in M(K_1, U_1) \cap \cdots \cap M(K_m, U_m) \subset M(K, U).$$

Let x be any point in K. Since $f(x)$ is a point of the open set U in Y, there are a finite number of sets in σ, say $U_1^x, \ldots, U_{n_x}^x$, such that

$$f(x) \in U_1^x \cap \cdots \cap U_{n_x}^x \subset U.$$

Since f is continuous, there is a neighborhood G_x of x in K such that

$$f(G_x) \subset U_1^x \cap \cdots \cap U_{n_x}^x.$$

As a compact Hausdorff space, K is regular. Hence there is an open neighborhood H_x of x in K such that the closure K_x of H_x is contained in G_x.

The collection $\{H_x \mid x \in K\}$ is an open cover of the compact space K and, therefore, there are a finite number of points in K, say $x_1, \ldots, x_q$, such that

$$K = H_{x_1} \cup \cdots \cup H_{x_q}.$$

In the subscripts and superscripts in the notations of the various sets involved above, we will simply replace x_j by j for every $j = 1, \ldots, q$.

Now the sets $K_1, \ldots, K_q$, as closed subsets of the compact set K, are compact. Moreover,

$$f(K_j) \subset f(G_j) \subset U_1^j \cap \cdots \cap U_{n_j}^j \subset U$$

for every $j = 1, \ldots, q$. Hence we have

$$f \in \bigcap_{j=1}^{q} [\bigcap_{i=1}^{n_j} M(K_j, U_i{}^j)].$$

Assume that $g \in \Omega$ is contained in the set on the right-hand side of the preceding formula. If $x \in K$, then x is in some H_j and hence is in K_j. Therefore, we have

$$g(x) \in U_1{}^j \cap \cdots \cap U_{n_j}{}^j \subset U.$$

This implies that $g \in M(K, U)$ and hence

$$f \in \bigcap_{j=1}^{q} [\bigcap_{i=1}^{n_j} M(K_j, U_i{}^j)] \subset M(K, U).$$

This completes the proof. ||

EXERCISES

1A. Prove that, if Y is a Fréchet, Hausdorff, or regular space, then so is Ω_π.

1B. State and prove a proposition for the pointwise topology π of Ω similar to (1.3).

1C. Show by example that Ω_π may fail to have a countable basis even when both X and Y are locally compact and satisfy the second axiom of countability.

1D. Prove that, if X is a Tychonoff space, then the set $\Omega = \text{Map } (X, R)$ is dense in the topological power R^X.

1E. Let Γ denote any given subset of $\Omega = \text{Map } (X, Y)$. For each topology τ in Ω, denote by Γ_τ the space obtained by giving Γ the relative topology in Ω_τ. Verify that a sub-basis for Γ_κ consists of all the sets $\{f \in \Gamma \mid f(K) \subset U\}$ for every compact set K in X and every open set U in Y.

2. ADMISSIBLE TOPOLOGIES

A great variety of topologies τ may be introduced into the set

$$\Omega = \text{Map } (X, Y)$$

to make it a space Ω_τ. There is a natural function

$$\omega : \Omega_\tau \times X \to Y$$

defined by $\omega(f, x) = f(x)$ for each $f \in \Omega_\tau$ and every $x \in X$. This function ω is called the *evaluation*.

A topology τ in Ω is said to be *admissible* iff the evaluation ω is continuous.

PROPOSITION 2.1. *If X is a locally compact regular space, then the compact-open topology κ of Ω is admissible; it is in fact the smallest of all admissible topologies in Ω.* [Arens 1.]

Proof. To prove the first assertion of the proposition, let $f \in \Omega$, $x \in X$, and an open set W of Y containing $f(x)$ be arbitrarily given. Since f is continuous, the inverse image $f^{-1}(W)$ in X is an open set containing x. Since X is a locally compact regular space, there exists an open neighborhood V of x such that the closure $\bar{V}$ of V is compact and is contained in $f^{-1}(W)$. Then $U = M(\bar{V}, W)$ is a sub-basic open set of Ω_κ containing f. Since $U = M(\bar{V}, W)$, it follows that the evaluation ω sends $U \times V$ into W. This proves that $\omega : \Omega_\kappa \times X \to Y$ is continuous and hence the compact-open topology κ of Ω is admissible.

For the second assertion of the proposition, we will prove that the compact-open topology κ of Ω is smaller than any other admissible topology τ of Ω without using our hypothesis on the space X. Let a sub-basic open set $M(K, W)$ of Ω_κ and a map $f \in M(K, W)$ be arbitrarily given. Since the topology τ is admissible, the evaluation

$$\omega : \Omega_\tau \times X \to Y$$

is by definition continuous. Hence, for each $x \in K$, there exists an open neighborhood V_x of x in X and an open neighborhood U_x of f in Ω_τ such that

$$\omega(U_x \times V_x) \subset W.$$

Since K is compact, there are a finite number of points $x_1, \ldots, x_n$ in K such that

$$K \subset V_{x_1} \cup \cdots \cup V_{x_n}.$$

Let U denote the open neighborhood of f in Ω_τ defined by

$$U = U_{x_1} \cap \cdots \cap U_{x_n}.$$

We will prove that $U \subset M(K, W)$. For this purpose, let $g \in U$. Then we have

$$g(K) = \omega(g \times K) \subset W.$$

This implies that $g \in M(K, W)$ and hence $U \subset M(K, W)$. Thus, we have proved that $M(K, W)$ is open in Ω_τ. Since the sub-basic sets form a sub-basis of κ, it follows that $\kappa \subset \tau$. ||

Since the hypothesis of (2.1) is not used in the proof of the second assertion, we have the following

COROLLARY 2.2. *The pointwise topology π of Ω is not admissible if it is different from the compact-open topology κ.*

In the remainder of this section we are concerned with the question whether local compactness of X is necessary for the admissibility of the compact-open topology κ of Ω.

A space Y is said to *contain a nondegenerate path* iff there exists a map $\phi : I \to Y$ such that the image $\phi(I)$ is not a single point. In this case, we can clearly assume that $\phi(0) \neq \phi(1)$.

PROPOSITION 2.3. *If X is a completely regular space and if Y is a Fréchet space containing a nondegenerate path, then a necessary and sufficient condition for the admissibility of the compact-open topology κ in Ω is the local compactness of X.* [Arens 1.]

Proof. Since the sufficiency is a special case of (2.1), it remains to prove the necessity.

Since Y contains a nondegenerate path, there exists a map $\phi : I \to Y$ such that $\phi(0) \neq \phi(1)$. Since Y is a Fréchet space, there exists an open neighborhood W_0 of $\phi(0)$ in Y which does not contain $\phi(1)$.

Let $\theta \in \Omega$ denote the constant map $\theta(X) = \phi(0)$ and consider an arbitrarily given point x_0 of X. Since κ is admissible, there exists an open neighborhood U of θ in Ω_κ and an open neighborhood V of x_0 in X such that $f(x) \in W_0$ for every $f \in U$ and each $x \in V$. We will prove that the closure $\bar{V}$ of V must be compact.

Let α be any collection of open sets in X which covers $\bar{V}$. Adjoin to α the open set $X \setminus \bar{V}$ and obtain an open cover α^* of X.

Consider the family σ of all sets $M(F, W)$, where F is a closed set of X contained in some member of α^* and W is an open set of Y. Then σ is a sub-basis of a topology in Ω. Denote this topology by τ.

We assert that the topology τ of Ω is admissible. In fact, let $f \in \Omega$, $x \in X$, and an open neighborhood W of $f(x)$ in Y be given. Since X is regular, there exists an open neighborhood G of x whose closure F is contained in $f^{-1}(W)$ and also in some member of the open cover α^*. Then $M(F, W)$ is an open neighborhood of f in Ω_τ. Clearly $g \in M(F, W)$ implies $g(G) \subset W$. Since x is arbitrary, this proves that τ is admissible.

Since τ is admissible, it follows from the proof of (2.1) that $\kappa \subset \tau$.

This implies that the open set U of Ω_κ is also open in Ω_τ. Hence there are a finite number of sets $M(F_i, W_i)$, $i = 1, \ldots, n$, in σ such that

$$\theta \in M(F_1, W_1) \cap \cdots \cap M(F_n, W_n) \subset U.$$

We assert that the open set

$$G = V \setminus (F_1 \cup \cdots \cup F_n)$$

of X must be empty. To prove this, let us assume that G is not void. Choose a point $p \in G$. Since X is completely regular, there exists a continuous real function $\psi : X \to I$ such that

$$\psi(X \setminus G) = 0, \qquad \psi(p) = 1.$$

Consider the composed map $\chi = \phi \circ \psi : X \to Y$. Clearly, $\chi \in \Omega$. Since $\chi(X \setminus G) = 0$, it follows that

$$\chi \in M(F_1, W_1) \cap \cdots \cap M(F_n, W_n) \subset U.$$

On the other hand, since $\chi(p) = \phi(1)$ is not in W_0, χ cannot be in U. This contradiction proves that G is empty.

Since G is empty, it follows that V is contained in $F_1 \cup \cdots \cup F_n$. Since the latter is closed, this implies that

$$\overline{V} \subset F_n \cup \cdots \cup F_n.$$

For each $i = 1, \ldots, n$, F_i is contained in some member V_i of α^*. Hence we obtain

$$\overline{V} \subset V_1 \cup \cdots \cup V_n.$$

Since $\overline{V}$ and $X \setminus \overline{V}$ are disjoint, we may assume that $V_i \in \alpha$ for each $i = 1, \ldots, n$. Hence α has a finite subcollection $V_1, \ldots, V_n$ covering $\overline{V}$. This proves that $\overline{V}$ is compact and hence X is locally compact. ‖

EXERCISES

2A. Prove that the discrete topology in $\Omega = \text{Map }(X, Y)$ is admissible.

2B. Prove that if a topology τ in Ω is admissible then every topology larger than τ is admissible.

2C. Let A be a locally compact regular closed subspace of a space X and y_0 an arbitrary point in a space Y. Let

$$\Gamma = \{f \in \text{Map }(X, Y) \mid f(X \setminus A) = y_0\}.$$

Prove that the restriction $\omega \mid \Gamma_\kappa \times X \to Y$ is continuous.

3. MAPS ON TOPOLOGICAL PRODUCTS

Throughout the present section, let T, X, Y be arbitrarily given spaces and denote by

$$\Omega \ = \ \text{Map } (X, Y),$$
$$\Phi \ = \ \text{Map } (X \times T, Y),$$
$$\Psi \ = \ \text{Map } (T, \Omega_\kappa)$$

the corresponding sets of all maps involved.

For each map $\phi \ : \ X \times T \to Y$, define a function $\theta(\phi) \ : \ T \to \Omega_\kappa$ by taking

$$[\theta(\phi)(t)](x) \ = \ \phi(x, t)$$

for every $t \in T$ and every $x \in X$. $\theta(\phi)$ is called the *associated function* of ϕ.

LEMMA 3.1.   *The associated function $\theta(\phi)$ of any $\phi \in \Phi$ is a map, called the associated map of the map ϕ.*   [Fox 1.]

Proof. Denote $\psi = \theta(\phi)$ and let $U = M(K, W)$ be any sub-basic open set in Ω_κ. It suffices to prove that $\psi^{-1}(U)$ is an open set of T. Let t_0 be any given point in $\psi^{-1}(U)$. By definition, we have

$$K \times \{t_0\} \ \subset \ \phi^{-1}(W).$$

Since ϕ is continuous and W is open, it follows that $\phi^{-1}(W)$ is an open set of the topological product $X \times T$. According to (III, Ex. 2D), there exists a neighborhood V of t_0 in T such that

$$K \times V \ \subset \ \phi^{-1}(W).$$

This implies that $V \subset \psi^{-1}(U)$. Hence $\psi^{-1}(U)$ is open. $\|$

Conversely, for each map $\psi \ : \ T \to \Omega_\kappa$ define a function $\rho(\psi) \ : \ X \times T \to Y$ by taking

$$[\rho(\psi)](x, t) \ = \ [\psi(t)](x)$$

for every $x \in X$ and every $t \in T$. This function $\rho(\psi)$ need not be continuous and is called the *associated function* of ψ. If $\rho(\psi)$ is continuous, then obviously

$$\theta[\rho(\psi)] \ = \ \psi.$$

If $\psi = \theta(\phi)$ for some $\phi \in \Phi$, then $\rho(\psi) = \phi$ is continuous.

By (3.1), the assignment $\phi \to \theta(\phi)$ for each $\phi \in \Phi$ defines a function

$$\theta \ : \ \Phi \to \Psi$$

which will be called the *association*.

LEMMA 3.2. *The association* θ : $\Phi \to \Psi$ *is injective.*

Proof. Let ϕ_1 and ϕ_2 be any two maps in Φ such that

$$\theta(\phi_1) = \theta(\phi_2).$$

Then we have

$$\phi_1 = \rho[\theta(\phi_1)] = \rho[\theta(\phi_2)] = \phi_2.$$

Hence θ is injective. ||

However, the association θ is not always surjective. The following lemma is now obvious.

LEMMA 3.3. *The association* θ *is surjective iff* $\rho(\psi)$ *is continuous for every* $\psi \in \Psi$.

PROPOSITION 3.4. *Let X and Y be two given spaces. The compact-open topology* κ *of* Ω *is admissible iff, for every space T, the association* θ *is surjective.*

Proof: Necessity. Assume that κ is admissible. Let $\psi \in \Psi$ be arbitrarily given. Consider the map

$$\chi : X \times T \to \Omega_\kappa \times X$$

defined by $\chi(x, t) = (\psi(t), x)$ for each $x \in X$ and each $t \in T$. Since κ is admissible, the evaluation

$$\omega : \Omega_\kappa \times X \to Y$$

is continuous. Hence we obtain a map $\phi = \omega \circ \chi \in \Phi$. Since

$$[\theta(\phi)(t)](x) = \phi(x, t) = \omega[\chi(x, t)]$$
$$= \omega[\psi(t), x] = [\psi(t)](x)$$

for each $x \in X$ and each $t \in T$, we obtain $\theta(\phi) = \psi$. Hence θ is surjective.

Sufficiency. Assume that the condition holds. In particular, select $T = \Omega_\kappa$ and take $\psi \in \Psi$ to be the identity map on Ω_κ. Since θ is surjective, there exists a map $\phi \in \Phi$ such that $\theta(\phi) = \psi$. Since ϕ is continuous and

$$\phi(x, f) = [\theta(\phi)(f)](x) = [\psi(f)](x) = f(x) = \omega(f, x)$$

for each $x \in X$ and each $f \in \Omega_\kappa$, the evaluation ω is also continuous. Hence κ is admissible. ||

As an immediate consequence of (2.1) and (3.4), we have the following

COROLLARY 3.5. *If X is a locally compact regular space, then the association* θ *is always surjective.* [Fox 1.]

PROPOSITION 3.6.   *If both X and T satisfy the first axiom of countability, then the association θ is surjective.*   [Fox 1.]

Proof.   Let $\psi \in \Psi$ be arbitrarily given and denote

$$\phi = \rho(\psi) : X \times T \to Y.$$

According to (3.3), it suffices to prove the continuity of ϕ.

Let W be any open set in Y and assume that $\phi^{-1}(W)$ is not open. Then there is a point (x_0, t_0) in $\phi^{-1}(W)$ which is also in the closure of the complement of $\phi^{-1}(W)$.

Since both X and T satisfy the first axiom of countability, clearly so does the topological product $X \times T$.   Let

$$\beta = \{G_n \mid n = 1, 2, \ldots\}$$

be a local basis at the point (x_0, t_0) in $X \times T$ and choose, for each n, a point (x_n, t_n) in the set

$$G_1 \cap \cdots \cap G_n \cap \phi^{-1}(W).$$

Since $\psi(t_0)$ is a map and

$$[\psi(t_0)](x_0) = \phi(x_0, t_0) \in W,$$

there is an open neighborhood U of x_0 in X with $\psi(t_0)$ in $M(U, W)$.   Let

$$K = U \cap \left(\bigcup_{n=0}^{\infty} \{x_n\} \right).$$

Since K is obviously compact, we obtain a sub-basic open set $M(K, W)$ of Ω_κ which contains $\psi(t_0)$.   Since ψ is continuous,

$$V = \psi^{-1}[M(K, W)]$$

is an open neighborhood of t_0 in T.   Therefore, there is an integer m such that $x_n \in U$ and $t_n \in V$ whenever $n > m$.   Hence

$$\phi(x_n, t_n) = [\psi(t_n)](x_n) \in W$$

for every $n > m$.   This contradicts the choice of the points (x_n, t_n) and proves that $\phi^{-1}(W)$ is open.   Hence ϕ is continuous. $\|$

For the special case where $T = I$ is the closed unit interval $[0, 1]$ of real numbers, if θ sends Φ onto Ψ, then there is a bijective correspondence between the homotopies of the maps Ω and the paths in the space Ω_κ.   In this case, the homotopy classes of the maps Ω are precisely the path-components of the space Ω_κ.

Now let us give compact-open topologies to the sets

$$\Phi = \text{Map} (X \times T, Y), \quad \Psi = \text{Map} (T, \Omega_\kappa)$$

and obtain spaces Φ_κ and Ψ_κ. Thus, the association

$$\theta : \Phi_\kappa \to \Psi_\kappa$$

becomes an injective function from a space Φ_κ into a space Ψ_κ.

PROPOSITION 3.7. *If T is a Hausdorff space, then the association θ is continuous.*

Proof. Since T is a Hausdorff space and the totality of the sub-basic open sets $M(K, U)$ is a sub-basis of Ω_κ, it follows from (1.3) that the family of all subsets

$$M[L, M(K, U)] = \{\psi \in \Psi \mid \psi(L) \subset M(K, U)\}$$

is a sub-basis of Ψ_κ, where L runs through the compact sets in T, K runs through the compact sets in X, and U runs through the open sets in Y. It follows clearly from the definition of θ that

$$\theta^{-1}\{M[L, M(K, U)]\} = M(K \times L, U).$$

Now, as a topological product of compact sets, $K \times L$ is compact and hence $M(K \times L, U)$ is an open set of Φ_κ. By (II, 3.1(*iv*)), this implies that θ is continuous. ||

PROPOSITION 3.8. *If both X and T are Hausdorff spaces, then the association θ is an imbedding.* [Jackson 2.]

Proof. Since θ is continuous and injective by (3.7) and (3.2), it remains to prove that θ^{-1} is continuous on $\theta(\Phi_\kappa)$. For this purpose, it suffices to show that, for each compact set J in $X \times T$ and each open set W in Y, the image $\theta[M(J, W)]$ is an open subset of $\theta(\Phi_\kappa)$.

Let $\psi \in \theta[M(J, U)]$ be arbitrarily given. Choose a $\phi \in M(J, U)$ with $\theta(\phi) = \psi$. Let J_X and J_T be the projections of J in X and T respectively. For each point $z = (x, t)$ in J, choose an open neighborhood U_z of x in J_X and an open neighborhood V_z of t in J_T, such that

$$\phi(U_z \times V_z) \subset W.$$

This is possible because ϕ is continuous. As compact Hausdorff spaces, J_X and J_T are regular. Hence we may shrink U_z and V_z a little bit so that

$$\phi(K_z \times L_z) \subset W,$$

where K_z denotes the closure of U_z in J_X and L_z that of V_z in J_T.

The collection $\{(U_z \times V_z) \cap J \mid z \in J\}$ is an open cover of the compact space J. Hence there are a finite number of points in J, say $z_1, \ldots, z_n$, such that

$$J \subset (U_{z_1} \times V_{z_1}) \cup \cdots \cup (U_{z_n} \times V_{z_n}).$$

For the subscripts in the notations of the various sets involved above, we will simply replace z_i by i for each $i = 1, \ldots, n$.

Now the sets K_i and L_i, $i = 1, \ldots, n$, as closed subsets of compact sets, are themselves compact. Moreover,

$$[\psi(L_i)](K_i) = \phi(K_i \times L_i) \subset W$$

for each $i = 1, \ldots, n$. Hence we obtain

$$\psi \in \theta(\Phi_\kappa) \cap \{ \bigcap_{i=1}^{n} M[L_i, M(K_i, W)]\}.$$

Assume that $\chi \in \Psi_\kappa$ is contained in the set on the right-hand side of the preceding formula. Since $\chi \in \theta(\Phi_\kappa)$, there is a $\xi \in \Phi_\kappa$ with $\chi = \theta(\xi)$. If $z = (x, t) \in J$, then z is contained in some $U_i \times V_i$ and hence in $K_i \times L_i$. Since χ is contained in $M[L_i, M(K_i, W)]$ and since $x \in K_i$ and $t \in L_i$, we have

$$\xi(z) = \xi(x, t) = [\chi(t)](x) \in W.$$

This proves that $\xi(J) \subset W$. Thus, $\xi \in M(J, W)$ and hence $\chi = \theta(\xi) \in \theta[M(J, W)]$. Therefore, we obtain

$$\psi \in \theta(\Phi_\kappa) \cap \{ \bigcap_{i=1}^{n} M[L_i, M(K_i, W)]\} \subset \theta[M(J, W)].$$

This proves that $\theta[M(J, W)]$ is an open set of $\theta(\Phi_\kappa)$. $\|$

As an immediate consequence of (3.5), (3.6), and (3.8), we have the following

THEOREM 3.9. *Let X and T be Hausdorff spaces and Y an arbitrary space. The association θ is a homeomorphism of Φ_κ onto Ψ_κ if either of the following conditions is satisfied:*
   (i) *X is locally compact.*
   (ii) *X and T satisfy the first axiom of countability.*

In following exercises, all spaces of maps involved are topologized by compact-open topology.

EXERCISES

3A. Prove that every map $d : X \to Q$ induces a map

$$d^* : \text{Map } (Q, Y) \to \text{Map } (X, Y)$$

given by $d^*(f) = f \circ d$ for every f in Map (Q, Y), and verify that:
   (a) d^* is injective if d is surjective.
   (b) d^* is an imbedding if, for each compact set K in Q, there exists a compact set L in X such that $d(L) = K$.

3B. Let Q be the quotient space obtained by collapsing a closed subspace A of a compact Hausdorff space X to a point and let $d : X \to Q$ denote the natural projection. Prove that the image of the induced map d^* is the subspace of Map (X, Y) which consists of all maps $f : X \to Y$ such that $f(A)$ is a single point.

3C. Let X be a compact Hausdorff space. Prove that the space

$$\text{Map } [S(X), Y]$$

of all maps from the suspension $S(X)$ of X into a space Y is homeomorphic to the subspace of the space

$$\text{Map } [I, \text{Map } (X, Y)]$$

consisting of all maps $f : I \to \text{Map } (X, Y)$ such that $f(0)$ and $f(1)$ are constant maps.

4. INJECTION AND PROJECTIONS

Throughout the present section, let X and Y be arbitrary spaces and Ω_κ the space

$$\Omega = \text{Map } (X, Y)$$

with the compact-open topology κ.

For each point $y \in Y$, let $j(y)$ denote the constant map in Ω which sends X into the single point y. The assignment $y \to j(y)$ defines a function

$$j : Y \to \Omega_\kappa$$

called the *injection* of Y into Ω_κ.

PROPOSITION 4.1. *The injection* $j : Y \to \Omega_\kappa$ *is an imbedding.*

Proof. First let us prove the continuity of j. Let $U = M(K, W)$ be an arbitrary sub-basic open set in Ω_κ. By the definition of j, we have $j^{-1}(U) = W$. Hence, by (II, 3.1 (*iv*)), j is continuous.

Next, let us prove that j is injective.   Let y_1 and y_2 be any two points in Y with $j(y_1) = j(y_2)$.   Then we have

$$y_1 \; = \; [j(y_1)](X) \; = \; [j(y_2)](X) \; = \; y_2.$$

Hence j is injective.

It remains to prove that j sends every open set W of Y onto an open set of $j(Y)$.   For this purpose, take a point $x \in X$ and consider the subbasic open set $M(x, W)$ of Ω_κ.   Clearly we have

$$j(W) \; = \; j(Y) \cap M(x, W).$$

Hence $j(W)$ is an open set in $j(Y)$. $\|$

PROPOSITION 4.2.   *If Y is a Hausdorff space, then $j(Y)$ is closed in Ω_κ.*

Proof.   We will prove that the complement

$$G \; = \; \Omega_\kappa \setminus j(Y)$$

is open.   Let $f \in G$.   Then there are two points a and b in X such that $f(a) \neq f(b)$.   Since Y is a Hausdorff space, there are two disjoint open sets U and V of Y such that $f(a) \in U$ and $f(b) \in V$.   Then

$$H \; = \; M(a, U) \cap M(b, V)$$

is an open set of Ω_κ with $f \in H$.   It remains to prove that $H \subset G$.   Let $h \in H$ be arbitrarily given.   Since U and V are disjoint, we have $h(a) \neq h(b)$ and hence $h \in G$. $\|$

Since Y is homeomorphic to the subspace $j(Y)$ of Ω_κ, we have the following converses of (1.1) and (1.2).

PROPOSITION 4.3.   *If Ω_κ is a Fréchet, Hausdorff, or regular space, then so is Y.*

PROPOSITION 4.4.   *If Ω_κ satisfies the second axiom of countability, then so does Y.*

Now, for any given point $a \in X$, let

$$p_a \; : \; \Omega_\kappa \to Y$$

denote the function defined by

$$p_a(f) \; = \; f(a)$$

for every $f \in \Omega_\kappa$.   This function is surjective since it sends the subset $j(Y)$ of Ω_κ onto Y.   Hereafter, we will call p_a the *projection* of Ω_κ onto Y determined by the given point $a \in X$.

PROPOSITION 4.5.   *The projection* p_a : $\Omega_\kappa \to Y$ *is continuous.*

Proof.   Let W be any open set of Y.   By the definition of p_a, the inverse image $p_a{}^{-1}(W)$ is clearly the sub-basic open set $M(a, W)$ of Ω_κ. Hence p_a is continuous. ||

PROPOSITION 4.6. $j(Y)$ *is a retract of* Ω_κ.

Proof.   Choose a point $a \in X$ and define a map

$$r \; : \; \Omega_\kappa \to j(Y)$$

by taking $r(f) = j[p_a(f)]$ for every $f \in \Omega_\kappa$.   If $f \in j(Y)$, then there is a point $y \in Y$ with $f = j(y)$.   Then we have

$$r(f) \; = \; j[p_a(f)] \; = \; j[f(a)] \; = \; j(y) \; = \; f.$$

Hence r is a retraction of Ω_κ onto $j(Y)$. ||

EXERCISES

4A. Verify that the propositions in this section are still true if we replace the compact-open topology κ by the pointwise topology π.

4B. For a given map d : $X \to Q$, prove that the following triangles are commutative:

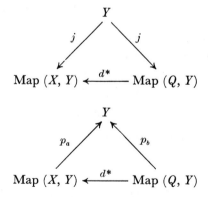

where d^* denotes the induced map in Exercise 3A, $a \in X$, and $b = d(a) \in Q$.

4C. Prove that every map e : $Y \to Z$ induces a map

$$e_* \; : \; \text{Map } (X, Y) \to \text{Map } (X, Z)$$

given by $e_*(f) = e \circ f$ for every f in Map (X, Y). Verify that the following rectangles are commutative:

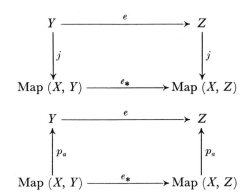

4D. A space X is said to be contractible relative to a point $a \in X$ iff there exists a contraction $\{h_t : X \to X \mid t \in I\}$ such that $h_t(a) = a$ for every $t \in I$.   Prove that $j(Y)$ is a strong deformation retract of $\Omega_\kappa =$ Map (X, Y) if X is a locally compact regular space and is contractible relative to a point $a \in X$.   In this case, the set $p_a^{-1}(y)$ is contractible relative to $j(y)$ for every $y \in Y$.

5. TOPOLOGY OF UNIFORM CONVERGENCE

Throughout the present section, we assume that Y is an arbitrarily given metrizable space.   Let d be any bounded distance function in Y which defines the topology of Y.   See (III, Ex. 8C).

There is a natural topology in the set

$$\Omega = \mathrm{Map}(X, Y)$$

induced by the distance function d for any given space X.   Define a real-valued function

$$d^* : \Omega^2 \to R$$

on the cartesian square $\Omega^2 = \Omega \times \Omega$ by taking

$$d^*(f, g) = \sup_{x \in X} d[f(x), g(x)]$$

for each pair of maps f and g in Ω.

LEMMA 5.1.   *The function $d^* : \Omega^2 \to R$ is a metric in Ω.*

Proof. We have to verify the conditions (M1) and (M2) in (III, § 8).

To verify (M1), let f, g, h be arbitrary maps in Ω. Let δ denote any given positive real number. Then, by definition, there exists a point x in X such that

$$d[f(x), g(x)] > d^*(f, g) - \delta.$$

Therefore, we obtain

$$d^*(f, g) < d[f(x), g(x)] + \delta \leqslant d[f(x), h(x)] + d[g(x), h(x)] + \delta$$

by the condition (M1) for the given metric d. This implies that

$$d^*(f, g) < d^*(f, h) + d^*(g, h) + \delta.$$

Since this holds for every $\delta > 0$, we must have

$$d^*(f, g) \leqslant d^*(f, h) + d^*(g, h).$$

To verify (M2), let f and g be any two maps in Ω. Then, by definition, we have $d^*(f, g) = 0$ iff $d[f(x), g(x)] = 0$ for every $x \in X$. By the condition (M2) for the given metric d, this holds iff $f(x) = g(x)$ for every $x \in X$. Hence, $d^*(f, g) = 0$ iff $f = g$. ‖

This metric d^* in Ω defines a topology in Ω will be called the d^*-*topology* induced by d, or the *topology of uniform convergence* with respect to d. We will denote by Ω_d the metric space formed by the set Ω together with the metric d^* defined above.

PROPOSITION 5.2. *The d^*-topology of Ω induced by any given bounded metric d on Y is admissible.*

Proof. We have to prove that the evaluation

$$\omega \; : \; \Omega_d \times X \to Y$$

is continuous. Let $f_0 \in \Omega_d$, $x_0 \in X$, and a real number $\delta > 0$ be arbitrarily given. Denote $y_0 = f_0(x_0)$. Since f_0 is continuous, there is a neighborhood V of x_0 in X such that

$$d[y_0, f_0(x)] < \tfrac{1}{2}\delta$$

for every $x \in V$. Let U denote the neighborhood of f_0 in Ω_d defined by

$$U = \{f \in \Omega_d \mid d^*(f_0, f) < \tfrac{1}{2}\delta\}.$$

Then we have

$$
\begin{aligned}
d[\omega(f_0, x_0),\, \omega(f, x)] &= d[f_0(x), f(x)] \\
&\leqslant d[f_0(x_0), f_0(x)] + d[f_0(x), f(x)] \\
&\leqslant d[y_0, f_0(x)] + d^*(f_0, f) < \delta
\end{aligned}
$$

for every $f \in U$ and every $x \in V$. This proves the continuity of ω. ‖

In the remainder of this section, we are concerned with the question whether or not the compact-open topology κ of Ω coincides with the d^*-topology.

Proposition 5.3. *If X is compact, then the compact-open topology κ of Ω coincides with the d^*-topology induced by any given bounded metric d on Y.*

Proof. By (5.2) and the proof of (2.1), every open set of Ω_κ is open in Ω_d. It remains to show that every open set of Ω_d is open in Ω_κ. For this, it suffices to prove that, for any $f \in \Omega$ and any real number $\delta > 0$, there exists an open set V of Ω_κ such that

$$ f \in V \subset U = \{ g \in \Omega \mid d^*(f, g) < \delta \}. $$

For every $x \in X$, let W_x denote the open set of Y defined by

$$ W_x = \{ y \in Y \mid d[f(x), y] < \tfrac{1}{3}\delta \}. $$

Since f is continuous and $f(x) \in W_x$, there is an open neighborhood G_x of x in X such that

$$ f(K_x) \subset W_x $$

where K_x denotes the closure of G_x in X. Since X is compact, there are a finite number of points in X, say $x_1, \ldots, x_n$, such that

$$ X = G_{x_1} \cup \cdots \cup G_{x_n}. $$

For the subscripts in the notations of the various sets involved above, we will simply replace x_i by i for each $i = 1, \ldots, n$.

As closed subsets of the compact space X, the sets $K_1, \ldots, K_n$ are compact. Hence

$$ V = M(K_1, W_1) \cap \cdots \cap M(K_n, W_n) $$

is an open set of Ω_κ and $f \in V$. It remains to prove that $V \subset U$. Let $g \in V$ and $x \in X$. Then there is an integer i with $1 \leqslant i \leqslant n$ such that $x \in G_i \subset K_i$. This implies that $f(x) \in W_i$ and $g(x) \in W_i$. Then we have

$$ d[f(x_i), f(x)] < \tfrac{1}{3}\delta, \qquad d[f(x_i), g(x)] < \tfrac{1}{3}\delta. $$

Hence we obtain

$$ d[f(x), g(x)] \leqslant d[f(x_i), f(x)] + d[f(x_i), g(x)] < \tfrac{2}{3}\delta. $$

Since x is arbitrary, this proves

$$ d^*(f, g) \leqslant \tfrac{2}{3}\delta < \delta $$

and hence $g \in U$. Thus we have proved that $V \subset U$. $\;\|$

Since the boundedness of the metric d is used only in the definition of d^* and is not necessary in case X is compact, we may delete the word "bounded" from the statement of (5.3).

The necessity of the compactness of X is shown by the following

PROPOSITION 5.4. *If X is a completely regular Hausdorff space and Y a metrizable space containing a nondegenerate path, then a necessary and sufficient condition for the compact-open topology κ of Ω to coincide with the d^*-topology induced by a given bounded metric d on Y is the compactness of X.* [Jackson 1.]

Proof. Since the sufficiency is a special case of (5.3), it remains to prove the necessity.

Since Y contains a nondegenerate path, there is a map $\phi : I \to Y$ such that $\phi(0) \neq \phi(1)$. Let

$$\delta = d[\phi(0), \phi(1)],$$

then $\delta > 0$. Let $\gamma : X \to Y$ denote the constant map $\gamma(X) = \phi(0)$ and U the open set of Ω_d defined by

$$U = \{ f \in \Omega \mid d^*(\gamma, f) < \delta \}.$$

Assume that the two topologies coincide. Then there must be compact sets $K_1, \ldots, K_n$ in X and open sets $W_1, \ldots, W_n$ in Y such that

$$\gamma \in M(K_1, W_1) \cap \cdots \cap M(K_n, W_n) \subset U.$$

We will complete the proof by contradiction. If

$$X \setminus (K_1 \cup \cdots \cup K_n)$$

is empty, then X is the union of a finite number of compact sets and hence is compact.

Otherwise, choose $x_0 \in X \setminus (K_1 \cup \cdots \cup K_n)$. As a compact set in a Hausdorff space, $K_1 \cup \cdots \cup K_n$ is closed in X. It follows from the complete regularity of X that there exists a continuous real function $\chi : X \to I$ such that

$$\chi(K_1 \cup \cdots \cup K_n) = 0, \qquad \chi(x_0) = 1.$$

Denote $f = \phi \circ \chi \in \Omega$.

For each $x \in K_i$, we have

$$f(x) = \phi[\chi(x)] = \phi(0) \in W_i.$$

Hence f is in $M(K_1, W_1) \cap \cdots \cap M(K_n, W_n)$. On the other hand,

$$\begin{aligned} d^*(\gamma, f) &\geq d[\gamma(x_0), f(x_0)] \\ &= d[\phi(0), \phi\chi(x_0)] \\ &= d[\phi(0), \phi(1)] = \delta. \end{aligned}$$

Hence f is not in U. This contradiction proves that X is compact. $\|$

The $d*$-topology of Ω is obviously easier to deal with than the compact-open topology; however, its principal defect is that it is usually
dependent not only on the topologies of X and Y, but also on the metric
d chosen for Y. Fortunately, we have (5.3).

EXERCISES

5A. Let X be the set of all positive integers and let Y consist of two points
0 and 1. Both X and Y are separable metric spaces with the
euclidean metric d of the real line R. Then $\Omega = \text{Map }(X, Y)$
consists of all sequences with terms 0 or 1. Prove that Ω_κ is separable
and Ω_d is not separable. Hence the two topologies do not coincide
even if Y is so simple as to contain only two points.

5B. Let X denote the set of all positive integers and let Q denote the set
of real numbers 0 and x^{-1} for all $x \in X$. Take $Y = X \times Q$ and
define metrics d and δ in the set Y by taking

$$d[(x_1, q_1), (x_2, q_2)] = \frac{[(x_1 - x_2)^2 + (q_1 - q_2)^2]^{1/2}}{1 + [(x_1 - x_2)^2 + (q_1 - q_2)^2]^{1/2}}$$

$$\delta[(x, q_1), (x, q_2)] = \min\{1, x|\, q_1 - q_2\,|\},$$

$$\delta[(x_1, q_1), (x_2, q_2)] = 1, \quad (\text{if } x_1 \neq x_2).$$

Prove that d and δ define the same topology in Y. However, the
induced metrics $d*$ and $\delta*$ define different topologies in $\Omega =$
Map (X, Y). Prove this by considering the map $f \in \Omega$ defined by
$f(x) = (x, 0)$ for all $x \in X$ and the sequence of maps $f_n \in \Omega$,
$n = 1, 2, \ldots$, defined by

$$f_n(x) = (x, 1/n), \quad (x \in X, n = 1, 2, \ldots).$$

This sequence converges to f in the $d*$-topology but not in the $\delta*$-
topology.

6. SPACES OF PATHS AND LOOPS

In this section, we are interested in the special case where X is the
closed unit interval $I = [0, 1]$ of real numbers. In this case, the maps

$$f : I \to Y$$

are called the paths in the space Y and the points $f(0)$ and $f(1)$ are called
the initial point and the final point of the path f. See (III, § 5).

The totality of paths in Y forms a space

$$\Omega(Y) \;=\; \text{Map } (I, Y)$$

with the compact-open topology. If Y is metrizable, then it follows from (5.3) and the compactness of I that the compact-open topology of $\Omega(Y)$ coincides with the d^*-topology induced by any metric d on Y. This justifies our omission of the subscript κ. This space $\Omega(Y)$ together with certain of its subspaces is of fundamental importance in modern topology.

Let $y_0 \in Y$ be a given point and consider the subspace

$$\Omega(Y, y_0) = \{f \in \Omega(Y) \mid f(0) = y_0\}.$$

PROPOSITION 6.1. *The space $\Omega(Y, y_0)$ is contractible relative to the constant path $\gamma = j(y_0)$.*

Proof. By (2.1), the evaluation

$$\omega \;:\; \Omega(Y, y_0) \times I \to Y$$

is continuous. Consider the map

$$\phi \;:\; I \times \Omega(Y, y_0) \times I \to Y$$

defined by

$$\phi(s, f, t) \;=\; \omega[f, s(1 - t)]$$

for every $s \in I, f \in \Omega(Y, y_0)$, and $t \in I$. By (3.1), the associated function

$$\psi \;=\; \theta(\phi) \;:\; \Omega(Y, y_0) \times I \to \Omega(Y)$$

is continuous. Define a homotopy

$$\{h_t \;:\; \Omega(Y, y_0) \to \Omega(Y) \mid t \in I\}$$

by setting $h_t(f) = \psi(f, t)$ for each $t \in I$ and each $f \in \Omega(Y, y_0)$.

For each $t \in I, f \in \Omega(Y, y_0)$, and $s \in I$, we have

$$\begin{aligned}
[h_t(f)](s) \;&=\; [\psi(f, t)](s) \;=\; \phi(s, f, t)\\
&=\; \omega[f, s(1 - t)] \;=\; f[s(1 - t)].
\end{aligned}$$

It follows that h_0 is the inclusion map, h_1 sends $\Omega(Y, y_0)$ into the single point $j(y_0)$, h_t sends $\Omega(Y, y_0)$ into itself and holds $j(y_0)$ fixed. This implies that $\Omega(Y, y_0)$ is contractible relative to $j(y_0)$. ∥

By a *loop* in Y, we mean a path $f : I \to Y$ such that $f(0) = f(1)$. The point $f(0) = f(1)$ will be called the *base point* of the loop f. The set of all loops in Y forms a subspace $\Lambda(Y)$ of the space $\Omega(Y)$ called the *space of loops* in Y.

Let $y_0 \in Y$ be a given point and consider the subspace

$$\Lambda(Y, y_0) \;=\; \{f \in \Omega(Y) \mid f(0) = y_0 = f(1)\}.$$

Then $\Lambda(Y, y_0)$ consists of all loops in Y with y_0 as base point. Clearly, we have

$$\Lambda(Y, y_0) \;=\; \Lambda(Y) \cap \Omega(Y, y_0).$$

There is a natural multiplication defined in the space $\Lambda(Y, y_0)$ as follows. For any two loops f and g in $\Lambda(Y, y_0)$, the *product* $fg \in \Lambda(Y, y_0)$ is the loop in Y defined by

$$(fg)(t) \;=\; \begin{cases} f(2t), & (\text{if } 0 \leqslant t \leqslant \tfrac{1}{2}), \\ g(2t - 1), & (\text{if } \tfrac{1}{2} \leqslant t \leqslant 1). \end{cases}$$

Intuitively speaking, fg is the loop in Y which travels along f in the first half of I and along g in the second half of I.

The assignment $(f, g) \to fg$ defines a function

$$\mu \;:\; \Lambda(Y, y_0) \times \Lambda(Y, y_0) \to \Lambda(Y, y_0)$$

called the *multiplication* in $\Lambda(Y, y_0)$.

PROPOSITION 6.2. *The multiplication μ in $\Lambda(Y, y_0)$ is continuous.*

Proof. Let $U = M(K, W) \cap \Lambda(Y, y_0)$ be any nonempty sub-basic open set in $\Lambda(Y, y_0)$. It suffices to prove that the inverse image $\mu^{-1}(U)$ is an open set of the topological product $\Lambda(Y, y_0) \times \Lambda(Y, y_0)$. Let $\xi, \eta \;:\; I \to I$ denote the maps defined by

$$\xi(t) \;=\; \tfrac{1}{2}t, \qquad \eta(t) \;=\; \tfrac{1}{2}(t + 1)$$

for every $t \in I$. Denote

$$A \;=\; \xi^{-1}(K), \qquad B \;=\; \eta^{-1}(K).$$

Then A and B are compact sets in I. Consider the sub-basic open sets

$$F \;=\; M(A, W) \cap \Lambda(Y, y_0), \qquad G \;=\; M(B, W) \cap \Lambda(Y, y_0)$$

in $\Lambda(Y, y_0)$. For any two loops $f, g \in \Lambda(Y, y_0)$, one can easily see that $fg \in M(K, W)$ iff $f \in M(A, W)$ and $g \in M(B, W)$. Therefore,

$$\mu^{-1}(U) \;=\; F \times G.$$

This proves that $\mu^{-1}(U)$ is open. ‖

COROLLARY 6.3. *Each loop $f \in \Lambda(Y, y_0)$ determines two maps*

$$L_f, R_f \;:\; \Lambda(Y, y_0) \to \Lambda(Y, y_0)$$

given by $L_f(g) \;=\; fg$ and $R_f(g) \;=\; gf$ for every g in $\Lambda(Y, y_0)$.

PROPOSITION 6.4. *If $\gamma \in \Lambda(Y, y_0)$ denotes the constant loop $\gamma(I) = y_0$, then L_γ and R_γ are homotopic to the identity map on $\Lambda(Y, y_0)$ relative to γ.*

Proof. By (2.1), the evaluation

$$\omega \; : \; \Lambda(Y, y_0) \times I \to Y$$

is continuous. Hence we may define a map

$$\phi \; : \; I \times \Lambda(Y, y_0) \times I \to Y$$

as follows. Let $s \in I$, $f \in \Lambda(Y, y_0)$, and $t \in I$ be arbitrarily given. We define

$$\phi(s, f, t) \;=\; \begin{cases} f\left(\dfrac{2s}{1+t}\right), & \left(\text{if } 0 \leqslant s \leqslant \dfrac{1+t}{2}\right), \\[2ex] y_0, & \left(\text{if } \dfrac{1+t}{2} \leqslant s \leqslant 1\right). \end{cases}$$

By (3.1), the associated function $\psi = \theta(\phi)$ is continuous. By definition, ψ is given by

$$[\psi(f, t)](s) \;=\; \phi(s, f, t)$$

for every $f \in \Lambda(Y, y_0)$, $t \in I$, and $s \in I$. Hence it can be easily seen that ψ sends $\Lambda(Y, y_0) \times I$ into the subspace $\Lambda(Y, y_0)$ of the space $\Omega(Y)$. Define a homotopy

$$\{ h_t : \Lambda(Y, y_0) \to \Lambda(Y, y_0) \mid t \in I \}$$

by taking $h_t(f) = \psi(f, t)$ for every $f \in \Lambda(Y, y_0)$ and every $t \in I$. Then it is easy to verify that $h_0 = R_\gamma$, h_1 is the identity map, and $h_t(\gamma) = \gamma$ for each $t \in I$. This proves that R_γ is homotopic to the identity map relative to γ. Similarly, one can prove that L_γ is homotopic to the identity map relative to γ. ‖

These properties of $\Lambda(Y, y_0)$ show that it belongs to the class of Hopf spaces defined as follows.

By a *continuous multiplication* in a space X, we mean a map

$$\mu \; : \; X \times X \to X.$$

Let μ be a given continuous multiplication in X. For any two points a and b of X, $\mu(a, b)$ is customarily denoted by ab and is called the *product* of a and b. For any given point a of X, the assignments $x \to ax$ and $x \to xa$ determine respectively the maps

$$L_a \; : \; X \to X, \qquad R_a \; : \; X \to X$$

called the *left* and the *right translation* of X by a. A point $a \in X$ is said to be a *left homotopy unit* if a is an idempotent, i.e. $aa = a$, and if L_a is homotopic to the identity map relative to a.   Similarly, one can define *right homotopy units* of X.   An idempotent $a \in X$ is said to be a *homotopy unit* if it is both a left and a right homotopy unit.   By a *Hopf space*, or simply an *H-space*, we mean a space X with a given continuous multiplication which has a homotopy unit.

The following theorem is an immediate consequence of (6.2) and (6.4).

THEOREM 6.5.   *The space* $\Lambda(Y, y_0)$ *is a Hopf space with the constant loop* $\gamma \in \Lambda(Y, y_0)$ *as a homotopy unit.*

By a *topological group*, we mean a space X together with a continuous multiplication μ in X which makes X a group.   Hence we have the following

PROPOSITION 6.6.   *Every topological group is a Hopf space with its neutral element as a homotopy unit.*

EXERCISES

6A. The projection $p_0 \: : \: \Omega(Y) \to Y$ defined by $p_0(f) = f(0)$ for every $f \in \Omega(Y)$ is called an *initial projection*.   The inverse image $p_0^{-1}(y_0)$ of a given point $y_0 \in Y$ is the subspace $\Omega(Y, y_0)$.   Prove that p_0 is open in case Y is locally pathwise connected.   In this case, p_0 is an identification.

6B. The map $p_1 \: : \: \Omega(Y, y_0) \to Y$ defined by $p_1(f) = f(1)$ for every $f \in \Omega(Y, y_0)$ is called the *final projection* of $\Omega(Y, y_0)$.   Prove that p_1 is surjective iff Y is pathwise connected and that p_1 is open if Y is locally pathwise connected.   Hence p_1 is an identification if Y is pathwise connected and locally pathwise connected.   The inverse image $p_1^{-1}(y_0)$ is the subspace $\Lambda(Y, y_0)$.

6C. Show that the subspace $F_n(Y, y_0)$ of the space Map (S^n, Y) which consists of all maps $f : S^n \to Y$ with $f(s_0) = y_0$, where $s_0 \in S^n$ is a given point, is homeomorphic to the subspace of Map (I^n, Y) consisting of all maps $g \: : \: I^n \to Y$ with $g(\partial I^n) = y_0$.

6D. Let $\Lambda^2(Y, y_0) = \Lambda[\Lambda(Y, y_0), \gamma]$, where γ denotes the constant loop $\gamma(I) = y_0$.   Define $\Lambda^n(Y, y_0)$ for every $n \geqslant 1$.   Prove that $\Lambda^n(Y, y_0)$ is homeomorphic to $F_n(Y, y_0)$ for every $n \geqslant 1$.

Chapter VI: FUNDAMENTAL GROUPS

For the benefit of students who take only one topology course we devote this last chapter to the fundamental group. In view of its many applications in other branches of mathematics, it is advisable that every student be acquainted with the fundamental group. For the instructor who can cover this chapter in the first semester, it serves as a natural transition from the set theoretic approach to the more advanced algebraic techniques such as homology theory. Our approach to the fundamental group differs from the traditional approach given in existing books. We first construct a much larger entity called the fundamental groupoid; then we obtain the fundamental group as a subgroup of the groupoid, thus making the proofs somewhat simpler.

1. EQUIVALENCE CLASSES OF PATHS

In the present chapter, let X be an arbitrarily given space. Consider the set

$$\Omega = \Omega(X) = \text{Map}\,(I, X)$$

of all paths in the space X. We are usually not interested in the topology of Ω unless otherwise stated.

Two paths $\sigma, \tau \in \Omega$ are said to be *equivalent*, in symbols $\sigma \sim \tau$, iff the following two conditions are satisfied:

(E1) $\sigma(0) = \tau(0)$ and $\sigma(1) = \tau(1)$.

(E2)   There exists a homotopy

$$\{h_t \ : \ I \to X \mid t \in I\}$$

such that $h_0 = \sigma$, $h_1 = \tau$, and $h_t(0) = \sigma(0)$, $h_t(1) = \sigma(1)$, for every $t \in I$.

In words, two paths $\sigma, \tau \ : \ I \to X$ are equivalent iff they have the same end points and are homotopic relative to the end points.

Note that (E2) implies (E1). For intuitive reasons, however, we like to have (E1) explicitly stated ahead of (E2).

Assume that $\sigma, \tau \in \Omega$ satisfy (E1) and let x_0 and x_1 denote their common end points. Define a map

$$F : \partial I^2 \to X$$

on the boundary ∂I^2 of the unit square I^2 by setting

$$\begin{array}{llll} F(s, 0) & = & \sigma(s), & F(s, 1) & = & \tau(s), & (s \in I); \\ F(0, t) & = & x_0, & F(1, t) & = & x_1, & (t \in I). \end{array}$$

Then (E2) is equivalent to the existence of an extension $H : I^2 \to X$ of F.

Let $\Lambda = \Lambda(X)$ denote the subset of Ω consisting of all loops in X. Then two loops $\sigma, \tau \in \Lambda$ are equivalent iff they have the same base point and are homotopic relative to the common base point.

The space X is said to be *simply connected* iff X is pathwise connected and, for any two paths σ, τ in X, (E1) implies (E2). In other words, a pathwise connected space X is simply connected iff every two paths in X with the same end points are homotopic relative to the common end points.

By the method used in proving (II, 7.3), one can easily verify that the relation $\sim$ in Ω is an equivalence relation. Let us denote by

$$\pi(X) = \Omega(X) \setminus \sim$$

the set of all equivalence classes in $\Omega(X)$ with respect to the equivalence relation $\sim$.

Let $e \in \pi(X)$ be an arbitrary equivalence class. Then, by (E1), all paths in the class e have the same initial point, say x_0, and the same final point, say x_1. We will denote

$$e(0) = x_0, \qquad e(1) = x_1$$

and call these the *initial point* and the *final point* of the class e respectively.

Let a, b be any two elements of $\pi(X)$ such that

$$a(1) = b(0).$$

Pick a path $\sigma \in a$ and path $\tau \in b$. Then we have

$$\sigma(1) = a(1) = b(0) = \tau(0).$$

Define a path $\chi : I \to X$ by taking

$$\chi(t) = \begin{cases} \sigma(2t), & (\text{if } 0 \geqslant t \geqslant \tfrac{1}{2}), \\ \tau(2t - 1), & (\text{if } \tfrac{1}{2} \geqslant t \geqslant 1). \end{cases}$$

Let $c \in \pi(X)$ denote the class which contains the path χ.

PROPOSITION 1.1. *The element $c \in \pi(X)$ depends only on the elements a and b.*

Proof. Let $\xi \in a$ and $\eta \in b$ be arbitrary paths. Then we have

$$\sigma \sim \xi, \qquad \tau \sim \eta.$$

Define a path $\zeta : I \to X$ by taking

$$\zeta(t) = \begin{cases} \xi(2t), & \text{(if } 0 \leqslant t \leqslant \tfrac{1}{2}), \\ \eta(2t - 1), & \text{(if } \tfrac{1}{2} \leqslant t \leqslant 1). \end{cases}$$

Then it suffices to prove that $\chi \sim \zeta$.

Since $\sigma \sim \xi$ and $\tau \sim \eta$, there exist homotopies

$$\{f_s : I \to X \mid s \in X\}, \qquad \{g_s : I \to X \mid s \in I\}$$

such that $f_0 = \sigma$, $f_1 = \xi$, $g_0 = \tau$, $g_1 = \eta$ and that

$$\begin{aligned} f_s(0) &= a(0), \\ f_s(1) &= a(1) = b(0) = g_s(0), \\ g_s(1) &= b(1) \end{aligned}$$

for all $s \in I$. Define a homotopy

$$\{h_s : I \to X \mid s \in I\}$$

by taking

$$h_s(t) = \begin{cases} f_s(2t), & \text{(if } 0 \leqslant t \leqslant \tfrac{1}{2}), \\ g_s(2t - 1), & \text{(if } \tfrac{1}{2} \leqslant t \leqslant 1), \end{cases}$$

for every $s \in I$. Then we have $h_0 = \chi$, $h_1 = \zeta$, and

$$h_s(0) = a(0), \qquad h_s(1) = b(1)$$

for every $s \in I$. Hence $\chi \sim \zeta$. ||

Because of (1.1), the element $c \in \pi(X)$ is called the *product* of a and b, denoted by

$$c = ab.$$

Note that ab is defined iff $a(1) = b(0)$.

For any element $a \in \pi(X)$, consider the two constant paths

$$\phi, \psi : I \to X$$

defined by $\phi(I) = a(0)$ and $\psi(I) = a(1)$. Denote by $\lambda(a)$ and $\rho(a)$ the elements of $\pi(X)$ containing the paths ϕ and ψ respectively. Then $\lambda(a)$ and $\rho(a)$ will be called the *left unit* and the *right unit* of the element a in $\pi(X)$. This is justified by the following

PROPOSITION 1.2. *For every $a \in \pi(X)$, $\lambda(a)a$ and $a\rho(a)$ are defined, and*
$$\lambda(a)a \;=\; a \;=\; a\rho(a).$$

Proof. Pick a path $\sigma \in a$. Since $\phi(1) = a(0)$, $\lambda(a)a$ is defined. Consider the homotopy
$$\{h_s \;:\; I \to X \mid s \in I\}$$
given by
$$h_s(t) \;=\; \begin{cases} \sigma(0), & (\text{if } 0 \leqslant t \leqslant \tfrac{1}{2}s), \\[2mm] \sigma\!\left(\dfrac{2t - s}{2 - s}\right), & (\text{if } \tfrac{1}{2}s \leqslant t \leqslant 1). \end{cases}$$

Then we have $h_0 = \sigma$, $h_1 \in \lambda(a)a$, and
$$h_s(0) \;=\; \sigma(0), \qquad h_s(1) \;=\; \sigma(1)$$
for every $s \in I$. This implies $\lambda(a)a \;=\; a$. Similarly, one can prove that $a\rho(a)$ is defined and is equal to a. ‖

On the other hand, the following proposition is obvious.

PROPOSITION 1.3. *For every $a \in \pi(X)$, $\lambda(a)\lambda(a)$ and $\rho(a)\rho(a)$ are defined, and*
$$\lambda(a)\lambda(a) \;=\; \lambda(a), \qquad \rho(a)\rho(a) \;=\; \rho(a).$$

Moreover, the following three propositions are also immediate consequences of the definitions.

PROPOSITION 1.4. *For every $a \in \pi(X)$, we have*
$$\lambda[\lambda(a)] \;=\; \lambda(a) \;=\; \rho[\lambda(a)],$$
$$\lambda[\rho(a)] \;=\; \rho(a) \;=\; \rho[\rho(a)].$$

PROPOSITION 1.5. *For any two elements $a, b \in \pi(X)$, ab is defined iff* $\rho(a) \;=\; \lambda(b)$.

PROPOSITION 1.6. *For any two elements $a, b \in \pi(X)$ with $\rho(a) = \lambda(b)$, we have*
$$\lambda(ab) \;=\; \lambda(a), \qquad \rho(ab) \;=\; \rho(b).$$

Before proceeding further, we will introduce the algebraic notion of a groupoid in the next section.

EXERCISES

1A. Prove that $\pi(X)$ is in a bijective correspondence with $X \times X$ if X is simply connected.

1B. Prove that the subsets $\Lambda(X)$, $\Omega(X, x_0)$ and $\Lambda(X, x_0)$ of the set $\Omega(X)$, where $x_0 \in X$, are unions of equivalence classes in $\Omega(X)$.

2. GROUPOIDS

With the properties of the equivalence classes of paths in a space as motivation, the notion of a groupoid will be defined as follows.

By a *groupoid*, we mean a set G together with two functions

$$\lambda, \rho \ : \ G \to G$$

and a product ab defined for any two elements $a, b \in G$ such that

$$\rho(a) \ = \ \lambda(b)$$

satisfying the conditions (G1)–(G6) given as follows.

(G1) $\lambda \circ \lambda \ = \ \lambda \ = \ \rho \circ \lambda, \qquad \lambda \circ \rho \ = \ \rho \ = \ \rho \circ \rho.$

Because of (G1), the products $\lambda(a)a$ and $a\rho(a)$ are defined for every $a \in G$. We require:

(G2) $\lambda(a)a \ = \ a \ = \ a\rho(a) \quad$ *for every* $a \in G$.

In view of (G2), $\lambda(a)$ is called the *left unit* of a and $\rho(a)$ the *right unit* of a.

Another consequence of (G1) is that $\lambda(a)\lambda(a)$ and $\rho(a)\rho(a)$ are defined for every $a \in G$. We require:

(G3) $\lambda(a)\lambda(a) \ = \ \lambda(a) \ $ *and* $\ \rho(a)\rho(a) \ = \ \rho(a) \ $ *for every* $a \in G$.

As to the product ab, we require:

(G4) $\lambda(ab) = \lambda(a) \ $ *and* $\ \rho(ab) = \rho(b) \ $ *for any two elements* $a, b \in G$ *with* $\rho(a) = \lambda(b)$.

Therefore, if a, b, c are any three elements of G with

$$\rho(a) \ = \ \lambda(b), \qquad \rho(b) \ = \ \lambda(c),$$

then the products $(ab)c$ and $a(bc)$ are defined in G. We require:

(G5) Associativity: $(ab)c \ = \ a(bc)$.

Hence it is not ambiguous to denote this element by abc.

Furthermore, we require:

(G6) Existence of inverses: *For each* $a \in G$, *there exist* $b \in G$ *and* $c \in G$ *such that*
$$\lambda(b) = \rho(a) = \lambda(c), \qquad \rho(b) = \lambda(a) = \rho(c)$$
and that
$$ab = \lambda(a), \qquad ca = \rho(a).$$

PROPOSITION 2.1. *For any two elements* $b, c \in G$ *satisfying* (G6) *for a given* $a \in G$, *we have* $b = c$.

Proof. The element cab is well-defined in G. We have

$$cab = (ca)b = \rho(a)b = \lambda(b)b = b,$$
$$cab = c(ab) = c\lambda(a) = c\rho(c) = c.$$

Hence we obtain $b = c$. ‖

As an immediate consequence of (2.1), we have the following

COROLLARY 2.2. *Foe every* $a \in G$, *there is a unique element* $a^{-1} \in G$ *such that*

$$\lambda(a^{-1}) = \rho(a), \qquad \rho(a^{-1}) = \lambda(a)$$

and that

$$aa^{-1} = \lambda(a), \qquad a^{-1}a = \rho(a).$$

Furthermore, for any two $a, b \in G$ *such that* $\rho(a) = \lambda(b)$, *we have*

$$(ab)^{-1} = b^{-1}a^{-1}.$$

This unique element $a^{-1} \in G$ is called the *inverse* of the given element $a \in G$.

As the important special case, a groupoid G is said to be a *group* iff $\lambda = \rho$ and both are constant maps. In this case, the *product* ab is defined for any two elements $a, b \in G$. The unique element

$$e = \lambda(G) = \rho(G)$$

is a two-sided unit of every element $a \in G$ and will be called the *neutral element* of the group G. Furthermore, for every $a \in G$, the *inverse* a^{-1} of a satisfies

$$aa^{-1} = e = a^{-1}a.$$

In the remainder of the present section, we are concerned with a given groupoid G.

A subset H of G is said to be *stable* in G iff it satisfies the following three conditions:

(S1) $\lambda(H) \subset H$ *and* $\rho(H) \subset H$.

(S2) $ab \in H$ *for any two elements* $a, b \in H$ *such that* $\rho(a) = \lambda(b)$.

(S3) $a^{-1} \in H$ *for every* $a \in H$.

If H is stable in G, then the restrictions $\lambda \mid H$ and $\rho \mid H$ together with the products ab for $a, b \in H$ turn H into a groupoid, called a *subgroupoid* of G. In particular, if H happens to be a group, then it is called a *subgroup* of the groupoid G. In the rest of the section, we are interested in certain of the subgroups of G.

By an *idempotent* of G, we mean an element $e \in G$ such that ee is defined and $ee = e$.

PROPOSITION 2.3. *For each idempotent $e \in G$, we have*

$$\lambda(e) = e = \rho(e).$$

Proof. Since ee is defined, we have $\lambda(e) = \rho(e)$. Next, consider the inverse e^{-1} of e. Then we have

$$eee^{-1} = e\lambda(e) = e\rho(e) = e.$$

On the other hand, we have

$$eee^{-1} = ee^{-1} = \lambda(e).$$

Hence we obtain $e = \lambda(e) = \rho(e)$. $\;\|$

Let E denote the set of all idempotents of G. Then, by (G3) and (2.3), we have the following

COROLLARY 2.4. $\lambda(G) = E = \rho(G)$.

Now, let $e \in E$ be an arbitrary idempotent of the given groupoid G. Let

$$G(e) = \{g \in G \mid \lambda(g) = e = \rho(g)\}.$$

PROPOSITION 2.5. $G(e)$ *is a subgroup of the groupoid G.*

Proof. First, by (2.3), we have $e \in G(e)$. Then, by the definition of $G(e)$, we have

$$\lambda[G(e)] = e \in G(e), \qquad \rho[G(e)] = e \in G(e).$$

This verifies (S1) for $G(e)$.

Next, for any two elements $a, b \in G(e)$, we have $\rho(a) = e = \lambda(b)$ and hence ab is defined in G. Moreover, since

$$\lambda(ab) = \lambda(a) = e = \rho(b) = \rho(ab),$$

it follows that $ab \in G(e)$. This verifies (S2) for $G(e)$.

Finally, for every $a \in G(e)$, we have

$$\lambda(a^{-1}) = \rho(a) = e = \lambda(a) = \rho(a^{-1}).$$

Hence $a^{-1} \in G(e)$. This verifies (S3) for $G(e)$.

Thus, we have proved that $G(e)$ is stable in G and hence is a sub-groupoid of G.   Besides, since

$$\lambda[G(e)] = e = \rho[G(e)],$$

$G(e)$ is a group and hence is a subgroup of G. ||

This group $G(e)$ will be called the *subgroup of the groupoid G defined by the idempotent e.*   Obviously, e is the neutral element of $G(e)$.

The following proposition is an obvious consequence of the definition.

PROPOSITION 2.6.   *If d and e are any two distinct idempotents of G, then*

$$G(d) \cap G(e) = \square.$$

Now, let a be an arbitrary element of the given groupoid G.   Because of (2.2), we may define a function

$$h_a : G[\lambda(a)] \to G[\rho(a)]$$

by taking $h_a(x) = a^{-1}xa$ for every element x of the group $G[\lambda(a)]$.

PROPOSITION 2.7.   *The function h_a is an isomorphism.*

Proof.   First, let x, y be any two elements in $G[\lambda(a)]$.   Then we have

$$\begin{aligned}
h_a(xy) &= a^{-1}xya = a^{-1}x\lambda(a)ya \\
&= a^{-1}xaa^{-1}ya = h_a(x)h_a(y).
\end{aligned}$$

Hence h_a is a homomorphism.

Next, let us prove that h_a is injective and hence is a monomorphism. For this purpose, let x be any element in $G[\lambda(a)]$ such that $h_a(x) = \rho(a)$. Then we have $a^{-1}xa = \rho(a)$ and therefore

$$aa^{-1}xaa^{-1} = a\rho(a)a^{-1} = aa^{-1} = \lambda(a).$$

On the other hand, we have

$$aa^{-1}xaa^{-1} = \lambda(a)x\lambda(a) = x.$$

Hence we obtain $x = \lambda(a)$.   This implies that h_a is a monomorphism.

Finally, let us prove that h_a is surjective and is an epimorphism. For this purpose, let y be any element in $G[\rho(a)]$.   Let $x = aya^{-1}$. Then $x \in G[\lambda(a)]$ and

$$h_a(x) = a^{-1}aya^{-1}a = \rho(a)y\rho(a) = y.$$

Hence h_a is an epimorphism.

This completes the proof that h_a is an isomorphism. ||

Now let a and b be any two elements in G with $\rho(a) = \lambda(b)$. Then the product ab is defined and we have the following isomorphisms

$$G[\lambda(a)] \xrightarrow{\ h_a\ } G[\rho(a)] = G[\lambda(b)] \xrightarrow{\ h_b\ } G[\rho(b)].$$

PROPOSITION 2.8. $h_{ab} = h_b \circ h_a$.

Proof. Let x be any element in $G[\lambda(a)]$. Then we have

$$
\begin{aligned}
h_{ab}(x) &= (ab)^{-1}x(ab) = b^{-1}a^{-1}xab \\
&= b^{-1}(a^{-1}xa)b = b^{-1}h_a(x)b \\
&= h_b[h_a(x)] = (h_b \circ h_a)(x).
\end{aligned}
$$

Hence $h_{ab} = h_b \circ h_a$. ‖

EXERCISES

2A. Let X be any set and π any group. Denote the neutral element of π by θ. Construct a groupoid G as follows. Take G as the Cartesian product

$$G = X \times X \times \pi$$

and define functions $\lambda, \rho : G \to G$ by taking

$$
\begin{aligned}
\lambda(x, y, \alpha) &= (x, x, \theta), \\
\rho(x, y, \alpha) &= (y, y, \theta)
\end{aligned}
$$

for every $x \in X$, $y \in X$, and $\alpha \in \pi$. For two points (x, y, α) and (y, z, β) in G, define the product by

$$(z, y, \alpha)(y, z, \beta) = (x, z, \alpha\beta).$$

Verify (G1)–(G6) and prove that

$$(x, y, \alpha)^{-1} = (y, x, \alpha^{-1})$$

for every $(x, y, \alpha) \in G$. For each idempotent $e = (x, x, \theta)$ in G, show that $\xi \to (x, x, \xi)$ defines an isomorphism $\pi \approx G(e)$. Finally, if $a = (x, y, \alpha) \in G$, then

$$h_a(x, x, \xi) = (y, y, \alpha^{-1}\xi\alpha)$$

for every $(x, x, \xi) \in G(e)$.

2B. Prove that the union of a disjoint family of groupoids is a groupoid.

2C. Prove that the intersection of any family of stable subsets in a given groupoid G is stable in G. Hence the intersection of any family of subgroupoids of G is a subgroupoid of G.

3. FUNDAMENTAL GROUPOID

Let X be an arbitrarily given space and now let us resume our investigation of the set

$$\pi(X) \;=\; \Omega(X) \diagdown \sim$$

of all equivalence classes of the paths in the space X.

We defined the functions $\lambda, \rho \;:\; \pi(X) \rightarrow \pi(X)$ and the product ab for $a, b \in \pi(X)$ such that $\rho(a) = \lambda(b)$ in Section 1 of this chapter.

THEOREM 3.1. $\pi(X)$ *is a groupoid, called the fundamental groupoid of the space* X.

Proof. We have to verify the conditions (G1)–(G6).

Obviously, (1.4) implies (G1), (1.2) implies (G2), (1.3) implies (G3), and (1.6) implies (G4). Hence it remains to verify (G5) and (G6).

To verify (G5), let a, b, c be three elements in $\pi(X)$ satisfying

$$\rho(a) \;=\; \lambda(b), \qquad \rho(b) \;=\; \lambda(c).$$

Pick paths $\alpha \in a$, $\beta \in b$, and $\gamma \in c$. Then the elements $(ab)c$ and $a(bc)$ of $\pi(X)$ are represented by the paths

$$\sigma \;:\; I \rightarrow X, \qquad \tau \;:\; I \rightarrow X$$

defined by

$$\sigma(t) \;=\; \begin{cases} \alpha(4t), & (\text{if } 0 \leqslant t \leqslant \tfrac{1}{4}), \\ \beta(4t-1), & (\text{if } \tfrac{1}{4} \leqslant t \leqslant \tfrac{1}{2}), \\ \gamma(2t-1), & (\text{if } \tfrac{1}{2} \leqslant t \leqslant 1), \end{cases}$$

$$\tau(t) \;=\; \begin{cases} \alpha(2t), & (\text{if } 0 \leqslant t \leqslant \tfrac{1}{2}), \\ \beta(4t-2), & (\text{if } \tfrac{1}{2} \leqslant t \leqslant \tfrac{3}{4}), \\ \gamma(4t-3), & (\text{if } \tfrac{3}{4} \leqslant t \leqslant 1). \end{cases}$$

To prove $\sigma \sim \tau$, let us consider the unit square I^2 and its three closed strips

$$A \;=\; \left\{ (s, t) \in I^2 \,\middle|\, 0 \leqslant t \leqslant \frac{s+1}{4} \right\},$$

$$B \;=\; \left\{ (s, t) \in I^2 \,\middle|\, \frac{s+1}{4} \leqslant t \leqslant \frac{s+2}{4} \right\},$$

$$C \;=\; \left\{ (s, t) \in I^2 \,\middle|\, \frac{s+2}{4} \leqslant t \leqslant 1 \right\}$$

as shown in the following diagram:

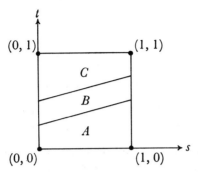

Define a function $H : I^2 \to X$ by taking for each $(s, t) \in I^2$

$$H(s, t) = \begin{cases} \alpha\left(\dfrac{4t}{s+1}\right), & \text{(if } (s, t) \in A), \\ \beta(4t - s - 1), & \text{(if } (s, t) \in B), \\ \gamma\left(\dfrac{4t - 2 - s}{2 - s}\right), & \text{(if } (s, t) \in C). \end{cases}$$

Since $\alpha(1) = \beta(0)$ and $\beta(1) = \gamma(0)$, H is well-defined on $A \cap B$ and $B \cap C$. Since $H \mid A$, $H \mid B$, and $H \mid C$ are continuous, so is H by (II, 4.3).

Define a homotopy $\{h_s : I \to X \mid s \in I\}$ by taking $h_s(t) = H(s, t)$ for each $s \in I$ and each $t \in I$. Then we have

$$h_0 = \sigma, \qquad h_1 = \tau$$

and

$$h_s(0) = \sigma(0), \qquad h_s(1) = \sigma(1)$$

for every $s \in I$. Hence $\sigma \sim \tau$ and

$$(ab)c = a(bc).$$

To verify (G6), let $a \in \pi(X)$ and pick a path $\sigma \in a$. Let $\tau : I \to X$ denote the *inverse path* of σ, i.e.

$$\tau(t) = \sigma(1 - t)$$

for every $t \in I$. Let $b \in \pi(X)$ denote the equivalence class containing τ. Since

$$\tau(0) = \sigma(1), \qquad \tau(1) = \sigma(0),$$

we have

$$\lambda(b) = \rho(a), \qquad \rho(b) = \lambda(a).$$

Hence ab and ba are both defined. In fact, ab contains the path

$$\xi \; : \; I \to X$$

defined by

$$\xi(t) \;=\; \begin{cases} \sigma(2t), & \text{(if } 0 \leqslant t \leqslant \tfrac{1}{2}\text{)}, \\ \tau(2t-1) = \sigma(2-2t), & \text{(if } \tfrac{1}{2} \leqslant t \leqslant 1\text{)}. \end{cases}$$

Define a function $K \; : \; I^2 \to X$ by taking

$$K(s,t) \;=\; \begin{cases} \sigma(2t-2st), & \text{(if } 0 \leqslant t \leqslant \tfrac{1}{2}\text{)}, \\ \sigma(2-2s-2t+2st), & \text{(if } \tfrac{1}{2} \leqslant t \leqslant 1\text{)}. \end{cases}$$

By (II, 4.3), K is continuous and hence gives a homotopy $\{k_s \; : \; I \to X \mid s \in I\}$ defined by $k_s(t) \;=\; K(s,t)$ for every $s \in I$ and every $t \in I$. Since $k_0 \;=\; \xi, k_1(I) \;=\; \sigma(0)$, and

$$k_s(0) \;=\; \sigma(0) \;=\; k_s(1)$$

for every $s \in I$, we obtain $ab \;=\; \lambda(a)$. Similarly, we can prove $ba \;=\; \rho(a)$. $\;\|$

COROLLARY 3.2. *If $a \in \pi(X)$ and $\sigma \in a$, then the inverse a^{-1} of a is the equivalence class containing the inverse path τ of σ.*

Now, let $x_0 \in X$ be an arbitrarily given point called a *base point*. Then the element $e \in \pi(X)$ which contains the constant path γ at x_0 is an idempotent. Let

$$\pi_1(X, x_0)$$

denote the subgroup $[\pi(X)](e)$ of the fundamental groupoid $\pi(X)$ defined by this idempotent e as described in the preceding section. This group is called the *fundamental group* of the space X at the base point x_0.

Let $a \in \pi_1(X, x_0)$. Then we have

$$\lambda(a) \;=\; e \;=\; \rho(a).$$

Therefore, a is an equivalence class of paths in X with end points both at x_0. Conversely, if a is an equivalence class of paths in X with end points both at x_0, then $\lambda(a) = e = \rho(a)$ and hence $a \in \pi_1(X, x_0)$.

Thus, the elements of the fundamental group $\pi_1(X, x_0)$ are the equivalence classes of the loops in X with base point at x_0; in symbols,

$$\pi_1(X, x_0) \;=\; \Lambda(X, x_0)/\!\sim.$$

By the results in (V, § 3), one can see clearly that a homotopy of loops in X relative to the base point at x_0 may be identified with a path in the space $\Lambda(X, x_0)$ topologized by the compact-open topology. Hence, the elements of the fundamental group $\pi_1(X, x_0)$ are precisely the path-components of the space $\Lambda(X, x_0)$; in symbols,

$$\pi_1(X, x_0) \;=\; \pi_0[\Lambda(X, x_0)].$$

Furthermore, the group operation in $\pi_1(X, x_0)$ is the multiplication of path-components of $\Lambda(X, x_0)$ induced by the continuous multiplication constructed in (V, § 6).

The following theorem is a direct application of (2.7).

THEOREM 3.3. *If $\sigma : I \to X$ is a path in X with $\sigma(0) = x_0$ and $\sigma(1) = x_1$, then σ determines an isomorphism*

$$\sigma^\# \;:\; \pi_1(X, x_0) \to \pi_1(X, x_1)$$

defined by

$$\sigma^\#(\xi) \;=\; h_{[\sigma]}(\xi)$$

for every $\xi \in \pi_1(X, x_0)$, where $[\sigma] \in \pi(X)$ denotes the element containing the path σ.

COROLLARY 3.4. *If X is pathwise connected, then the fundamental group $\pi_1(X, x_0)$ of X, as an abstract group, does not depend on the choice of the base point x_0.*

Because of (3.4), the fundamental group of a pathwise connected space X is usually denoted by $\pi_1(X)$.

COROLLARY 3.5. *The isomorphism $\sigma^\#$ depends only on the equivalence class $[\sigma]$ of σ.*

Let σ and τ be any two paths in X with same end points, i.e.

$$\sigma(0) \;=\; x_0 \;=\; \tau(0), \qquad \sigma(1) \;=\; x_1 \;=\; \tau(1).$$

Then, by (3.3), we have the isomorphisms

$$\sigma^\# \;:\; \pi_1(X, x_0) \to \pi_1(X, x_1),$$
$$\tau^\# \;:\; \pi_1(X, x_0) \to \pi_1(X, x_1).$$

For each $\xi \in \pi_1(X, x_0)$, we have

$$\sigma^\#(\xi) \;=\; \alpha^{-1}\xi\alpha, \qquad \tau^\#(\xi) \;=\; \beta^{-1}\xi\beta$$

where $\alpha = [\sigma]$ and $\beta = [\tau]$ are elements in $\pi(X)$. Therefore,

$$
\begin{aligned}
\tau^\#(\xi) \;&=\; \beta^{-1}\xi\beta \;=\; \beta^{-1}\alpha\alpha^{-1}\xi\alpha\alpha^{-1}\beta \\
&=\; \beta^{-1}\alpha[\sigma^\#(\xi)]\alpha^{-1}\beta \\
&=\; (\alpha^{-1}\beta)^{-1}[\sigma^\#(\xi)](\alpha^{-1}\beta).
\end{aligned}
$$

Here $\gamma = \alpha^{-1}\beta$ is an element of $\pi_1(X, x_1)$ which contains the loop

$$\theta = \sigma^{-1}\tau : I \to X$$

defined by

$$\theta(t) = \begin{cases} \sigma(1 - 2t), & \text{(if } 0 \leqslant t \leqslant \tfrac{1}{2}), \\ \tau(2t - 1), & \text{(if } \tfrac{1}{2} \leqslant t \leqslant 1). \end{cases}$$

Thus we have the following

PROPOSITION 3.6. *If $\sigma, \tau : I \to X$ are two paths with*

$$\sigma(0) = x_0 = \tau(0), \qquad \sigma(1) = x_1 = \tau(1),$$

then $\tau^{\#}$ is the composition of $\sigma^{\#}$ followed by the inner automorphism of $\pi_1(X, x_1)$ defined by the element $\gamma \in \pi_1(X, x_1)$ which contains the loop $\theta = \sigma^{-1}\tau$.

EXERCISES

3A. Let X be any given pathwise connected space and $x_0 \in X$ a given base point. Let $\pi = \pi_1(X, x_0)$ and consider the groupoid

$$G = X \times X \times \pi$$

constructed in Ex. 2A. For each point $x \in X$, choose an element $d_x \in \pi(X)$ such that $d_x(0) = x_0$ and $d_x(1) = x$. Define a function $H : \pi(X) \to G$ by taking

$$H(a) = [a(0), a(1), d_{a(0)}ad_{a(1)}^{-1}]$$

for every $a \in \pi(X)$. Prove that H is an isomorphism. Hence $\pi(X)$ is essentially determined by the set X and the fundamental group $\pi = \pi_1(X, x_0)$.

3B. A pathwise connected space X is said to be 1-*simple* iff, for any two paths σ and τ in X with same end points, we have $\sigma^{\#} = \tau^{\#}$. Prove that X is 1-simple iff its fundamental group $\pi_1(X)$ is abelian.

3C. Prove that the fundamental groupoid $\pi(X)$ of a space X is the disjoint union of the fundamental groupoids of the path-components of X.

3D. Prove that the fundamental group $\pi_1(X, x_0)$ of a space X at a point $x_0 \in X$ depends only on the path-component Γ of X containing x_0. In fact, $\pi_1(X, x_0) = \pi_1(\Gamma, x_0)$.

3E. If X is the topological sum of two disjoint spaces U and V, and if $u_0 \in U$ and $v_0 \in V$, prove that

$$\pi_1(X, u_0) = \pi_1(U, u_0),$$
$$\pi_1(X, v_0) = \pi_1(V, v_0).$$

Hence the fundamental groups of a space at base points in different path-components are mutually independent.

4. INDUCED HOMOMORPHISMS

Consider an arbitrarily given map

$$f : X \to Y,$$

and consider the fundamental groupoids $\pi(X)$ and $\pi(Y)$ of X and Y respectively.

Let $a \in \pi(X)$ and pick a path

$$\alpha : I \to X$$

from the equivalence class a. Then the composition of α and f is a path

$$f \circ \alpha : I \to Y$$

in Y.

LEMMA 4.1. *The element of $\pi(Y)$ which contains the path $f \circ \alpha$ does not depend on the choice of the path α from the equivalence class a.*

Proof. Let $\alpha' \in a$ be any other path in a. Then $\alpha \sim \alpha'$. By definition, there exists a homotopy

$$\{h_s : I \to X \mid s \in I\}$$

such that $h_0 = \alpha$, $h_1 = \alpha'$, and

$$h_s(0) = \alpha(0), \qquad h_s(1) = \alpha(1)$$

for every $s \in I$. Then the homotopy

$$\{k_s = f \circ h_s : I \to Y \mid s \in I\}$$

satisfies $k_0 = f \circ \alpha$, $k_1 = f \circ \alpha'$, and

$$k_s(0) = (f \circ \alpha)(0), \qquad k_s(1) = (f \circ \alpha)(1)$$

for every $s \in I$. Hence $f \circ \alpha \sim f \circ \alpha'$. This proves that the element $[f \circ \alpha] \in \pi(Y)$ does not depend on the choice of $\alpha \in a$. ||

Because of (4.1), the element $[f \circ \alpha]$ of $\pi(Y)$ depends only on the given element a and the given map f. This element will be denoted by

$$f_*(a) \in \pi(Y).$$

The assignment $a \to f_*(a)$ for each $a \in \pi(X)$ defines a function

$$f_* : \pi(X) \to \pi(Y).$$

LEMMA 4.2. *f_* is a homomorphism.*

By this, we mean that, for any two elements a, $b \in \pi(X)$ such that ab is defined, the element $f_*(a)f_*(b)$ is defined in $\pi(Y)$ and

$$f_*(ab) \;=\; f_*(a)f_*(b).$$

Proof. Pick $\alpha \in a$ and $\beta \in b$. Then $\alpha(1) = \beta(0)$ and ab is the equivalence class which contains the path $\gamma : I \to X$ defined by

$$\gamma(t) \;=\; \begin{cases} \alpha(2t), & (\text{if } 0 \leqslant t \leqslant \tfrac{1}{2}), \\ \beta(2t-1), & (\text{if } \tfrac{1}{2} \leqslant t \leqslant 1). \end{cases}$$

Since $(f \circ \alpha)(1) = f[\alpha(1)] = f[\beta(0)] = (f \circ \beta)(0)$, it follows that $f_*(a)f_*(b)$ is defined in $\pi(Y)$ and is represented by the path $f \circ \gamma$. Since γ represents the element $ab \in \pi(X)$, $f \circ \gamma$ also represents the element $f_*(ab)$. Hence $f_*(ab) = f_*(a)f_*(b)$. $\;\|$

The homomorphism f_* is called the *homomorphism induced* by f on the fundamental groupoid, denoted by

$$\pi(f) \;=\; f_*.$$

The following two propositions are obvious.

PROPOSITION 4.3.   *If* $i : X \to X$ *is the identity map on* X, *then*

$$\pi(i) \;:\; \pi(X) \to \pi(X)$$

is the identity homomorphism on $\pi(X)$.

PROPOSITION 4.4.   *If* $f : X \to Y$ *and* $g : Y \to Z$ *are maps, then*

$$\pi(g \circ f) \;=\; \pi(g) \circ \pi(f).$$

THEOREM 4.5.   *If* $f : X \to Y$ *is a homeomorphism of a space* X *onto a space* Y, *then*

$$\pi(f) \;:\; \pi(X) \to \pi(Y)$$

is an isomorphism, i.e. $\pi(f)$ *is bijective.*

Proof. Let $g = f^{-1} : Y \to X$. Then we have

$$\pi(g) \circ \pi(f) \;=\; \pi(g \circ f) \;=\; \pi(i_X),$$
$$\pi(f) \circ \pi(g) \;=\; \pi(f \circ g) \;=\; \pi(i_Y),$$

where i_X and i_Y denote the identity maps on X and Y respectively. By (4.3), it follows that $\pi(f)$ and $\pi(g)$ are both bijective. $\;\|$

COROLLARY 4.6.   *The fundamental groupoid* $\pi(X)$ *of a space* X *is a topological invariant.*

LEMMA 4.7. *If* $f(x_0) = y_0$, *then* $\pi(f)$ *carries* $\pi_1(X, x_0)$ *into* $\pi_1(Y, y_0)$ *and hence defines a homomorphism*

$$\pi_1(f) \; : \; \pi_1(X, x_0) \to \pi_1(Y, y_0).$$

Proof. Let $a \in \pi_1(X, x_0)$ and pick a loop $\alpha \in a$. Then

$$\alpha(0) \; = \; x_0 \; = \; \alpha(1).$$

The composed map $f \circ \alpha \; : \; I \to Y$ represents the element $[\pi(f)](a)$ in $\pi(Y)$. Since

$$(f \circ \alpha)(0) \; = \; f[\alpha(0)] \; = \; y_0 \; = \; f[\alpha(1)] \; = \; (f \circ \alpha)(1),$$

we have $[\pi(f)](a) \in \pi_1(Y, y_0)$. $\;\;||$

The homomorphism $\pi_1(f)$ is said to be the *induced homomorphism* of the map $f \; : \; (X, x_0) \to (Y, y_0)$.

Obviously, we have propositions about $\pi_1(f)$ corresponding to (4.3) and (4.4).

Now let $f, g \; : \; X \to Y$ be any two maps and $x_0 \in X$ a given point. Assume that $f \simeq g$; that is, there exists a homotopy

$$\{h_t \; : \; X \to Y \mid t \in I\}$$

such that $h_0 = f$ and $h_1 = g$. Let $y_0 = f(x_0)$ and $y_1 = g(x_0)$. Then we have

$$\pi_1(f) \; : \; \pi_1(X, x_0) \to \pi_1(Y, y_0),$$
$$\pi_1(g) \; : \; \pi_1(X, x_0) \to \pi_1(Y, y_1).$$

Furthermore, let $\sigma \; : \; I \to Y$ denote the path in Y defined by $\sigma(t) = h_t(x_0)$ for every $t \in I$. Then σ determines an isomorphism

$$\sigma^\# \; : \; \pi_1(Y, y_0) \to \pi_1(Y, y_1).$$

THEOREM 4.8. $\pi_1(g) = \sigma^\# \circ \pi_1(f)$.

Proof. Let $a \in \pi_1(X, x_0)$ and pick a loop $\alpha : I \to X$ in the equivalence class a. Define a map $H : I \times I \to Y$ by taking

$$H(s, t) \; = \; h_t[\alpha(s)]$$

for each (s, t) in $I \times I$. Then we have

$$H(0, t) \; = \; \sigma(t), \qquad H(1, t) \; = \; \sigma(t),$$
$$H(s, 0) \; = \; (f \circ \alpha)(s), \qquad H(s, 1) \; = \; (g \circ \alpha)(s)$$

on the boundary of the unit square $I \times I$ as indicated by the following diagram:

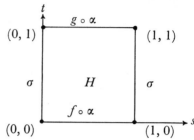

This implies that $g \circ \alpha \sim \sigma^{-1}(f \circ \alpha)\sigma$ and hence

$$[\pi_1(g)](a) = \sigma^{\#}\{[\pi_1(f)](a)\}.$$

Since a is arbitrary, this proves the theorem. ‖

COROLLARY 4.9. *If* f, g : $(X, x_0) \to (Y, y_0)$ *are homotopic relative to* x_0, *then*

$$\pi_1(f) = \pi_1(g).$$

THEOREM 4.10. *If* f : $X \to Y$ *is a homotopy equivalence and if* $f(x_0) = y_0$, *then*

$$\pi_1(f) : \pi_1(X, x_0) \to \pi_1(Y, y_0)$$

is an isomorphism.

Proof. By the definition of a homotopy equivalence in (II, § 7), there exists a map g : $Y \to X$ such that $g \circ f$ and $f \circ g$ are both homotopic to the identity maps. Let $x_1 = g(y_0)$. Then we have

$$\pi_1(X, x_0) \xrightarrow{\pi_1(f)} \pi_1(Y, y_0) \xrightarrow{\pi_1(g)} \pi_1(X, x_1).$$

Since $g \circ f$ is homotopic to the identity map on X, there exists a homotopy

$$\{h_t : X \to X \mid t \in I\}$$

such that h_0 is the identity map and $h_1 = g \circ f$. Let σ : $I \to X$ denote the path defined by $\sigma(t) = h_t(x_0)$ for every $t \in I$. Then we have $\sigma(0) = x_0$, $\sigma(1) = x_1$, and an isomorphism

$$\sigma^{\#} : \pi_1(X, x_0) \to \pi_1(X, x_1).$$

By (4.8), we have

$$\pi_1(g \circ f) = \sigma^{\#} \circ \pi_1(i)$$

where i : $X \to X$ denotes the identity map. By (4.3) and (4.4), it follows that

$$\pi_1(g) \circ \pi_1(f) = \sigma^{\#}$$

which is an isomorphism. This implies that $\pi_1(f)$ is a monomorphism and $\pi_1(g)$ is an epimorphism.

Similarly, since $f \circ g$ is homotopic to the identity map on Y, one can prove that $\pi_1(g)$ is a monomorphism and $\pi_1(f)$ is an epimorphism. Consequently, both $\pi_1(f)$ and $\pi_1(g)$ are isomorphisms. ||

COROLLARY 4.11. *The fundamental group $\pi_1(X)$ of a pathwise connected space X is a homotopy invariant.*

EXERCISES

4A. Prove that $\pi_1(X) = 0$ for every contractible space X. Here, if G is a group, $G = 0$ means that G consists of a single element.

4B. Prove that a pathwise connected space X is simply connected iff $\pi_1(X) = 0$.

4C. Prove that the fundamental group of a connected cellular polytope P is isomorphic to that of its 2-dimensional skeleton P_2.

5. FUNDAMENTAL GROUPS OF SPHERES

In the present section, we will determine the fundamental group

$$\pi_1(S^n)$$

of the n-sphere S^n for every $n > 0$.

THEOREM 5.1. $\pi_1(S^n) = 0$ *for every* $n > 1$.

Proof. The n-sphere S^n is homeomorphic with the cellular polytope K obtained by adjoining the unit n-simplex Δ_n to a point v_0 by a map $\kappa : \partial \Delta_n \to v_0$. Thus, we may identify S^n with K and choose the vertex $v_0 \in K$ as the base point of the fundamental group. Let

$$\sigma : I \to K$$

be an arbitrary loop with v_0 as base point. By (IV, Ex. 6C) and its proof, σ is equivalent to a loop

$$\gamma : I \to K$$

which is a cellular map of the cellular polytope I into the cellular polytope K. Since I is 1-dimensional, it follows that $\gamma(I)$ is contained in the 1-dimensional skeleton K^1 of K. Since $n > 1$, we have $K^1 = v_0$. Hence γ is the constant loop. This implies that $\pi_1(S^n) = 0$. ||

For the remaining case $n = 1$, we have the following theorem.

THEOREM 5.2. $\pi_1(S^1)$ *is an infinite cyclic group.*

To establish this theorem, let us represent the 1-sphere S^1 as the unit circle in the space C of all complex numbers, i.e.

$$S^1 = \{z \in C \mid |z| = 1\}.$$

Thus S^1 is a compact abelian topological group with the usual multiplication of complex numbers as group operation.

Consider the *exponential map* $p : R \to S^1$ defined on the real line R by the formula

$$p(x) = \exp(2\pi x i) = e^{2\pi x i}$$

for every $x \in R$, where e stands for the base of natural logarithms and i the unit of imaginary numbers. Obviously, p is continuous and is a homomorphism, i.e.

$$p(x + y) = p(x)p(y)$$

for any x and y in R. The kernel $p^{-1}(1)$ is the subgroup Z of all integers. Furthermore, for every proper connected subspace U of S^1, p carries every component of $p^{-1}(U)$ homeomorphically onto U.

LEMMA 5.3. (COVERING PATH PROPERTY). *For any path* $\sigma : I \to S^1$ *and any point* $x_0 \in R$ *satisfying* $p(x_0) = \sigma(0)$, *there exists a unique path* $\tau : I \to R$ *such that*

$$\tau(0) = x_0, \qquad p \circ \tau = \sigma.$$

Proof. Since I is compact and σ is continuous, there exists a partition

$$0 = t_0 < t_1 < \ldots < t_{n-1} < t_n = 1$$

of I such that the image of each closed subinterval

$$I_i = [t_i, t_{i+1}], \qquad 0 \leqslant i < n,$$

under σ is a proper connected subspace U_i of S^1.

We will establish the lemma by proving inductively the following assertion A_i: There is a unique map τ_i defined on the closed interval $[0, t_i]$ into R satisfying

$$\tau_i(0) = x_0, \qquad p \circ \tau_i = \sigma \mid [0, t_i].$$

A_0 is trivial. Assume $0 \leqslant i < n$. We will prove that A_i implies A_{i+1}.

For this purpose, we assume A_i. By the choice of the partition of I, $U_i = \sigma(I_i)$ is a proper connected subspace of S^1. Denote by V_i the component of $p^{-1}(U_i)$ containing the point $\tau_i(t_i)$. Then the restriction $p_i = p \mid V_i$ is a homeomorphism of V_i onto U_i and, therefore, the inverse map $p_i^{-1} : U_i \to V_i$ is well defined. Define a map $\tau_{i+1} : [0, t_{i+1}] \to R$ by setting

$$\tau_{i+1}(t) = \begin{cases} \tau_i(t), & \text{(if } 0 \le t \le t_i), \\ p_i^{-1}[\sigma(t)], & \text{(if } t_i \le t \le t_{i+1}). \end{cases}$$

This establishes the existence of τ_{i+1}. The uniqueness of τ_{i+1} follows easily by the fact that V_i is a component of $p^{-1}(U_i)$ and that p_i is a homeomorphism. This completes the induction. ‖

If the reader is familiar with the logarithmic function and its analytic continuations, then he will be able to see that the unique covering path τ in (5.3) is given by

$$\tau(0) = x_0, \qquad \tau(t) = \frac{1}{2\pi i} \log_e \sigma(t)$$

for every $t \in I$.

LEMMA 5.4. (COVERING HOMOTOPY PROPERTY). *For an arbitrary map* $f : X \to R$ *of a space* X *into* R *and any homotopy* $h_t : X \to S^1$, $(0 \le t \le 1)$, *of the map* $h = p \circ f$, *there is a unique homotopy* $f_t : X \to R$, $(0 \le t \le 1)$, *of* f *satisfying*

$$p \circ f_t = h_t$$

for every $t \in I$.

Proof. For each point $x \in X$, define a path $\sigma_x : I \to S^1$ by taking

$$\sigma_x(t) = h_t(x)$$

for every $t \in I$. By (5.3), there is a unique path $\tau_x : I \to R$ such that

$$\tau_x(0) = f(x), \qquad p \circ \tau_x = \sigma_x.$$

Let $H : X \times I \to S^1$ and $F : X \times I \to R$ be defined by taking

$$H(x, t) = h_t(x), \qquad F(x, t) = \tau_x(t)$$

for every $x \in X$ and every $t \in I$. Then we have $p \circ F = H$ and $F(x, 0) = f(x)$ for each $x \in X$. For the existence part of the proof, it remains to show the continuity of F.

Let x_0 be any point in X. By the continuity of H and the compactness of I, there exist a neighborhood M of x_0 in X and a partition

$$0 = t_0 < t_1 < \cdots < t_{n-1} < t_n = 1, \qquad I = [t_i, t_{i+1}]$$

of I such that $H(M \times I_i)$ is contained in a proper connected subspace of S^1.   By means of an inductive construction similar to that used in the proof of (5.3), one can define a map $G : M \times I \to R$ satisfying

$$G(x, 0) = f(x), \qquad p[G(x, t)] = H(x, t)$$

for every $x \in M$ and $t \in I$.   Because of the uniqueness part of (5.3), this implies that

$$G = F \mid M \times I.$$

Since M is a neighborhood of x_0 in X, F is continuous at (x_0, t) for each $t \in I$.   Since x_0 is arbitrary, F is continuous.   ‖

Now let $\sigma : I \to S^1$ be any loop in S^1 with 1 as base point.   Since

$$p(0) = 1 = \sigma(0),$$

it follows by (5.3) that there is a unique path $\tau : I \to R$ such that

$$\tau(0) = 0, \qquad p \circ \tau = \sigma.$$

Since $p[\tau(1)] = \sigma(1) = 1$, $\tau(1)$ is in $p^{-1}(1) = Z$ and hence is an integer.   This integer $\tau(1)$ is called the *degree* of the loop σ and will be denoted by

$$\deg (\sigma) = \tau(1).$$

LEMMA 5.5.   *For any two equivalent loops σ and σ' in S^1 with 1 as base point, we have*

$$\deg (\sigma) = \deg (\sigma').$$

Proof.   Since σ and σ' are equivalent, there exists a homotopy $h_t : I \to S^1$, $(0 \leqslant t \leqslant 1)$, such that $h_0 = \sigma$, $h_1 = \sigma'$, and

$$h_t(0) = 1 = h_t(1)$$

for every t.   Let $\tau : I \to R$ denote the unique path such that $\tau(0) = 0$ and $p \circ \tau = \sigma$.   Then, by (5.4), there exists a unique homotopy $f_t : I \to R$, $(0 \leqslant t \leqslant 1)$, such that $f_0 = \tau$ and $p \circ f_t = h_t$ for every t.

Define a map $\theta : I \to R$ by taking $\theta(t) = f_t(0)$ for every $t \in I$.   Since

$$p[\theta(t)] = p[f_t(0)] = h_t(0) = 1$$

for every $t \in I$, it follows that $\theta(I)$ is contained in $p^{-1}(1) = Z$.   Since Z is discrete and $\theta(I)$ is connected, this implies that $\theta(I)$ consists of a single point.   Hence

$$f_t(0) = \theta(t) = \theta(0) = \tau(0) = 0$$

for every $t \in I$.   Let $\tau' = f_1$.   Then we have $\tau'(0) = 0$ and $p \circ \tau' = \sigma'$.   Hence

$$\deg (\sigma) = \tau(1), \qquad \deg (\sigma') = \tau'(1).$$

Next define a map $\rho : I \to R$ by taking $\rho(t) = f_t(1)$ for every $t \in I$. By a similar argument as used in the preceding paragraph, one can prove that $\rho(I)$ consists of a single point. Hence

$$\tau'(1) \;=\; \rho(1) \;=\; \rho(0) \;=\; \tau(1).$$

This implies that deg (σ) = deg (σ'). $\|$

Because of (5.5), the assignment $\sigma \to$ deg (σ) for the loops σ with 1 as base point induces a function

$$\deg : \pi_1(S^1, 1) \to Z$$

from the fundamental group $\pi_1(S^1, 1)$ of S^1 at the base point 1 into the additive group Z of all integers. Then Theorem 5.2 is an immediate consequence of the following lemma.

LEMMA 5.6. *The function* deg *is an isomorphism of* $\pi_1(S^1, 1)$ *onto* Z.

Proof. First, let us prove that deg is a homomorphism. For this purpose, let α and β be any two elements in $\pi_1(S^1, 1)$ and pick loops σ and ρ representing the elements α and β respectively. Then the element $\alpha\beta$ in $\pi_1(S^1, 1)$ is represented by the loop $\lambda : I \to S^1$ defined by

$$\lambda(t) = \begin{cases} \sigma(2t), & (\text{if } 0 \le t \le \tfrac{1}{2}), \\ \rho(2t - 1), & (\text{if } \tfrac{1}{2} \le t \le 1). \end{cases}$$

Let $\tau, \theta : I \to R$ denote the paths uniquely determined by the conditions

$$\tau(0) = 0 = \theta(0), \qquad p \circ \tau = \sigma, \qquad p \circ \theta = \rho.$$

Then we obtain by definition

$$\deg (\alpha) \;=\; \tau(1), \qquad \deg (\beta) \;=\; \theta(1).$$

Define a path $\mu : I \to R$ by taking

$$\mu(t) = \begin{cases} \tau(2t), & (\text{if } 0 \le t \le \tfrac{1}{2}), \\ \tau(1) + \theta(2t - 1), & (\text{if } \tfrac{1}{2} \le t \le 1). \end{cases}$$

Then we have $\mu(0) = 0$. Since p is a homomorphism and $\tau(1)$ is contained in the kernel of p, we obtain

$$p \circ \mu = \lambda.$$

This implies that

$$\deg (\alpha\beta) \;=\; \mu(1) \;=\; \tau(1) + \theta(1) \;=\; \deg (\alpha) + \deg (\beta).$$

Hence deg is a homomorphism.

Next, let us prove that deg is an epimorphism. For this purpose let $k \in Z$ be an arbitrarily given integer. Define a path $\psi_k : I \to R$ by taking

$$\psi_k(t) = kt$$

for every $t \in I$. Since $\psi_k(0) = 0$ and $\psi_k(1) = k$, it follows that the composition

$$\phi_k = p \circ \psi_k : I \to S^1$$

is a loop with 1 as base point. This loop ϕ_k represents an element $[\phi_k]$ of $\pi_1(S^1, 1)$

$$\deg [\phi_k] = \psi_k(1) = k.$$

Hence deg is an epimorphism.

It remains to prove that deg is a monomorphism. Let α and β be any two elements of $\pi_1(S^1, 1)$ such that

$$\deg (\alpha) = \deg (\beta).$$

Pick two loops σ and ρ representing the elements α and β respectively. Let $\tau, \theta : I \to R$ denote the paths uniquely determined by the conditions

$$\tau(0) = 0 = \theta(0), \qquad p \circ \tau = \sigma, \qquad p \circ \theta = \rho.$$

Then we have

$$\tau(1) = \deg (\alpha) = \deg (\beta) = \theta(1).$$

Define a homotopy $f_t : I \to R$, $(0 \leqslant t \leqslant 1)$, by taking

$$f_t(x) = (1 - t)\tau(x) + t\theta(x)$$

for every $x \in I$. Then we have $f_0 = \tau, f_1 = \theta$, and

$$f_t(0) = 0, \qquad f_t(1) = \tau(1) = \theta(1)$$

for every $t \in I$. Therefore, the composition

$$h_t = p \circ f_t : I \to S^1, \qquad (0 \leqslant t \leqslant 1),$$

is a homotopy such that $h_0 = \sigma, h_1 = \rho$, and

$$h_t(0) = 1 = h_t(1)$$

for every $t \in I$. This implies that $\sigma \sim \rho$ and hence $\alpha = \beta$. Therefore, deg is an isomorphism. ‖

As an application of this result, let us consider the unit disk

$$E^2 = \{z \in C \mid |z| \leqslant 1\}$$

in the space C of all complex numbers. Then $S^1 \subset E^2$.

THEOREM 5.7. S^1 *is not a retract of* E^2.

Proof. Suppose that S^1 were a retract of E^2. Then, by definition, there exists a retraction

$$r : E^2 \supset S^1;$$

that is, r is a map of E^2 onto S^1 such that its composition

$$r \circ i : S^1 \to S^1$$

with the inclusion map $i : S^1 \subset E^2$ is the identity map on S^1.

Choose the complex number $1 \in S^1 \subset E^2$ as the base point for the fundamental groups of S^1 and E^2. The maps r and i induce homomorphisms

$$\pi_1(S^1) \xrightarrow{\ i_* \ } \pi_1(E^2) \xrightarrow{\ r_* \ } \pi_1(S^1).$$

Since $r \circ i$ is the identity map, it follows that $r_* \circ i_*$ is the identity automorphism of $\pi_1(S^1)$. This implies that r_* is an epimorphism, i.e.

$$\pi_1(S^1) \ = \ r_*[\pi_1(E^2)].$$

Since E^2 is contractible, it follows from Exercise 4A that $\pi_1(E^2) = 0$. This implies $\pi_1(S^1) = 0$ which contradicts Theorem 5.2. ‖

As a consequence of (5.7), we will prove the following special 2-dimensional case of the Brouwer fixed-point theorem.

THEOREM 5.8. *Every map* $f : E^2 \to E^2$ *has a fixed point, that is to say, there exists a point* x *of* E^2 *such that* $f(x) = x$.

Proof. Assume that $f : E^2 \to E^2$ is free of fixed points. Then we may define a map $r : E^2 \to S^1$ as follows: Let $x \in E^2$. Since f has no fixed points, we have $f(x) \neq x$. Draw the line from $f(x)$ to x and produce until it intersects S^1 at a point $r(x)$. One verifies that the assignment $x \to r(x)$ defines a map $r : E^2 \to S^1$. If $x \in S^1$, it is obvious from the construction that $r(x) = x$. Hence r is a retraction of E^2 onto S^1. This contradicts (5.7). ‖

EXERCISES

5A. Prove that the fundamental group $\pi_1(\infty)$ of the space ∞ which consists of two tangent circles in R^2 is the free group generated by two elements.

5B. Prove that the fundamental group $\pi_1(T^2)$ of the torus T^2 is a free abelian group of rank 2.

5C. Prove that the fundamental group $\pi_1(P^n)$ of the real projective space of dimension $n > 1$ is cyclic of order 2.

6. HIGHER HOMOTOPY GROUPS

Let X be an arbitrarily given space and $x_0 \in X$ a given base point. Denote

$$Y = \Lambda(X, x_0)$$

the space of all loops in X with base point x_0 topologized by the compact-open topology and let $y_0 \in Y$ stand for the constant loop $y_0(I) = x_0$.

For every integer $n > 1$, we define the n-dimensional homotopy group $\pi_n(X, x_0)$ of the space X at the base point x_0 recurrently by the formula

$$\pi_n(X, x_0) = \pi_{n-1}(Y, y_0).$$

Among the most important properties of homotopy groups is the following

THEOREM 6.1. $\pi_n(X, x_0)$ is an abelian group for every $n > 1$.

Proof. By our recurrent definition, it suffices to prove the theorem for the special case $n = 2$. According to (V, 6.5), Y is a Hopf space with y_0 as a homotopy unit. Hence, (6.1) is an immediate consequence of the following lemma.

LEMMA 6.2. If X is a Hopf space with x_0 as a homotopy unit, then $\pi_1(X, x_0)$ is an abelian group.

Proof. Let a and b be any two elements in $\pi_1(X, x_0)$. We have to prove that $ab = ba$. For this purpose, choose loops $\alpha \in a$ and $\beta \in b$.

Using the continuous multiplication in X, we define a map $\gamma : I \to X$ by taking

$$\gamma(t) = \alpha(t)\beta(t)$$

for every $t \in I$. Then we have

$$\gamma(i) = \alpha(i)\beta(i) = x_0 x_0 = x_0, \qquad (i = 0, 1).$$

Hence γ is a loop with base point at x_0 and represents an element c in $\pi_1(X, x_0)$.

We will prove that $c = ab$ and $c = ba$. For this purpose, let us consider the neutral element e of $\pi_1(X, x_0)$. It is represented by the constant loop $\kappa : I \to X$ with $\kappa(I) = x_0$.

Since $ae = a$, α is equivalent to the loop α' : $I \to X$ defined by

$$\alpha'(t) = \begin{cases} \alpha(2t), & (\text{if } 0 \leqslant t \leqslant \tfrac{1}{2}), \\ x_0, & (\text{if } \tfrac{1}{2} \leqslant t \leqslant 1). \end{cases}$$

Similarly, β is equivalent to the loop β' : $I \to X$ defined by

$$\beta'(t) = \begin{cases} x_0, & (\text{if } 0 \leqslant t \leqslant \tfrac{1}{2}), \\ \beta(2t - 1), & (\text{if } \tfrac{1}{2} \leqslant t \leqslant 1). \end{cases}$$

Let $\{h_s, k_s : I \to X \mid s \in I\}$ be homotopies such that $h_0 = \alpha$, $h_1 = \alpha'$, $k_0 = \beta$, $k_1 = \beta'$, and

$$h_s(0) = x_0 = h_s(1), \qquad k_s(0) = x_0 = k_s(1)$$

for every $s \in I$. Define a homotopy $\{\phi_s : I \to X \mid s \in I\}$ by taking

$$\phi_s(t) = h_s(t)k_s(t)$$

for every $s \in I$ and every $t \in I$. Hence we obtain $\phi_0 = \gamma$ and $\phi_s(0) = x_0 = \phi_s(1)$ for every $s \in I$.

Now the loop ϕ_1 is given by

$$\phi_1(t) = \begin{cases} \alpha(2t)x_0, & (\text{if } 0 \leqslant t \leqslant \tfrac{1}{2}), \\ x_0\beta(2t - 1), & (\text{if } \tfrac{1}{2} \leqslant t \leqslant 1). \end{cases}$$

Since x_0 is a homotopy unit of X, there exist two homotopies

$$\{\xi_t, \eta_t : X \to X \mid t \in I\}$$

such that $\xi_0 = \eta_0$ is the identity map on X, $\xi_1(x) = xx_0$ and $\eta_1(x) = x_0x$ for each $x \in X$, and $\xi_t(x_0) = x_0 = \eta_t(x_0)$ for every $t \in I$. Define a homotopy $\{\psi_s : I \to X \mid s \in I\}$ by taking

$$\psi_s(t) = \begin{cases} \xi_s[\alpha(2t)], & (\text{if } 0 \leqslant t \leqslant \tfrac{1}{2}), \\ \eta_s[\beta(2t - 1)], & (\text{if } \tfrac{1}{2} \leqslant t \leqslant 1). \end{cases}$$

Then ψ_0 represents ab, $\psi_1 = \phi_1$, and $\psi_s(0) = x_0 = \psi_s(1)$ for every $s \in I$. Since

$$\psi_0 \sim \psi_1 = \phi_1 \sim \phi_0 = \gamma,$$

it follows that $ab = c$.

Similarly, one can prove that $ba = c$. Hence we obtain $ab = ba$. ‖

COROLLARY 6.3. *If X is a topological group with x_0 as neutral element, then $\pi_1(X, x_0)$ is an abelian group.*

To conclude the book, we will give one more property of homotopy groups.

Theorem 6.4. *If $Z = X \times Y$ is the topological product of two spaces X and Y, and if $z_0 = (x_0, y_0) \in Z$, then $\pi_n(Z, z_0)$ is isomorphic to the direct product*

$$\pi_n(X, x_0) \times \pi_n(Y, y_0)$$

for every $n \geqslant 1$.

Proof. Since $\Lambda(Z, z_0)$ is obviously homeomorphic to the topological product

$$\Lambda(X, x_0) \times \Lambda(Y, y_0)$$

by (V, 1.3), it suffices to prove the theorem for the case $n = 1$.

For this purpose, let

$$p : (Z, z_0) \to (X, x_0), \qquad q : (Z, z_0) \to (Y, y_0)$$

denote the natural projections defined by $p(z) = x$ and $q(z) = y$ for every $z = (x, y)$ in Z. On the other hand, let

$$i : (X, x_0) \to (Z, z_0), \qquad j : (Y, y_0) \to (Z, z_0)$$

denote the maps (called injections) defined by $i(x) = (x, y_0)$ and $j(y) = (x_0, y)$ for each $x \in X$ and each $y \in Y$. Then $p \circ i$ and $q \circ j$ are identity maps, and $p \circ j$ and $q \circ i$ are constant maps.

The maps p, q, i, j induce homomorphisms

$$p_* : \pi_1(Z, z_0) \to \pi_1(X, x_0), \qquad q_* : \pi_1(Z, z_0) \to \pi_1(Y, y_0),$$
$$i_* : \pi_1(X, x_0) \to \pi_1(Z, z_0), \qquad j_* : \pi_1(Y, y_0) \to \pi_1(Z, z_0).$$

Since $p \circ i$ and $q \circ j$ are identity maps, it follows that $p_* \circ i_*$ and $q_* \circ j_*$ are the identity homomorphisms. Hence, i_* and j_* are monomorphisms, and p_* and q_* are epimorphisms. On the other hand, since $p \circ j$ and $q \circ i$ are constant maps, we have

$$p_* \circ j_* = 0 = q_* \circ i_*.$$

Here, if $h : G \to H$ is a homomorphism, then $h = 0$ means that $h(G)$ consists of only the neutral element of H.

Now, consider the *direct product*

$$\pi_1(X, x_0) \times \pi_1(Y, y_0).$$

As a set, this is the Cartesian product of the sets $\pi_1(X, x_0)$ and $\pi_1(Y, y_0)$. Its elements are ordered pairs (ξ, η) of elements $\xi \in \pi_1(X, x_0)$ and $\eta \in \pi_1(Y, y_0)$. Its group operation is defined by

$$(\xi_1, \eta_1)(\xi_2, \eta_2) = (\xi_1 \xi_2, \eta_1 \eta_2).$$

Define a function

$$h : \pi_1(Z, z_0) \to \pi_1(X, x_0) \times \pi_1(Y, y_0)$$

by setting

$$h(\zeta) = [p_*(\zeta), q_*(\zeta)]$$

for every $\zeta \in \pi_1(Z, z_0)$. Since p_* and q_* are homomorphisms, so is h. It remains to prove that h is an isomorphism.

Let $\xi \in \pi_1(X, x_0)$ and $\eta \in \pi_1(Y, y_0)$ be arbitrarily given. Let

$$\zeta = i_*(\xi)j_*(\eta) \in \pi_1(Z, z_0).$$

Then we have

$$\begin{aligned}
h(\zeta) &= [p_*(\zeta), q_*(\zeta)] \\
&= [p_*\{i_*(\xi)\}p_*\{j_*(\xi)\}, q_*\{i_*(\xi)\}q_*\{j_*(\xi)\}] \\
&= (\xi\xi_0, \eta_0\eta) = (\xi, \eta),
\end{aligned}$$

where $\xi_0 \in \pi_1(X, x_0)$ and $\eta_0 \in \pi_1(Y, y_0)$ denote the neutral elements. Hence h is an epimorphism.

On the other hand, let $\zeta \in \pi_1(Z, z_0)$ be any element such that

$$h(\zeta) = (\xi_0, \eta_0).$$

Then, by definition, we have

$$p_*(\zeta) = \xi_0, \qquad q_*(\zeta) = \eta_0.$$

Let $f : I \to Z$ be a loop in the class ζ. Then $p \circ f$ and $q \circ f$ are equivalent to the constant loops at x_0 and y_0 respectively. Therefore, there exist homotopies

$$\{g_t : I \to X \mid t \in I\},$$
$$\{h_t : I \to Y \mid t \in I\}$$

such that

$$\begin{aligned}
g_0 &= p \circ f, & h_0 &= q \circ f, \\
g_1(I) &= x_0, & h_1(I) &= y_0, \\
g_t(0) &= x_0 = g_t(1), & h_t(0) &= y_0 = h_t(1)
\end{aligned}$$

for every $t \in I$. Define a homotopy

$$\{f_t : I \to Z \mid t \in I\}$$

by taking $f_t(s) = (g_t(s), h_t(s))$ for every $t \in I$ and every $s \in I$. Then clearly we have

$$\begin{aligned}
f_0 &= f, \\
f_1(I) &= z_0, \\
f_t(0) &= z_0 = f_t(1), \qquad (t \in I).
\end{aligned}$$

This implies that ζ is the neutral element of $\pi_1(Z, z_0)$. Hence h is also a monomorphism. $\|$

EXERCISES

6A. By means of (V, Exs. 6C and 6D), prove that the elements of $\pi_n(X, x_0)$ can be identified with the path-components of the space $F_n(X, x_0)$. Hence, these can be considered as the homotopy classes of the maps $f : (S^n, s_0) \to (X, x_0)$ relative to s_0.

6B. If X is pathwise connected, prove that $\pi_n(X, x_0)$, as an abstract group, does not depend on the base point x_0. Hence it may be denoted by $\pi_n(X)$ and called the *n-dimensional homotopy group of X*.

6C. Prove that the n-dimensional homotopy group $\pi_n(X)$ of a pathwise connected space X is a homotopy invariant.

6D. Prove that the n-dimensional homotopy group of a connected cellular polytope P is isomorphic to that of its $(n + 1)$-dimensional skeleton P_{n+1}.

BIBLIOGRAPHY

BOOKS

[A–H]   Alexandroff, P., and H. Hopf: *Topologie* I. Springer-Verlag, Berlin, 1935.

[A]   Alexandroff, P. S.: *Combinatorial Topologie* Vol. I–III, Graylock Press, Rochester, N.Y., 1956–60.

[Ar]   Arnold, B. H.: *Intuitive Concepts in Elementary Topology*. Prentice-Hall, Inc., Englewood Cliffs, N.J., 1962.

[Ba]   Barim, J. D.: *Elements of Point Set Topology*. Prentice-Hall, Inc., Englewood Cliffs, N.J., 1964.

[Be]   Berge, C.: *Topological Spaces*. Macmillan Company, New York, 1963.

[Bo]   Bourbaki, N.: *Éléments de Mathématiques*. Hermann & Cie, Paris, 1939–48.

[Bu]   Bushaw, D.: *Elements of General Topology*. John Wiley & Sons, New York, 1963.

[C]   Cairns, S. S.: *Introductory Topology*. Ronald Press, New York, 1961.

[E–S]   Eilenberg, S., and N. E. Steenrod: *Foundations of Algebraic Topology*. Princeton Univ. Press, Princeton, N.J., 1952.

[F]   Franz, W.: *Topologie I, Allgemeine Topologie*. Walter de Gruyter & Co., Berlin, 1960.

[H–S]   Hall, D. W., and G. L. Spencer: *Elementary Topology*. John Wiley & Sons, Inc., New York, 1955.

[Hi]   Hilton, P. J.: *An Introduction to Homotopy Theory*. Cambridge University Press, London, 1953.

[Hi–W]   Hilton, P. J., and S. Wylie: *Homology Theory, an Introduction to Algebraic Topology*. Cambridge University Press, London, 1960.

[Hu]   Hu, S. T.: *Homotopy Theory*. Academic Press, New York, 1959.

[H–Y]   Hocking, J. G., and Young, G. S.: *Topology*. Addison-Wesley, Reading, Mass., 1961.

[Hu–W]   Hurewicz, W., and H. Wallman: *Dimension Theory*. Princeton Univ. Press, Princeton, N.J., 1941.

[K]   Kelley, J. L.: *General Topology*. D. Van Nostrand Co. Inc., Princeton, N.J., 1955.

[Ko]   Kowalski, H. J.: *Topologische Räume*. Birkhäuser Verlag, Basel, 1961.

[Ku1]   Kuratowski, C.: *Topologie* I–II (Polska Akademia Nauk. Monografie matematyczne, tom 20–21), Warsaw, 1948.

[Ku2]   Kuratowski, C.: *Introduction to Set Theory and Topology*. Pergamon Press, New York, 1962.

[L1]   Lefschetz, S.: *Introduction to Topology*. Princeton Univ. Press, Princeton, N.J., 1949.

[L2]   Lefschetz, S.: *Algebraic Topology.* Amer. Math. Soc. Coll. Publ., Vol. 27, 1942.

[L3]   Lefschetz, S.: *Topics in Topology.* (Annals of Math. Studies, No. 10) Princeton Univ. Press, Princeton, N.J., 1942.

[M]   Mamuzić, Z. P.: *Introduction to General Topology.* P. Noordhoff Ltd., Groningen, 1963.

[Ma]   Mansfield, M. J.: *Introduction to Topology.* D. Van Nostrand Co. Inc., Princeton, N.J., 1963.

[Me]   Mendelson, B.: *Introduction to Topology.* Allyn & Bacon, Inc., Boston, 1962.

[Mi]   Milnor, J.: *Morse Theory.* (Annals of Math. Studies, No. 51), Princeton Univ. Press, 1963.

[Mu]   Munkres, J. R.: *Elementary Differential Topology.* (Annals of Math. Studies, No. 54), Princeton Univ. Press, Princeton, N.J., 1963.

[N]   Newman, M. H. A.: *Elements of the Topology of Plane Sets of Points.* Second Ed., Cambridge Univ. Press, London, 1954.

[Pa]   Patterson, E. M.: *Topology.* Oliver and Boyd, London, 1956.

[Po1] Pontryagin, L. S.: *Topological Groups.* Princeton Univ. Press., 1939.

[Po2] Pontryagin, L. S.: *Foundations of Combinatorial Topology.* Graylock Press, Rochester, N.Y., 1952.

[R–R] Rado, T. and P. V. Reichelderfer: *Continuous Transformations in Analysis.* Springer-Verlag, Berlin, 1955.

[Re]   Reidemeister, K.: *Topologie der Polyeder.* Edwards Bros., Ann. Arbor, Michigan, 1944.

[S1]   Sierpinski, W.: *Introduction to General Topology.* Univ. of Toronto Press, 1934.

[S2]   Sierpinski, W.: *General Topology.* Univ. of Toronto Press, 1952.

[Si]   Simmons, G. F.: *Introduction to Topology and Modern Analysis.* McGraw-Hill Book Co., New York, 1963.

[S–T] Seifert, H. and Threllfall, W.: *Lehrbuch der Topologie.* B. G. Teubner Verlagsgesellschaft, Stuttgart, 1934.

[St]   Steenrod, N. E.: *The Topology of Fiber Bundles.* Princeton Univ. Press, Princeton, N.J., 1951.

[T]   Tukey, J. W.: *Convergence and Uniformity in Topology.* (Annals of Math. Studies, No. 2) Princeton Univ. Press, Princeton, N.J., 1940.

[Va]   Vaidyanathaswamy, R.: *Set Topology.* Second Ed., Chelsea Publ. Co., New York, 1960.

[Ve]   Veblen, O.: *Analysis Situs.* Amer. Math. Soc. Coll. Publ. Vol. 5, 1931.

[Wa]   Wallace, A. H.: *An Introduction to Algebraic Topology.* Pergamon Press, New York, 1957.

[Wh1] Whyburn, G. T.: *Analytic Topology.* Amer. Math. Soc. Coll. Publ. Vol. 28, 1942.

[Wh2] Whyburn, G. T.: *Topological Analysis.* Princeton Univ. Press, 1958.

[Wi]   Wilder, R. L.: *Topology of Manifolds.* Amer. Math. Soc. Coll. Publ. Vol. 32, 1949.

PAPERS

Arens, R.
1. *A topology for spaces of transformations.* Ann. of Math. (2), **47** (1946), 480–495.

Dieudonné, J.
1. *Une généralization des espace compacts.* J. Math. Pures Appl., **23** (1944), 65–76.

Fox, R. H.
1. *On topologies for function spaces.* Bull. Amer. Math. Soc., **51** (1945), 429–432.

Frink, A. H.
1. *Distance functions and the metrization problem.* Bull. Amer. Math. Soc., **43** (1937), 133–142.

Gottlieb, D. H.
1. *Homotopy and isotopy properties.* Dissertation, UCLA, 1962.

Hanner, O.
1. *Solid spaces and absolute retracts.* Arkiv Mat. Svenska Vetens. Akad., **1** (1951), 375–382.
2. *Retraction and extension of mappings of metric and non-metric spaces.* Arkiv Mat. Svenska Vetens. Akad. **2** (1952), 315–360.

Hu, S. T.
1. *Homotopy and isotopy properties of topological spaces.* Canadian J. Math., **13** (1961), 167–176.

Iséki, K.
1. *A note on retraction in completely normal spaces.* Revista Fac. Ciências de Lisboa, Second Ser., **3** (1954), 176–180.

Jackson, J. R.
1. *Comparison of topologies on function spaces.* Proc. Amer. Math. Soc., **3** (1952), 156–158.
2. *Spaces of mappings on topological products with applications to homotopy theory.* Proc. Amer. Math. Soc., **3** (1952), 327–333.

Morita, K.
1. *On spaces having the weak topology with respect to closed coverings,* I–II. Proc. Japan Acad., **29** (1953), 537–545, **30** (1954), 711–717.

Morita, K., and Hanai, S.
1. *Closed mappings and metric spaces.* Proc. Japan Acad., **32** (1956), 10–14.

Stone, A. H.
1. *Paracompactness and product spaces.* Bull. Amer. Math. Soc., **54** (1948), 977–982.
2. *Metrizability of decomposition spaces.* Proc. Amer. Math. Soc., **7** (1956), 690–700.

Tsuda, M.
1. *On adjunction spaces.* Proc. Japan Acad., **38** (1962), 23–26.

Whitehead, J. H. C.
1. *Combinatory homotopy.* Bull. Amer. Math. Soc., **55** (1949), 213–245.

INDEX